DYNAMIC PROGRAMMING
AND THE
CALCULUS OF VARIATIONS

MATHEMATICS
IN SCIENCE
AND ENGINEERING

A SERIES OF MONOGRAPHS AND TEXTBOOKS

Edited by Richard Bellman
University of Southern California

MATHEMATICS IN SCIENCE AND ENGINEERING

DYNAMIC PROGRAMMING
AND THE
CALCULUS OF VARIATIONS

Stuart E. Dreyfus

THE RAND CORPORATION
SANTA MONICA, CALIFORNIA

1965

ACADEMIC PRESS   New York and London

ACADEMIC PRESS INC.
111 Fifth Avenue, New York, New York 10003

United Kingdom Edition published by
ACADEMIC PRESS INC. (LONDON) LTD.
Berkeley Square House, London W.1

LIBRARY OF CONGRESS CATALOG CARD NUMBER: 65-26394

First Printing 1965
Second Printing 1967

PRINTED IN THE UNITED STATES OF AMERICA

To my parents

Preface

One of the earliest aims and accomplishments of modern science was the mathematical expression of the laws governing the behavior of physical systems. More recently, scientists have sought and found underlying rules of behavior in economic, military, social, and biological processes. Once a law of causality has been determined—or, as is more often the case, approximated—for a given system, it is often seen that the behavior of the system can be influenced by the choice of certain parameters which man can control. For example, the direction and magnitude of the thrust of a rocket are parameters that can be controlled and used to influence the rocket's trajectory; similarly, the demand for an economic good is affected by its price and the price can be set by the entrepreneur.

A question then arises as to how these controllable parameters can be chosen so as to attain some desired goal. Sometimes the goal may be merely that the behavior of the controlled system exhibit certain qualitative features, such as stability or convergence or growth. When this is the case, the goal can often be attained via any one of a large set of control parameter values. To find one such configuration is a traditional problem in control theory.

In recent years, interest has focused on *optimizing* the behavior of the system. Some output of the system, such as the range of a rocket or the profit produced by an economic enterprise, is to be either maximized or minimized, subject to the laws governing the behavior of the system. Usually, a unique control configuration achieves the goal. The search for the control that maximizes or minimizes a well-defined system criterion constitutes a fundamental problem of *optimization theory*.

The *calculus of variations* is a mathematical discipline that treats certain problems in the area of optimization theory. A more recent mathematical formalism, *dynamic programming*, is also applicable to optimization problems. In this book the relationships between these two techniques are developed.

The different rules of causality of various systems are described by mathematical relationships having a great variety of forms and in which the control parameters appear in many ways. However, only problems with rather special equations and types of control are investigated in this book. Specifically, the mathematical model treated associates values with functions and seeks a function with minimum or maximum associated value. Though restrictive, this particular mathematical model is capable of describing a very large number of important processes, and has been the subject of continuous mathematical study for over 250 years.

Many different rules can be formulated for associating a numerical value with each function in a given set of functions. Any such rule is called a *functional*. The calculus of variations, and this book, considers problems in which the rule relating values to functions is expressed (or can be expressed by a variable change) in a particular form involving a definite integral. Then, that function is sought which has associated with it, by the given rule, a numerical value less than that associated with any other function in the specified set of functions. The search for maximizing functions is also a problem in variational theory. For concreteness, the theory is usually developed in terms of minimization problems alone, since the results for maximization and minimization problems differ only in sign and not in form.

The systematic study of the problems considered began in the late seventeenth century with the work of John and James Bernoulli. Early in the eighteenth century, Euler, a pupil of John Bernoulli, discovered a differential equation which a minimizing function must satisfy. Lagrange, later in the century, simplified and generalized this work. The approach of these pioneers, naturally enough, was to examine functions (given a specific rule for associating values with functions) that were candidates for the title of "function of minimum value" and to deduce properties that the minimizing function must possess. Usually, these properties followed from the principle that a minimizing function must yield, at the very least, a smaller value of the criterion functional than that associated with any neighboring function.* Neighboring functions were constructed by *varying* the candidate function; hence, the name *calculus of variations*. Attention was focused upon the function that yielded the minimum value of the functional rather than upon the actual numerical value of the minimized functional. This was reasonable, since the value of the functional follows easily, in theory, once an argument-function is specified, while the shape

---

* The term *neighboring* and other technical terms used in this Preface will be given precise mathematical meaning in the text.

of the minimizing function cannot be deduced from the minimum value of the functional.

Recently, a new approach to a wide variety of optimization problems, including as a special case those usually associated with the calculus of variations, has been developed. In this approach, a particular optimization problem is solved by studying a collection, or family, of problems which contains the particular problem as a member. (As an example, let us consider the problem of finding the curve of shortest length connecting two specified points A and B. The family of problems for this example might be the problems of finding the minimum-length curves connecting *any* given initial point and B.) Each member of the family of problems has its own solution curve (i.e., a minimum-value curve), and that curve has a value. (In this example, for any given initial point C, the solution curve is the straight line connecting C with B and the value of the curve is given by the formula for distance.) In this manner, an optimal value can be associated with each member of the family of problems and each member can be identified by its initial point. The rule associating an optimal value (i.e., a minimum distance to B in our example) with each initial point is called the *optimal value function*. Dynamic programming studies the optimal value function, rather than the solution curve yielding the value. All this would appear rather academic and indirect were it not for one important fact: The optimal value function has certain intuitive local properties in the space of points on which it is defined that allow it to be mathematically characterized, usually as the solution of a partial differential equation. Knowledge of the optimal value associated with a particular problem that has particular initial and terminal points provides no way of determining the minimizing curve itself. However, knowledge of the more general optimal value function associated with a family of problems having a variety of initial points *does* allow one to determine the minimizing curve for any particular member of the family of problems.

To summarize, the dynamic programming viewpoint centers its attention upon a function—the optimal value function—and upon its attributes. The classical variational theory, on the other hand, studies minimizing curves and their properties.

As stated, the classical approach compares a potential solution function with neighboring functions. For a problem with definite integral criterion, this naturally leads to the study of a definite integral involving the candidate function and its neighbors. Yet, results, if they are to be useful, should concern properties that are independent of the neighboring comparison functions and that hold *at each point* of a minimizing function. The classical theory successfully eliminates all explicit appearances of the neighboring comparison functions from its results and transforms statements about definite integrals into conclusions concerning properties that hold at each point of the minimizing function; but, in doing so, it gives up much of its intuitive content.

The existence of an intuitive geometric appreciation of almost every derivational step and conclusion justifies, I feel, the dynamic programming approach to variational problems. Actually, there are two aims in this volume. The first is to convey to the reader the simple and intuitive nature of many of the results of the calculus of variations that becomes apparent when these results are deduced from the dynamic programming viewpoint. A second goal of this book is to familiarize the reader with the application of dynamic programming methods to classical problems in order that he may appreciate how the same dynamic programming techniques apply to stochastic and adaptive variational problems.

Although rigorous derivations of results are not presented, a paper which was written jointly with L. D. Berkovitz is summarized and referenced and, under certain specific assumptions, attains this end. Indeed, a completely rigorous presentation would necessarily be at odds with the primary goal of intuitive clarity. Similarly, the question is left open as to whether the dynamic programming approach to problems of the calculus of variations, if pursued for several hundred years (as has been the classical theory) and if rendered completely rigorous, might yield results that are either slightly sharper or slightly weaker than those of the classical theory. At this moment of its infancy, it is fairly safe to say that the dynamic programming results, at a rather subtle level, are weaker.

In the initial chapter, the basic ideas of dynamic programming are introduced. Only discrete and finite problems are considered in this chapter, since for such problems the fundamental tenet of dynamic programming, called the *principle of optimality*, is easily justified and numerically illustrated.

After the concepts of dynamic programming are developed in the first chapter, the calculus of variations is discussed in Chapter II. The domain of problems traditionally considered is defined, the classical mathematical arguments used in their study are outlined, and the more important results that have been obtained are discussed. I have not actually presented the details of any derivations since these derivations already fill a great many books.

The principles of dynamic programming are applied to the simplest variational problem in Chapter III, and new derivations and interpretations of many of the classical results stated in Chapter II are produced.

Dynamic programming is used in Chapter IV to study the problem of Mayer, which is a somewhat different classical formulation of a variational problem from that of Chapter III. The form of the problem and the results obtained are particularly suited to trajectory optimization and other modern engineering control problems.

The problem of Chapter IV is modified in Chapter V by the introduction of inequality constraints on admissible functions. First, the minimizing function is sought in a restricted set of functions whose derivatives satisfy certain inequalities. Dynamic programming is used to reproduce and reinterpret classical results for this problem. Restrictions upon the functions themselves are then considered and results for this more difficult problem are developed.

Some special problems to which the general theory of the earlier chapters is inapplicable are treated in Chapter VI. Some results are deduced, but in general I feel that these problems are more perplexing than they are practical and that the intensive study of such problems, while challenging, is not particularly rewarding.

This completes the portion of the book which is primarily concerned with using dynamic programming for developing and interpreting known results of the classical variational theory. I emphasize that, with respect to the deterministic problems customarily considered by means of the calculus of variations, any result that follows from the dynamic programming approach is also obtainable by classical arguments. Conversely, I feel that any conclusion that can be derived classically can also be deduced, at least formally, using dynamic programming. Only the nature of the derivations and the intuitive insight afforded by the results are at variance between the two theories.

In Chapter VII, the concepts of stochastic and adaptive optimization problems are introduced and the applicability of dynamic programming to this new and challenging area of application is shown. It is the existence of this vast, important class of problems, and the apparent inapplicability of classical methods to these problems, that has motivated much of the research on the dynamic programming method. I feel that it is in this exciting problem domain that the insights and interpretations afforded by dynamic programming, and developed in this book, will ultimately prove most useful. The text of this book terminates at the point where, I feel, the greatest potential contribution of dynamic programming begins.

Nothing in mathematics is ever completely new nor is the independent work of different persons ever identical. Indeed, "identical" and "distinct" are relative terms dependent upon the view and the viewer. Prior work in the calculus of variations which might be considered most closely related to dynamic programming is probably that of Carathéodory (1935). Bellman (1957) is responsible for the name "dynamic programming" and for most of the pioneering work in the area. Current approaches to optimization theory akin to dynamic programming and to the ideas of Carathéodory are being developed by Kalman (1963), Halkin (1963), and Blaquiere and Leitmann (1964).

I would like to thank Dr. Richard Bellman for motivating my original interest in the topic of this volume and for his encouragement and aid in the preparation of the manuscript. I am also indebted to Professor A. E. Bryson, Jr., of Harvard University for supervising my doctoral dissertation which contains much of the material included in this volume. My thanks go to Professor Howard Raiffa and to Russell Shaver for careful and critical readings of the complete manuscript, and to Stanley Azen, Leonard Berkovitz, Barry Boehm, Marshall Freimer, Y. C. Ho, Kenneth Saunders, and Michael Warshaw for enlightening conversations and other assistance of various sorts. Editors Wade Holland and Linda Colbert, while they may not have understood what I had to say, greatly improved the way I said it. Finally, I would like to thank typist Joan Pederson, without whose help the manuscript would have been written.

The results presented in this volume were obtained in the course of mathematical research carried out at The RAND Corporation under a broad research program sponsored by the United States Air Force. I would like to express my appreciation for the opportunities thus afforded me.

STUART E. DREYFUS

Santa Monica, California
September, 1965

Contents

CHAPTER III

The Simplest Problem

CHAPTER IV

The Problem of Mayer

CHAPTER V

Inequality Constraints

CHAPTER VI

Problems with Special Linear Structures

CHAPTER VII

Stochastic and Adaptive Optimization Problems

DYNAMIC PROGRAMMING
AND THE
CALCULUS OF VARIATIONS

CHAPTER I

Discrete Dynamic

Programming

1. Introduction

In this chapter we treat certain decision problems from the point of view of dynamic programming. The problems we treat have the property that at each of a finite set of times $(t_1, t_2, \ldots, t_n)$ a decision is to be chosen from a finite set of decisions. Such problems are examples of discrete multistage decision process problems. If one out of, say, three possible decisions must be chosen at each decision time, and the process consists of, say, ten such decision times, there are 3^{10} possible different sequences of ten decisions each. If a rule somehow associates a value with each of these sequences, we might ask for the decision sequence with maximum, or minimum, value. We would then have a multistage optimization problem of discrete type and, if sufficient structure is present in the process, the technique of dynamic programming is applicable.

We shall develop the theory of dynamic programming with respect to certain finite multistage decision process problems in this initial chapter. We begin by studying discrete processes of finite duration since there is no difficulty in the rigorous justification of the technique we employ and because, due to the finite set of possibilities, simple numerical examples can be easily and exactly solved by hand calculation.

In later chapters we shall see that the ideas and interpretations developed in this chapter are easily extended to problems involving continuous processes. What is not so easy is the rigorous mathematical justification of the steps and results. While some rigorous theory for continuous problems is presented in the literature and is discussed in Section 34 of Chapter III, rigor is not the primary aim of this book. Comforted by our ability to check our somewhat heuristic results against the rigorously supported conclusions of the 300-year-old classical variational theory, we shall strive

1

more for simplicity of deduction and for geometric or physical interpretation of results than for mathematical rigor.

2. An Example of a Multistage Decision Process Problem

Rather than speak abstractly of the particular type of process with which
we are concerned, we present a simple illustrative example. Consider the
network shown in Fig. I.1. We use the name *vertices* for the points of intersection of the straight lines shown in the figure, and we label them by
letters; we designate the line segments shown connecting certain vertices
as *arcs*. A *continuous path* is an ordered sequence of arcs, each adjacent pair
having one vertex in common. For example, the sequence of arcs $\widehat{AC}$, $\widehat{CF}$,
$\widehat{FD}$, $\widehat{DG}$, $\widehat{GJ}$, $\widehat{JM}$, $\widehat{MP}$, $\widehat{PB}$ constitutes a continuous path connecting
vertices A and B. A path will be said to be *monotonic-to-the-right* if the
noncommon vertex of the second arc of each pair of adjacent arcs lies to the
right, in Fig. I.1, of the noncommon vertex of the first arc. The path
enumerated above is not monotonic-to-the-right since the vertex D is the
noncommon vertex of the second arc of the pair $\widehat{CF}$, $\widehat{FD}$, and vertex D does
not lie to the right of vertex C.

By the above definitions, each monotonic-to-the-right continuous path
connecting A and B consists of six arcs. One such path is the sequence of
arcs $\widehat{AC}$, $\widehat{CF}$, $\widehat{FJ}$, $\widehat{JM}$, $\widehat{MP}$, $\widehat{PB}$. Shown on the figure is a number associated
with each arc, which we shall call the *value* of the arc. The value of a path is
taken to be the sum of the values of its component arcs. The value of the
monotonic-to-the-right path connecting A and B that we enumerated in
this paragraph is 18.

The first multistage decision process problem we consider seeks that
monotonic-to-the-right continuous path, henceforth called *admissible path*
(or merely *path*), connecting A and B which has minimum value.*

One could simply enumerate all 20 admissible paths and choose the one
with minimum value, but we shall proceed otherwise. To lend the problem
of choosing the minimum-value path a sequential or dynamic flavor, let us
imagine that we begin to construct the path by first choosing an arc leading
from the initial vertex A. We call this choice the first *stage* of the decision
process. Then, at the second stage, an arc leading to the right from the
terminal vertex of the first arc is selected. To make this selection, we need

---

* Generally, when discussing the solution of a problem, the exposition will refer to a
unique optimal solution. If the optimal solution is not unique, the statements that are
made concern *any* optimal solution unless otherwise noted.

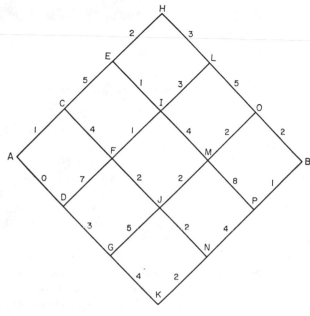

FIG. I.1

to know which of the two vertices, C or D, is the terminal vertex at the end of stage one. We call the designation of the terminal vertex at the end of stage one the *state* at the beginning of stage two. At stage three, we can again pick an arc if we know the state—i.e., the vertex from which the arc should originate. From this viewpoint, we have a six-stage decision process problem, with the decision at each stage depending on the state at that stage.

3. The Dynamic Programming Solution of the Example

Having described a sequential choice procedure, how shall we generate the sequence of decisions which produces the path with minimum value? To answer this question within the framework of dynamic programming, we reason as follows: Suppose we somehow know the value of the minimum-value path associated with each of two shorter problems, one requiring the connection of C and B (see Fig. I.1), and one requiring the connection of D and B. Then we can easily evaluate the particular path from A to B that has $\overgroup{AC}$ as its initial arc, and of which the remaining five arcs constitute the path of minimum value from C to B, by adding the value of arc $\widehat{AC}$ to the value of the minimum-value path from C to B. Any other path with $\widehat{AC}$ as initial arc and any sequence of remaining arcs will be inferior to the above one. Similarly, we can add the value of arc $\widehat{AD}$ to the value of the minimum-value path starting from D and going to B. This yields the value of the minimum-value path connecting A and B which has $\widehat{AD}$ as its initial arc. Since there are only two decisions possible at A, these are the only two candidates for a path of minimum value connecting A and B. The minimum-value path from A to B is that path, of the just-described two paths, with smaller value. So it is clear that we would have no trouble determining the initial arc and the over-all value of the minimum-value path from A to B is we knew the values of the minimum-value paths from both C and D to B. Note that it is not the optimal path, but the *value* of the optimal path, that is the vital information.

Continuing, we could easily determine the values of the minimum-value paths from both C and D to B if we knew beforehand the values of the best paths from E, F, and G to B. Just as we reasoned that we could solve the original six-stage problem if we had already solved two five-stage problems, we now can relate the five-stage solution to four-stage processes. This recursive reasoning can be repeated until we need only the values of the minimum-value paths from O and P, respectively, to B in order to calculate the values starting at L, M, and N, etc. But the value of the path of minimum value connecting either O or P with B is easily obtained since there is no free choice associated with picking an admissible path from either of these vertices to B. For each of these vertices, the value of the best and only admissible path is the value of the arc connecting the vertex with the terminal point B.

Suppose we put these ideas into practice. We first compute the minimum path-value associated with connecting vertex O with B, which is 2; and with connecting vertex P with B, which is 1. We next solve the three relevant two-stage problems in terms of the known one-stage solutions. The minimum (and only) value of an admissible path joining L with B is 7. If we start at M, we can choose the arc to O with a value 2 and continue optimally to B by a path of value 2 (this fact is indicated by the 2 we have already associated with vertex O), for a total of 4. Or, we can choose arc $\widehat{MP}$ initially for a total value of $8 + 1$, or 9. Since 4 is less than 9, we associate the value 4 with starting at vertex M; with N, we associate the value 5. We complete the association of a value with each initial vertex by working backward, determining a minimum-path-to-B value that we associate with each vertex by comparing (at most) two different sums, each of two

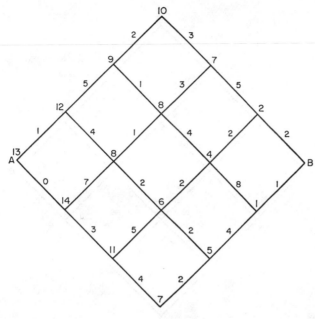

FIG. I.2

numbers. This generates Fig. I.2. From this calculation, we conclude that the value of the path of minimum value connecting A with B is 13.

We would also know the particular path that has the value 13 if we had recorded, at each vertex, an arrow indicating which of the two possible arcs emanating from the vertex initiates the minimum-value path from that vertex to B. We determined that arc when we chose the minimum of two sums to obtain the value associated with the vertex. If we had recorded this information, we would have obtained Fig. I.3. Now, to find the minimum-value path from A to B, we follow the arrow from A up to the vertex that was called C in Fig. I.1, down to F, down to J, up to M, up to O, and down to B.

Before formalizing what we have done, let us demonstrate the efficiency of this algorithm for this problem. At each of the nine vertices where there was a real choice of the initial arc, we have performed two additions and one binary comparison; at six other vertices we performed one addition. Hence, we have performed 24 additions and nine binary comparisons. The direct evaluation by enumeration of all 20 admissible paths would involve five additions per path, yielding 100 additions, and a comparison of 20 results.

The general formulas for the n-stage problem ($n = 6$ in our example) better illustrate the computational savings. The dynamic programming

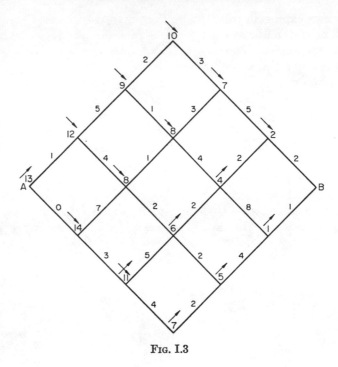

Fig. I.3

algorithm above involves $(n^2/2) + n$ additions, while the direct enumeration generates

$$\binom{n}{\frac{1}{2}n} = \frac{n!}{(\frac{1}{2}n)!(\frac{1}{2}n)!}$$

paths or

$$\frac{(n-1)n!}{(\frac{1}{2}n)!(\frac{1}{2}n)!}$$

additions. For $n = 20$, dynamic programming requires an easily manageable 220 additions, while enumeration would require more than 1,000,000 additions.

In spite of the obvious superiority of the dynamic programming method of enumeration over direct enumeration of all possible paths, the aspect of dynamic programming with respect to continuous processes that will occupy us in later chapters is analytical rather than computational. This is because continuous processes have a structure that discrete processes lack, and there are computational alternatives to direct enumeration which exploit this structure and are even more efficient than the dynamic programming algorithm illustrated above.

Let us now express in mathematical notation the dynamic programming formulation of the above example of a discrete and finite multistage decision process problem. Then we shall consider several other examples which illustrate various properties of the dynamic programming procedure and several results that have analogs to continuous processes.

4. The Dynamic Programming Formalism

We have introduced the concepts of stage and state with respect to the above example. Briefly, if an optimal sequence of n decisions is sought, the stage is the position in the sequence of the particular decision being considered. The state is the specific information necessary to render that decision, given the stage. The stage may be identified by a single number; the state may be identified by a single number in some cases and by a set of numbers or a vector in others. For the example presented in Fig. I.1, let us

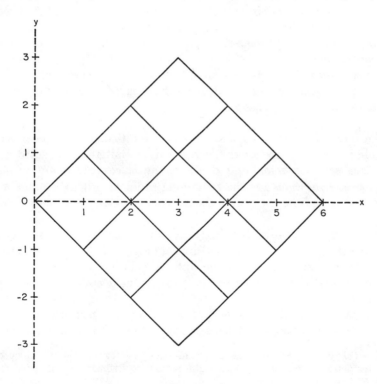

FIG. I.4

establish a coordinate system as shown in Fig. I.4. Then, the stage can be identified by the x-coordinate and the state by the y-coordinate.

The solution of a multistage decision process problem can be viewed as a sequence of transformations. Each member of the sequence transforms a stage and state into a new stage and state. In the example at hand, a stage and state determine a vertex (for example, the vertex A can be identified as stage 0 and state 0, or simply as $(0, 0)$), and a sequence of vertices represents a path. The path of minimum value can be represented by the transformation of $(0, 0)$ into $(1, 1)$, then $(1, 1)$ into $(2, 0)$, $(2, 0)$ into $(3, -1)$, $(3, -1)$ into $(4, 0)$, $(4, 0)$ into $(5, 1)$, and $(5, 1)$ into $(6, 0)$. In order to use the recursive method developed in Section 3, the stage variable and its numbering system must be chosen so that the stage number evolves monotonically along all admissible paths. The state need not exhibit this property, and will not in general. If more than one variable is monotonic along all admissible paths, any such variable can be considered as the stage. If no such monotonic variable can be found or conveniently adjoined to the problem, the algorithm that we shall develop is inapplicable, although other dynamic programming techniques may still prove useful.* It was to assure the monotonicity of the stage variable that we restricted our attention to only monotonic-to-the-right paths in the artificial example we have been considering.

We shall now state the basic principle of dynamic programming in terms of the concepts thus far developed. It has been called by Bellman "the principle of optimality," and asserts:

> An optimal sequence of decisions in a multistage decision process problem has the property that whatever the initial stage, state, and decision are, the remaining decisions must constitute an optimal sequence of decisions for the remaining problem, with the stage and state resulting from the first decision considered as initial conditions.†

This principle was used implicitly in solving the example in Section 3 when we observed that the optimal initial decision for an n-stage problem can be determined in terms of the optimal solution to all $(n - 1)$-stage problems whose initial states result from initial decisions in the n-stage problem.

Specifically, for the example of Section 3, adopting the coordinate system of Fig. I.4, we can now write a mathematical description of the reasoning

---

* For an algorithm that yields the minimum-value path for our example, independent of the restriction to monotonic-to-the-right paths, see Bellman and Dreyfus (1962), pp. 229–230.

† Bellman and Dreyfus (1962), p. 15.

employed to solve the problem. We begin by introducing an auxiliary function $S(x, y)$ of the integer variables x and y. The function $S(x, y)$ is defined at the vertices (x, y) of the network under discussion by

$S(x, y)$ = the value of the minimum-value admissible path connecting the vertex (x, y) and the terminal vertex $(6, 0)$.

We shall call the function $S(x, y)$ the *optimal value function*.

Let us now associate the symbol $a_u(x, y)$ with the value of the arc connecting the vertices (x, y) and $(x + 1, y + 1)$, the subscript u signifying the arc going diagonally *up* from (x, y); and let us associate the symbol $a_d(x, y)$ with the value of the arc connecting (x, y) with $(x + 1, y - 1)$, the d indicating *down*. We let either $a_u(x, y)$ or $a_d(x, y) = \infty$ if there is no associated arc of the network.

In terms of these symbols, the principle of optimality asserts the relation

$$S(x, y) = \min\left[\begin{array}{c} a_u(x, y) + S(x + 1, y + 1) \\ a_d(x, y) + S(x + 1, y - 1) \end{array}\right], \qquad (4.1)$$

where the symbol

$$\min\left[\begin{array}{c} c_1 \\ c_2 \end{array}\right]$$

denotes the smaller of the two quantities c_1 and c_2. Equation (4.1) is called a *recurrence relation* since it relates the values of S associated with a given stage x to the values for the following stage $x + 1$, and allows the computation of S in an iterative fashion.

The fact that the minimum-value path *from* the terminal point *to* the terminal point has zero value, since it contains no arcs, yields the boundary condition on the function $S(x, y)$,

$$S(6, 0) = 0. \qquad (4.2)$$

Equations (4.1) and (4.2) determine the value of $S(x, y)$ at each vertex of the network. The reader can easily verify that the above recurrence relation characterizing $S(x, y)$ is satisfied by the function tabulated in Fig. I.2.

Let us summarize the essence of the dynamic programming formalism. First, one thinks small, seeking to isolate a property that an optimal decision sequence satisfies *at each decision point*. That local property, expressed by the principle of optimality, concerns the optimal value associated with starting the process in any state that can be reached in one stage from the initial state. This fact requires several conceptual developments. One must think in terms of a more general problem than the original one—i.e., rather than analyze a particular problem with specific initial and terminal conditions, one must consider many problems, each with a different initial stage and state. This is termed imbedding the problem in a family of problems. Since each problem in this family has its own optimal sequence of decisions, one cannot seek *the* optimal sequence but must think of an optimal decision associated with each of the various possible initial stages and states of problems that belong to the family of problems. Hence, one seeks an *optimal policy*, the optimal decision for each possible initial stage and state, rather than an optimal sequence of decisions. Finally, to use the principle of optimality to determine the optimal policy, one needs to know the optimal value associated with all states that can immediately succeed each initial one. This results in the definition and use of the auxiliary optimal value function.

Very briefly, then, the practitioner of discrete dynamic programming will imbed a specific given problem in a more general family of problems, will define the optimal value function which associates a value with each of the various possible initial conditions of problems in that family, will invoke the principle of optimality in order to deduce a recurrence relation characterizing that function, and will seek the solution of the recurrence relation in order to obtain the optimal policy function which furnishes the solution to the specific given problem and all other problems in the more general family as well.

5. Two Properties of the Optimal Value Function

Let us return to the illustrative example of Section 2 and its numerical solution in Section 3. In the present section, we wish to discuss some aspects of that solution that recur in the continuous problems that will occupy us later. Then, in subsequent sections, we shall modify the example problem in various ways. We shall solve these modified problems and exhibit other properties of the solutions that have continuous analogs.

The optimal sequence of decisions in the example—the decisions that yield the path connecting A and B shown by the thick line in Fig. I.5—has two fundamental properties that can be expressed in terms of the optimal value function $S(x, y)$ and the optimal policy function. These functions were defined, in the above section, on the vertices of the network and were tabulated in Section 3, Fig. I.3; they are duplicated in Fig. I.6.

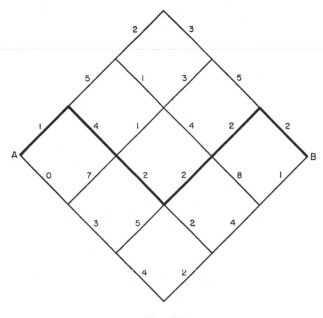

FIG. I.5

Consider the initial arc of the path of minimum value connecting A and B. The value of the optimal value function at A, the point $(0, 0)$, is related to the value at C, the point $(1, 1)$, by the equation

$$S(0, 0) = a_u(0, 0) + S(1, 1). \tag{5.1}$$

Hence,

$$S(1, 1) - S(0, 0) = -a_u(0, 0), \tag{5.2}$$

or, for the specific values of our example,

$$12 - 13 = -1. \tag{5.3}$$

Similarly, for the second arc of the optimal path connecting A to B, which is the initial arc of the optimal path connecting C and B, we have

$$S(2, 0) - S(1, 1) = -a_d(1, 1) \tag{5.4}$$

or, for our example

$$8 - 12 = -4. \tag{5.5}$$

If we call the difference between the value of the optimal value function at

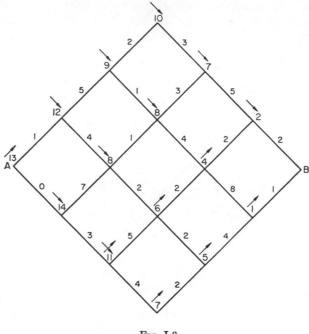

FIG. I.6

the right end of an arc and the value at its left end the *forward difference at its left end* with respect to the included arc, we can state:

Property 1. Evaluated at any initial point, the forward difference of the optimal value function taken with respect to the initial arc of the optimal path emanating from that point equals the negative of the value of the included arc.

Note that Property 1 does not hold at a vertex for the forward difference with respect to an included arc that is not on the optimal path emanating from that vertex. For example, the arc $\overset{\frown}{AD}$ is not on the optimal path emanating from A. For that arc, we have the forward difference one (14–13) which does not equal zero, the negative of the value of the included arc. Note also that Property 1 can easily be used to construct the optimal policy function (in this example, the set of arrows shown in Fig. I.6) from the optimal value function. Each arrow points in the direction (or directions) in which the forward difference between adjacent values of the optimal value function equals the negative of the included arc number. We mentioned in the Preface that knowledge of the single number which gives the optimal value of the path connecting specific initial and final points (such as A and B) was of no use in determining the optimal path itself, but that knowledge of the complete optimal value function was. The truth of this assertion should now be obvious.

The second characteristic property of the optimal path also follows from the definition of the optimal value function.

Property 2. The optimal choice of an arc emanating from a particular vertex renders the sum of

(1)   the forward difference of the optimal value function taken with respect to that arc, and
(2)   the value of the included arc

minimum over all possible decisions.

Property 1 implies that each arc of the optimal path renders this sum equal to zero. If a different decision rendered this sum negative, that decision would be a better decision than the optimal one, which would be a contradiction.

The above two obvious properties of the optimal path, stated in terms of the optimal value function, are equivalent to the fundamental recurrence relation (4.1), deduced from the principle of optimality.

6. An Alternative Method of Solution

Putting aside properties of the optimal path for a moment, let us now make an observation about the method of solution of the example problem. We chose to imbed the particular problem in a family of problems, each with the same terminal vertex B but with various initial vertices. This led to a recursive solution working backward from the terminal vertex and eventually including the initial vertex A. We call this the *backward* solution. We could equally well have imbedded the specific problem in a family of problems with fixed initial vertex and various terminal vertices. We call this the *forward* method of solution, and to use it we proceed as follows: Define the optimal value function $S(x, y)$ by

$S(x, y)$ = the value of the minimum-value admissible path connecting the initial vertex A to the vertex (x, y).

Then, this function $S(x, y)$, which differs from the optimal value function of the previous section, satisfies the recurrence relation

$$S(x, y) = \min \begin{bmatrix} a_u(x-1, y-1) + S(x-1, y-1) \\ a_d(x-1, y+1) + S(x-1, y+1) \end{bmatrix}, \quad (6.1)$$

with boundary condition

$$S(0, 0) = 0. \quad (6.2)$$

We have used here a sort of reversed principle of optimality stating:

An optimal sequence of decisions in a multistage decision process problem has the property that whatever the final decision and state preceding the terminal one, the prior decisions must constitute an optimal sequence of decisions leading from the initial state to that state preceding the terminal one.

The computation begins by using the value of $S(0, 0)$ to compute $S(1, 1)$ and $S(1, -1)$. Then these values are used in order to compute $S(2, 2)$,

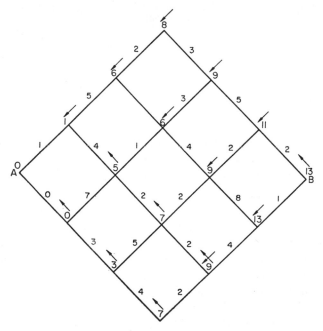

Fig. I.7

$S(2, 0)$, and $S(2, -2)$, etc. The arrows associated with vertices, constituting the optimal policy, indicate the preceding vertex from which it was optimal to come, and not as in the previous algorithm, the vertex to which it would be optimal to go. The solution to the problem of Section 2 is shown in Fig. I.7. The numbers represent the optimal value function and the arrows are the optimal decisions, as defined above. Of course, we find that the minimum-value path and its value have not changed due to the different imbedding technique.

7. Modified Properties of the Optimal Value Function

Property 1, stated in Section 5, must be modified for the forward method of solution.

We define the difference between the value of the optimal value function at the right end of an arc and the value at the left end as the *backward difference at its right end* with respect to the included arc. Then modified Property 1 is: Evaluated at any terminal point, the backward difference of the optimal value function taken with respect to the terminal arc of the optimal path to that point equals the value of the included arc.

Modified Property 2 is that: the optimal arc leading into a particular vertex renders the sum of the negative of the backward difference and the value of the included arc minimum over all possible arcs leading into the vertex.

8. A Property of Multistage Decision Processes

One further observation about the nature of multistage decision processes will be illustrated here in order to forewarn the reader against a possible pitfall. One cannot solve a multistage decision process problem by making, sequentially, the optimal single-stage decisions. That is, although the arc leading diagonally down from A in Fig. I.5 has value 0 while the arc leading up has value 1, the minimum-value sequence begins with the upward arc since it turns out that this arc leads to a much more desirable state than does the downward arc. So, not only the arc value but the effect of the different changes in state must be considered in making each decision. It is the value of these composite effects that is calculated and minimized at each application of the fundamental recurrence relation. This situation has been characterized by one decision-theorist as a case where the two birds in the bush might well be worth more than the one in the hand.

9. Further Illustrative Examples

So far we have studied a problem with fixed end points. Let us now consider a different problem. In the network shown in Fig. I.8, the minimum-value path is sought connecting the initial point A with any vertex on the terminal line B. Such a problem is said to have one *variable end point*. Let us see what new properties can be deduced.

To solve the problem, we define the optimal value function $S(x, y)$, which

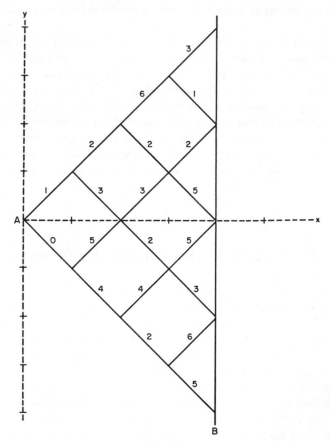

Fig. I.8

associates a value with each vertex, by

$S(x, y)$ = the value of the minimum-value admissible path connecting the vertex (x, y) with any vertex on the terminal line $x = 4$.

The function $S(x, y)$ satisfies the recurrence relation

$$S(x, y) = \min \begin{bmatrix} a_u(x, y) + S(x + 1, y + 1) \\ a_d(x, y) + S(x + 1, y - 1) \end{bmatrix}. \tag{9.1}$$

The boundary condition on the solution of (9.1) follows from the definition of S and the fact that the minimum-value path *from* any vertex on the terminal line *to* any vertex on the terminal line equals zero; the boundary

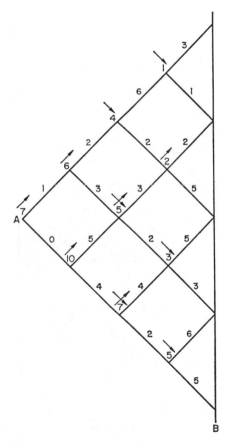

FIG. I.9

condition is

$$S(4, y) = 0. \tag{9.2}$$

Note by comparison with Eqs. (4.1) and (4.2) that allowing the terminal condition to be any vertex of an admissible set rather than a specified vertex affects only the boundary condition and not the recurrence relation.

The optimal value function and optimal policy function, as determined by (9.1) and (9.2) for the example of Fig. I.8, are shown by the numbers and arrows, respectively, in Fig. I.9. The optimal path from point A to line B has sum 7 and consists of two arcs going diagonally up, then one going down, and finally one going up.

An alternative method of solution could proceed in the opposite direction,

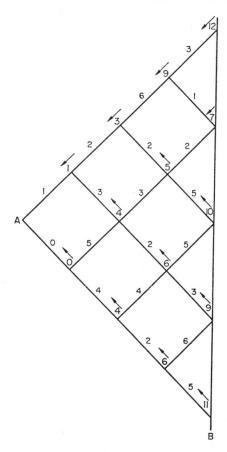

FIG. I.10

just as did the example of Section 6. We define

$S(x, y)$ = the value of the minimum-value admissible path connecting the initial vertex A with the vertex (x, y).

This leads to the recurrence relation

$$S(x, y) = \min \begin{bmatrix} a_u(x - 1, y - 1) + S(x - 1, y - 1) \\ a_d(x - 1, y + 1) + S(x - 1, y + 1) \end{bmatrix}, \quad (9.3)$$

with boundary condition

$$S(0, 0) = 0. \quad (9.4)$$

The optimal value function satisfying this relation is shown in Fig. I.10. The arrow associated with a vertex indicates the preceding vertex from which it is optimal to come.

Construction of this figure does not quite solve the problem. We now know the minimum value of paths from vertex A to each of the five possible terminal vertices. To decide to which terminal vertex the optimal path to the line B should go, we minimize $S(4, y)$ over the five admissible y values. Doing this, we find that the solution path to the original problem with variable end point should go to the vertex $(4, 2)$ and has associated with it a value of 7. We can then follow the arrows back from $(4, 2)$ to $(0, 0)$ to find the optimal path. As in the earlier example, correct use of either the backward or forward formulation gives the same (correct) result.

On the basis of the above observations, we state Property 3, applicable to problems with the terminal vertex not completely specified.

Property 3. If the backward recursion scheme is used, the optimal value function is zero at all admissible terminal vertices. If the forward recursion scheme is adopted, the optimal terminal vertex is found by minimizing the optimal value function over all admissible terminal vertices.

Suppose both initial and terminal vertices, as well as the connecting path, are to be picked optimally subject to constraints. For example, the initial vertex may be required to lie on a given line A and the terminal vertex on a given line B (see Fig. I.11). Then, whether the forward or backward recursion is used, a combination of the two computational devices developed above is required. First, the optimal value function is defined to be zero

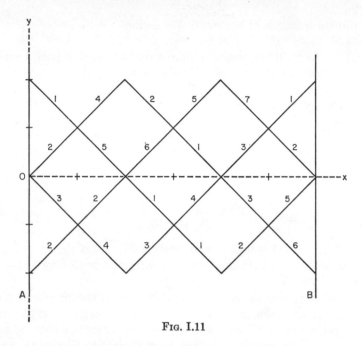

Fig. I.11

at each of the set of vertices constituting one admissible end point, and the optimal value function is computed. Then the optimal value function is minimized over the vertices that are admissible as the other end point. This minimization determines one end point of the optimal path. With one end point and the optimal policy function calculated, tracing out of the optimal path as specified by the optimal policy function determines the other end point. The reader should verify by dynamic programming methods that the minimum-value path from line A to line B in the network shown in Fig. I.11 starts at $(0, 2)$, terminates at $(6, 2)$, and has value 12.

All the problems above require the determination of a path which minimizes a summation. The continuous analog of this type of problem requires the determination of a curve which minimizes an integral. The dynamic programming solution of such problems will be the subject of Chapter III.

10. Terminal Control Problems

In all the prior examples, each arc of a path was assigned a value and the value of a path was the sum of the values of its arcs. We now consider a different type of problem, in which each path is assigned a value solely on the basis of its point of termination, independent of how it got there. We seek the path of minimum value under this new valuation rule. Such a problem is called a *terminal control problem*. We treat the continuous analog of this problem in Chapters IV and V.

If a terminal control problem is to be mathematically interesting, the set of admissible paths must be constrained so that only a limited number of points satisfying the definition of possible terminal points is attainable. Otherwise, we would have a calculus problem seeking the terminal point of minimum value, rather than a variational problem seeking the optimal *attainable* terminal point. Terminal control problems are not easily illustrated by simple discrete examples. It is difficult to find meaningful constraints on admissible paths that limit the set of attainable terminal points without simultaneously rendering the problem trivial. In the continuous theory, exemplified by missile or airplane trajectory optimization problems, the path constraints are the kinematical and dynamical equations of motion and arise quite naturally and necessarily from physical considerations.

11. Example of a Terminal Control Problem

Let us consider a six-stage problem as an illustrative example. Paths emanate from the origin. From each vertex (x, y) of a path, either an arc leading diagonally upward to $(x + 1, y + 1)$ or diagonally downward to $(x + 1, y - 1)$ is to be chosen, just as in the earlier examples. The problem terminates when $x = 6$. The value of a path is taken to be equal to its terminal y-coordinate, hence we have a terminal control problem. The path of minimum value is sought. While this problem is admittedly trivial it will serve to illustrate some points.

12. Solution of the Example

We initiate the solution by defining the optimal value function by

$S(x, y) =$ the value of the minimum-value admissible path starting at the point (x, y) and terminating at some vertex on the line $x = 6$,

where x and y are integers with $x = 0, 1, \ldots, 6$. The optimal value function satisfies the recurrence relation

$$S(x, y) = \min \begin{bmatrix} S(x + 1, y + 1) \\ S(x + 1, y - 1) \end{bmatrix}. \qquad (12.1)$$

where, it should be noted, there is no sum of terms on the right side of Eq. (12.1) since the value of a path depends on its point of termination but not explicitly upon the rest of the path. The terminal boundary condition is

$$S(6, y) = y \qquad (12.2)$$

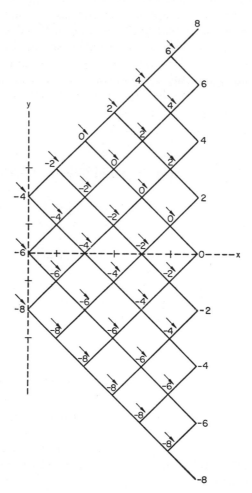

Fig. I.12

since the value of the minimum-value path starting, and terminating, at the point $(6, y)$ is y. Note that the boundary values are not zero as in the minimum-sum examples.

Numerical solution of this problem is accomplished by backward iteration of (12.1) starting from the terminal line $x = 6$, with the value of S along along that line given by (12.2). One starts this computational procedure from a sufficiently large set of potential terminal vertices to be sure of including all terminal vertices that are actually attainable from the specified initial point (in this case, the origin). The optimal value and optimal policy functions are shown in Fig. I.12. It is hardly surprising that the optimal path from the origin has value -6 and consists exclusively of diagonally downward arcs.

13. Properties of the Solution of a Terminal Control Problem

For a terminal control problem, the analog of Property 1 that was stated, for minimum-sum problems, in Section 5 is: Evaluated at any initial point, the forward difference of the optimal value function taken with respect to the initial arc of the optimal path emanating from that point is zero. That is, the optimal value function is constant along an optimal path.

Property 2 becomes: The optimal decision at a particular vertex renders the forward difference of the optimal value function minimum over all possible decisions.

Suppose that the problem is generalized to a third dimension so that paths are sought in (x, y, z)-space. Let the value of the path be, as before, its y-coordinate when $x = 6$. Then, if $S(x, y, z)$ is defined as in Section 12, the appropriate terminal boundary values of S are given by

$$S(6, y, z) = y. \tag{13.1}$$

Consequently, we see that the function S, at points of termination of paths, has the same value for all those points that have a fixed y-value and any z-value. In general, if a particular state variable does not enter into the terminal criterion, and the terminal value of the monotonic stage-variable is explicitly specified, the partial difference of the optimal value function, with respect to the variable not entering into the terminal criterion, is zero at the end point.

Suppose that the initial point is not specified explicitly but must belong to a given set of points. The optimal initial point is found by first computing, as described, the optimal value function by means of backward recursion from a large set of possible terminal points, and then by minimizing the optimal value function over all admissible initial points.

The above conclusions concerning terminal control problems whose end points are not completely specified will be called Property 3 of terminal control problems.

14. Summary

This completes our discussion of the dynamic programming solution of discrete deterministic problems of finite duration.

We have seen how our desire for a local characterization of optimality—that is, for some property holding for each decision of the optimal sequence of decisions—has led to the imbedding of a particular problem in a more general family of problems. Each member of the family can be characterized by a stage and state, and two functions—the optimal value function and the optimal policy function—can be defined on the set of stage and state values. These functions satisfy a recurrence relation deduced from the principle of optimality. The appropriate boundary condition for this relation follows from the definition of the optimal value function and depends on the manner in which the problem was specified. If either the optimal value or the optimal policy function has been determined (by the algorithms of this chapter they are determined simultaneously), the specific multistage decision process problem that initiated the analysis (as well as all other problems in the family in which the particular problem was imbedded) has been solved. We have emphasized the actual numerical solution of problems in this chapter in order to exhibit optimal value and optimal policy functions. In later chapters we shall be more concerned with the analysis of the fundamental recurrence relation than with its analytical or numerical solution.

We shall return briefly to simple discrete illustrative examples in Chapter VII where we introduce the concepts of stochastic and adaptive multistage decision process problems. Chapters II–VI, however, concern themselves solely with continuous deterministic problems.

CHAPTER II

The Classical Variational Theory

1. Introduction

In this chapter we shall indicate the nature of the problems generally studied by means of the calculus of variations, the types of mathematical arguments employed, and the kinds of results that have been obtained. A vast subject such as this can receive only cursory treatment in but one chapter and we unfortunately cannot include all the important topics, techniques, and results.

This chapter may be omitted with no loss of continuity by the reader interested specifically in the techniques of dynamic programming. We have included it for several reasons. First, we feel that the subsequent exposition of dynamic programming will be clearer if the reader has been provided with an overview of the types of problems to be studied and the results to be obtained. Second, by using simple examples in this chapter for illustrating the application of results, we avoid the necessity of doing so in the next chapter, thereby breaking the continuity of the presentation. Finally, since one of our major theses is the conceptual homogeneity of the dynamic programming approach, stemming as it does from one fundamental principle, we feel we should indicate to the interested reader the rather eclectic nature of the classical arguments.

We have chosen in this chapter to free ourselves from most of the actual manipulative analysis that is necessarily found in a mathematical text specifically devoted to the classical theory. Due to this decision, we hope that we can convey to those readers who are not enamored of the details of mathematical rigor some appreciation of the nature of the classical theory not otherwise easily available.

2. A Problem

Suppose that we were asked to find the curve, lying in a given plane and connecting two specified points in the plane, which is of shortest length. This is a typical example of the type of problem found in the domain of variational theory.

3. Admissible Solutions

While the problem just stated has everyday conversational meaning, it is a bit too imprecise for mathematical treatment. We must begin by defining the set of admissible curves among which the one of shortest length is sought. In the calculus of variations it is traditional to include in the set of *admissible curves* only continuous curves which consist of a finite number of segments on each of which the tangent turns continuously. Figure II.1 shows a particular pair of points and an admissible candidate for the title "curve of shortest length" connecting them. This curve consists of three segments, along each of which it has a continuously turning tangent.

While the consideration of only those rather well-behaved curves described here is a restriction accepted in almost all variational studies, the statement of the specific problem often includes further requirements on admissible curves. For example, the problem stated in Section 2 admits only planar curves passing through two specified points. When we speak of admissible curves, with respect to a particular problem, we mean those curves satisfying the above continuity properties and any further properties required by the problem statement.

Unless otherwise noted, the modifier "admissible" should be understood when we consider a curve or, synonymously, an arc, in what follows. A

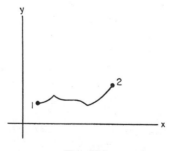

Fig. II.1

curve, which is a geometric entity, can be described by an equation of the form

$$y = y(x). \tag{3.1}$$

When we proceed analytically we shall consider *admissible functions* $y(x)$. This means that the function is continuous over the interval of interest and that the interval can be subdivided into a finite number of parts, on each of which $y(x)$ has a continuous derivative. In addition, the function satisfies any further conditions explicitly required in the statement of the problem. An admissible function $y(x)$ defines an admissible curve or arc $y = y(x)$.

4. Functions

Let us digress for a moment. Recall that a function of one real variable can be regarded as a rule that associates, with each real value of the independent variable (or argument) lying within some specified range, a numerical value of what is called the dependent variable. For example, the function $y(x)$ given by

$$y(x) = 2x^2 - x + 1 \tag{4.1}$$

together with the equation

$$y = y(x), \tag{4.2}$$

associates the value 7 of the dependent variable y with the value 2 of the independent variable x. Let x_0 be the value of the argument x, which has associated with it the smallest value of y. Suppose that $y(x)$ is continuously differentiable. The determination of x_0 is a classical minimization problem of calculus.

5. Functionals

We can also conceive of a rule that associates a dependent numerical value with an independent argument which is a curve (rather than a real number), and we can seek the curve with smallest associated value. As we have mentioned, a rule relating numerical values to numerical arguments is called a function. A rule associating numerical values with curves is an example of a *functional*.

With regard to the problem of finding the curve of minimum length connecting two points, we can begin by defining a particular functional which associates numbers, which are lengths, with curves. In these terms, the problem of Section 2 is to find the admissible curve that has related to it, by the arc-length functional, the smallest numerical value. The calculus of variations can be defined as the study of certain problems involving functional optimization.

6. Minimization and Maximization

For concreteness, we shall almost always discuss minimization problems. It should be understood that the variational theory is equally applicable to maximization problems. Any results for minimization problems can be reexpressed for maximization problems by observing that minimizing any quantity F is equivalent to maximizing $-F$. The curve of minimum length is also the curve the negative of whose length is maximum.

7. Arc-Length

Each admissible curve that we are going to consider has an arc-length associated with it. The mathematical formula giving the arc-length A of a curve $y = y(x)$ that connects the points $(x_0, y(x_0))$ and $(x_1, y(x_1))$ and that is continuous and has a continuous derivative is

$$A[y] = \int_{x_0}^{x_1} (1 + y'^2)^{1/2} \, dx. \tag{7.1}$$

We use the square brackets to enclose the function that is the argument of a functional.* Given a function $y(x)$, we can differentiate it to obtain its derivative $y'(x)$ and then perform the indicated integration of the function of x

$$(1 + y'^2)^{1/2}, \tag{7.2}$$

to obtain a number that equals the arc-length contained between the points $(x_0, y(x_0))$ and $(x_1, y(x_1))$ on the curve $y = y(x)$.

---

* If the curve has a discontinuous derivative, we replace the integral (7.1) by the sum of integrals taken over the intervals of continuity of the derivative.

8. The Simplest General Problem

The first general problem that we consider in this chapter is a generalization of the problem of the shortest arc-length. In the arc-length problem, the integrand

$$(1 + y'^2)^{1/2} \tag{8.1}$$

of the integral (7.1) to be minimized, was a function of the derivative of the unknown solution curve. More generally, we shall consider integrands that explicitly depend on the independent variable x and the unknown function $y(x)$ itself, as well as its derivative. Hence, the simplest general problem is to find that admissible curve $y = y(x)$ that minimizes a given functional $J[y]$ of the form

$$J[y] = \int_{x_0}^{x_1} F(x, y, y') \, dx. \tag{8.2}$$

Here, F is a given function of its three arguments. Note that (7.1) is simply a special case of (8.2) with x and y not appearing as arguments of F.

It is no coincidence that the problem posed in Section 2 led to a rule relating a value to a curve taking the form of a definite integral. The calculus of variations concerns itself only with the definite integral (single or multiple integral) functional and problems transformable into that form.

The particular problem posed in Section 2 admitted only solution curves connecting two fixed points. A problem is still considered to be of the simple type if the end points of the curve sought are merely stipulated to lie somewhere on specified curves. Such a problem is said to have *variable end points*. An example is the problem of finding the curve of minimum

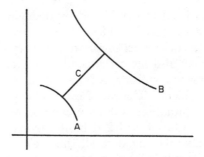

FIG. II.2

length connecting two given curves. In Fig. II.2, the curve C is the curve of minimum length connecting curves A and B.

A variational problem is not termed "simple" if there are supplementary side conditions that must be satisfied by admissible curves (see, for example, Section 36, this chapter). Such problems still lie, however, in the domain of the calculus of variations.

9. The Maximum-Value Functional

While the definite integral is an excellent and common example of a functional, it is by no means the only one. Another rule assigning numerical values to curves would be

$$J[y] = \max_{x_0 \le x \le x_1} [F(x, y, y')] \tag{9.1}$$

where F is some definite given function of x, y, and y'. Here, the choice of $y(x)$ determines F as a particular function of x, and the value of J associated with that $y(x)$ is the maximum value assumed by the function F in the given interval $x_0 \le x \le x_1$. That $y(x)$ might be sought which either maximizes or minimizes this maximum value of F. We might mention that, in a sense, the dynamic programming approach is conceptually more general than the calculus of variations, including, for example, the above maximum-value functional. We shall not, however, pursue this topic further in this book.

10. The Nature of Necessary Conditions

The classical variational theory begins by deducing conditions that the minimizing curve must satisfy. These are called *necessary conditions*. While the minimizing curve *must* satisfy a necessary condition, other non-minimizing curves may also meet the condition. Hence, the set of curves satisfying any necessary condition is larger than, or equal to, the set of curves solving the problem. (The set of solution curves usually consists of just one curve.) The situation is diagrammed schematically in Fig. II.3, where necessary conditions 1 and 2 delimit the set of solution curves to the set $A \cap B$ (this symbol denotes all those elements common to both sets A and B), which still is larger than the solution set (i.e., it includes nonsolution functions). Necessary conditions serve the useful purpose of

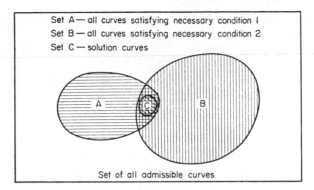

Set A — all curves satisfying necessary condition I
Set B — all curves satisfying necessary condition 2
Set C — solution curves

A   C   B

Set of all admissible curves

FIG. II.3

telling one where, in the set of all admissible curves, one should look for the solution curve.

11. Example

Consider the calculus problem: Given a function $f(x)$, find the point x_0, $a \leq x_0 \leq b$, having associated with it the minimum value of the function. A necessary condition, if the function has continuous derivative and does not take on its minimum value at a or b, is that

$$f'(x_0) = 0. \tag{11.1}$$

But, as is evident for the particular function $f(x)$ shown in Fig. II.4,

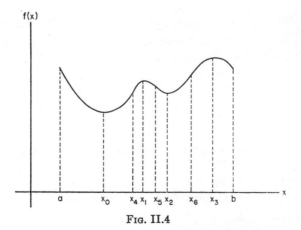

$f(x)$

a x_0 x_4 x_1 x_5 x_2 x_6 x_3 b x

FIG. II.4

nonminimizing points x_1, x_2, and x_3 also satisfy the necessary condition. The further necessary condition that

$$f''(x_0) \geq 0, \tag{11.2}$$

admits all points between a and x_4 and between x_5 and x_6. In conjunction with the necessary condition (11.1), it eliminates x_1 and x_3 from the set of possible solution points. The points x_0 and x_2 remain as contenders.

12. The Nature of Sufficient Conditions

Since the process of eliminating possible solutions by the stipulation of additional necessary conditions has no obvious termination,* one next asks about properties which, if satisfied by a curve, definitely establish it as a solution curve. Such properties are termed *sufficient conditions*.

A sufficient condition for a given problem which *does* have a solution may be satisfied by a vacuous set of curves. For example, since, by its definition, the arc-length of a curve is always nonnegative, the statement "any curve with arc-length 0 is a solution curve for the minimum arc-length problem" is a valid sufficient condition, yet not a very useful one.

13. Necessary and Sufficient Conditions

If a set of properties exactly defines the set of solution curves, the condition that a curve satisfy the properties is both necessary and sufficient.

The ultimate goal of our investigation would logically be the statement of a set of necessary and sufficient conditions for the general variational problem. Unfortunately, for general problems in the calculus of variations this has never been done, due to the immense variety of special situations that can arise, and no such conditions will be found in this book.

14. The Absolute Minimum of a Functional

Let us consider the problem: Find that admissible function $y(x)$ satisfying the end point conditions $y(x_0) = y_0$ and $y(x_1) = y_1$ (i.e., the curve

---

* In the calculus of variations, an important new necessary condition was discovered by Weierstrass more than a hundred years after the first few.

$y = y(x)$ connecting the two points (x_0, y_0) and (x_1, y_1)) which renders minimum the functional $J[y]$ given by

$$J[y] = \int_{x_0}^{x_1} F(x, y, y') \, dx, \tag{14.1}$$

where $F(x, y, y')$ is a specified function.

Assuming the solution curve is unique, what we seek is the curve that yields a number J, by Eq. (14.1), that is smaller than the number yielded by any other admissible curve. The value of J corresponding to such a curve is called the *absolute minimum* of the functional $J[y]$ and the associated curve is the *absolutely minimizing curve*. However, in practice, the classical variational theory is generally less ambitious in what it seeks, as we shall see below.

15. A Relative Minimum of a Function

Since functional minimization can be regarded as a generalization of function minimization, it is reasonable initially to look to the ideas and results of the ordinary calculus for guidance in our study of the more general situation.

Suppose that we are given a function $y(x)$ and asked to find the value x_0 of the independent variable x for which y, given by $y = y(x)$, assumes its minimum value. A curve $y = y(x)$ is sketched in Fig. II.5.

Following classical calculus theory, we define a concept called *relative minimality* by: The point $\bar{x}$ yields a relative minimum of $y = y(x)$ if there exists an $\epsilon > 0$ with a corresponding neighborhood N_ϵ of the point $\bar{x}$ given by $| x - \bar{x} | \leq \epsilon$ such that $y(\bar{x}) \leq y(x)$ for all x in N_ϵ. By this definition, the points A, B, and C yield relative minima of the function

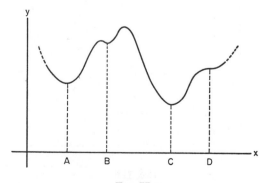

Fig. II.5

shown in Fig. II.5, but D (where $y' = y'' = 0$, but $y''' \neq 0$) does not. the function

$$y = x^3 \tag{15.1}$$

exhibits, at the origin, the behavior ascribed to the point D.

16. A Strong Relative Minimum of a Functional

Returning to variational theory, we seek a curve $y = y(x)$ which minimizes a functional $J[y]$. We define a *strong neighborhood* N_ϵ in function space of an admissible function $\bar{y}(x)$, where $x_0 \leq x \leq x_1$, as the collection of all admissible functions $y(x)$ for which the inequality

$$| y(x) - \bar{y}(x) | \leq \epsilon \tag{16.1}$$

holds for all x in $[x_0, x_1]$, where $\epsilon > 0$. A different strong neighborhood corresponds to each value of ϵ. A curve $y = \bar{y}(x)$ is said to yield a *strong relative minimum* of $J[y]$ if there exists a strong neighborhood of $\bar{y}(x)$ such that $J[\bar{y}] \leq J[y]$ for all $y(x)$ in the neighborhood.

Shown in Fig. II.6 is a curve $y = \bar{y}(x)$, a strong neighborhood, and a curve $y = y(x)$ in the neighborhood.

17. A Weak Relative Minimum of a Functional

It is convenient in variational theory to define also a *weak neighborhood* N_ϵ of an admissible function $\bar{y}(x)$, where $x_0 \leq x \leq x_1$, as the collection

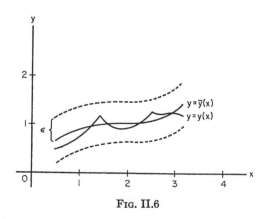

FIG. II.6

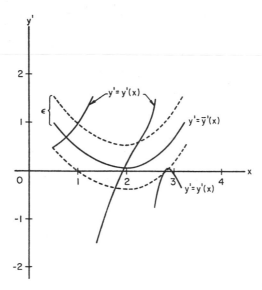

FIG. II.7

of all admissible functions $y(x)$ for which the two inequalities

$$| y(x) - \bar{y}(x) | \leq \epsilon \tag{17.1}$$

$$| y'(x) - \bar{y}'(x) | \leq \epsilon \tag{17.2}$$

hold for all x in $[x_0, x_1]$ where $\epsilon > 0$. A different weak neighborhood corresponds to each value of ϵ. A curve $y = \bar{y}(x)$ is said to yield a *weak relative minimum* of $J[y]$ if there exists a weak neighborhood of $\bar{y}(x)$ such that $J[\bar{y}] \leq J[y]$ for all $y(x)$ in the neighborhood.

It may surprise the reader that the definition of a weak neighborhood is more restrictive than the definition of a strong neighborhood. However, the statement that a result holds, given ϵ, for all curves in the weak neighborhood asserts less than the statement that the result holds for the larger class of curves in the strong neighborhood corresponding to the same ϵ. Hence, the choice of terminology, which, incidentally, is traditional and not ours.

For a function $y(x)$ to lie in a weak neighborhood of $\bar{y}(x)$ corresponding to a small value of ϵ, its derivative at each point as well as its value must closely approximate those of $\bar{y}(x)$. The curve $y = y(x)$ in Fig. II.6 does not lie within the weak neighborhood of $y = \bar{y}(x)$ corresponding to the value of ϵ shown. To show this, we sketch in Fig. II.7 the derivative of the curve $y = \bar{y}(x)$ and the derivative of the curve $y = y(x)$ which was seen in Fig. II.6 to lie within the strong neighborhood N_ϵ of $y = \bar{y}(x)$.

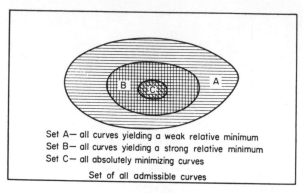

Set A— all curves yielding a weak relative minimum
Set B— all curves yielding a strong relative minimum
Set C— all absolutely minimizing curves

Set of all admissible curves

FIG. II.8

Inequality (17.2) is clearly violated for the given value of ϵ. The curve $y = y(x)$ *does* lie within a weak neighborhood of $y = \bar{y}(x)$ for sufficiently large ϵ. In what follows, however, we are going to be concerned only with very small $|\epsilon|$.

If no constraints bound the domain of admissible curves, and if a curve yielding an absolute minimum exists, then the curve yielding the absolute minimum of a given functional must be a member of the set of curves yielding strong relative minima. Each member of this set, in turn, must be a curve yielding a weak relative minimum. This fact is shown schematically in Fig. II.8. Hence, conditions which are necessary for a curve to yield a weak relative minimum are necessary for the curve to be the solution. The classical theory begins by studying conditions necessary for a curve to yield a weak relative minimum.

18. Weak Variations

Suppose that we wish to test the curve $y = y(x)$ to see if it yields a weak relative minimum of the functional (14.1). For comparison purposes, we can deform the curve into another curve $y = g(x)$ in the following *arbitrary* manner: Choose a function $\eta(x)$ so that the curve given by

$$y = g(x) = y(x) + \epsilon\eta(x) \qquad (18.1)$$

is admissible for all ϵ. Once $\eta(x)$ is specified, every value of ϵ yields a deformation of $y(x)$.

For example, suppose that the curve $y = y(x)$ that we wish to deform is given by

$$y = x^2; \qquad (18.2)$$

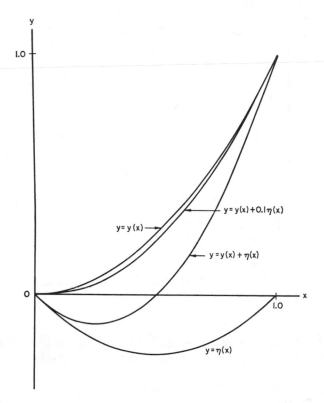

Fig. II.9

that by the problem statement admissible curves must satisfy the usual continuity properties and also must pass through the points (0, 0) and (1, 1); and that we let $\eta(x)$ in (18.1) take the particular form

$$\eta(x) = x(x - 1). \tag{18.3}$$

Shown in Fig. II.9 is the curve $y = x^2$ and the deformations $y = g(x)$ corresponding to the values of ϵ in Eq. (18.1) of 0.1 and 1, as well as a plot of $y = \eta(x)$.

If a different $\eta(x)$ had been chosen, the deformation would be different. For $\eta(x)$ given by

$$\eta(x) = 10x \qquad\qquad 0 \leq x \leq 0.1$$

$$\eta(x) = 2 - 10x \qquad 0.1 \leq x \leq 0.2$$

$$\eta(x) = 0 \qquad\qquad 0.2 \leq x \, 1 < \tag{18.4}$$

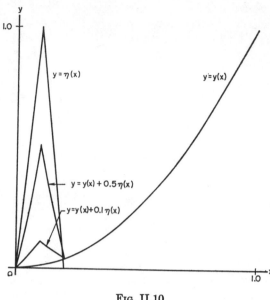

FIG. II.10

we have the situation shown in Fig. II.10 where $y = y(x)$ is deformed only between 0 and 0.2. Two of these deformations are indicated in the figure.

Note that in order for the deformed curve to pass through the points $(0, 0)$ and $(1, 1)$, no matter what the value of ϵ, we must have $\eta(0) = \eta(1) = 0$. Also note that as long as η and η' remain finite, by choosing $|\epsilon|$ sufficiently small, $g(x)$ defined in (18.1) and its derivative $g'(x)$ can be made arbitrarily close to $y(x)$ and $y'(x)$, respectively. Hence, given a function $y(x)$, an admissible $\eta(x)$, and a weak neighborhood N_δ of $y(x)$, we can choose $|\epsilon|$ sufficiently small so that the deformation given by Eq. (18.1) lies in the weak neighborhood. Such deformations will be called *weak variations* of $y(x)$.

19. The First and Second Variations

Given any $y(x)$ and $\eta(x)$ such that $y = y(x) + \epsilon\eta(x)$ is admissible, and given any weak neighborhood of $y(x)$, for $|\epsilon|$ sufficiently small $y(x) + \epsilon\eta(x)$ will lie within the weak neighborhood. Therefore, if there is to exist a weak neighborhood of $y(x)$ such that no curve in the neighborhood yields a smaller value of the functional than does $y(x)$, all weak variations of $y(x)$ generated by an admissible $\eta(x)$ and sufficiently small $|\epsilon|$ must yield functional values larger than or equal to that produced by $y(x)$. Consequently, for the functional (14.1) to have a weak relative minimum corresponding to some particular curve $y = y(x)$, the inequality

$$\int_{x_0}^{x_1} F(x, y, y') \, dx \leq \int_{x_0}^{x_1} F(x, y + \epsilon\eta, y' + \epsilon\eta') \, dx \qquad (19.1)$$

must hold for $|\epsilon|$ sufficiently small and for every function $\eta(x)$ such that $y(x) + \epsilon\eta(x)$ is admissible.

Expansion in ordinary Taylor series of the right-hand side of (19.1) and cancellation yields the series in ϵ

$$0 \leq \epsilon \int_{x_0}^{x_1} (F_y\eta + F_{y'}\eta') \, dx$$

$$+ \tfrac{1}{2}\epsilon^2 \int_{x_0}^{x_1} (F_{yy}\eta^2 + 2F_{yy'}\eta\eta' + F_{y'y'}\eta'^2) \, dx + o(\epsilon^2) \qquad (19.2)$$

where $o(\epsilon^2)$ signifies terms which, after division by ϵ^2, approach zero as ϵ approaches zero. A subscripted function denotes partial differentiation of the function with respect to the subscripted variable. The partial derivatives of $F(x, y, y')$ are evaluated along the curve $y = y(x)$ and, therefore, should be considered as particular functions of x once F and $y = y(x)$ are specified.

The numerical coefficient of ϵ, which depends on $y(x)$ and $\eta(x)$, which is denoted by the symbol $V_1[y, \eta]$, and which is given by the formula

$$V_1[y, \eta] = \int_{x_0}^{x_1} (F_y\eta + F_{y'}\eta') \, dx, \qquad (19.3)$$

is called the *first variation* with respect to the deformation (18.1). The numerical coefficient of $\epsilon^2/2$, denoted by $V_2[y, \eta]$ and given by

$$V_2[y, \eta] = \int_{x_0}^{x_1} (F_{yy}\eta^2 + 2F_{yy'}\eta\eta' + F_{y'y'}\eta'^2) \, dx, \qquad (19.4)$$

is called the *second variation*.

20. The Euler-Lagrange Equation

For inequality (19.2) to hold, for given $y(x)$, and all sufficiently small $|\epsilon|$, the first variation (19.3) must equal zero for all choices of $\eta(x)$. In order for this to occur, $y(x)$ must satisfy the relationship*

$$F_{y'} = \int_{x_0}^{x} F_y \, dx + c. \tag{20.1}$$

This condition on the function $y(x)$ is called the *integrated form of the Euler-Lagrange equation*. For a given integrand F and function $y(x)$, each side of Eq. (20.1) is a function of x, and the condition asserted is that $y(x)$ must be chosen so that the two functions of x are identical. On any subarc with continuously turning tangent, (20.1) takes the form of the famous *Euler-Lagrange differential equation*

$$(d/dx)F_{y'} - F_y = 0. \tag{20.2}$$

It is important to note that (20.1), involving no derivative of $y(x)$ higher than the first, must hold all along the curve $y = y(x)$, even at points of discontinuous $y'(x)$. Equation (20.2) involves, in general, the second derivative of $y(x)$, since F, and hence $F_{y'}$, depends on the first derivative of $y(x)$. But $y''(x)$ is not defined at points of discontinuity of $y'(x)$, so (20.2) holds only between such points. Thus, result (20.1) is more powerful than result (20.2) and can be used, as we shall indicate later in this chapter, to deduce conditions that hold at points of discontinuous $y'(x)$, points that are called *corners*.

The remarkable fact here is that the condition that the equation

$$V_1[y, \eta] = 0 \tag{20.3}$$

must hold for all admissible functions $\eta(x)$, implies the condition that $y(x)$ satisfy Eq. (20.1); yet Eq. (20.1) does not involve $\eta(x)$ at all. This result is quite fortuitous. We may be willing to perform a calculation to check a condition such as (20.1) at each point of a single function $y(x)$ (even here we often actually substitute many discrete points for the continuum). However, it would be out of the question, practicably speaking, to check the condition that the integral (19.3) equals zero for every function $\eta(x)$ in an infinite set of such functions.

Converting conditions involving the candidate $y(x)$ and arbitrary perturbing functions $\eta(x)$ into conditions on just the function $y(x)$ is the

---

* This result is not expected to be obvious. However, due to the nature of this book we must omit the details of the derivations of the classical theory. While it is tempting to repeat the very famous classical derivation of the above result, we draw the line here for fear that otherwise we shall never draw the line. References are provided at the end of this chapter to standard texts which contain the details of the derivations that we have omitted. The above result and many others will, of course, be derived from the dynamic programming viewpoint in the next chapter.

heart of the difficulty in the derivations of the classical necessary conditions which we shall state below.

21. Example

Turning to the minimum-distance problem where

$$F(x, y, y') = (1 + y'^2)^{1/2}, \tag{21.1}$$

we see that the Euler-Lagrange equation (20.2) becomes, in this case, the equation

$$(d/dx) \left[y'/(1 + y'^2)^{1/2} \right] = 0. \tag{21.2}$$

This equation implies that

$$y'/(1 + y'^2)^{1/2} = c, \tag{21.3}$$

where c is a constant, and thus that

$$y' = c/(1 - c^2)^{1/2}. \tag{21.4}$$

Hence, between possible corners at which y' is discontinuous, we see that the curve $y = y(x)$ of minimum arc-length, if it exists, must be a straight line.

22. The Legendre Condition

It is necessary that $y(x)$ satisfy Eq. (20.1) if the curve $y = y(x)$ is to yield a smaller value of the integral (14.1) than the curves $y = g(x)$, given by (18.1), for any admissible $\eta(x)$ and for all $| \epsilon |$ sufficiently small. This is necessary for weak relative minimality, which is necessary for strong relative minimality, which, in turn, is necessary for absolute minimality. Consequently, while we may be sure we have caught the answer, if one exists, in the net of our first necessary condition, we have possibly also caught a wide assortment of other curves. Among the catch, indeed, are all functions yielding relative maxima of the integral (14.1).

It is next shown in texts on the classical theory that if we add the condition that

$$F_{y'y'} \geq 0 \tag{22.1}$$

for all x in $[x_0, x_1]$, then we eliminate most weak relative maxima (and other sorts of undesirable stationary solutions) while excluding no actual solutions. This condition is called the *Legendre necessary condition*. Such rare relative maxima as have $F_{y'y'} = 0$ for some range of x and certain properties of higher derivatives might still sneak in.

For the minimum-distance example, the reader can verify that

$$F_{y'y'} = (1 + y'^2)^{-3/2}. \qquad (22.2)$$

Consequently, $F_{y'y'}$ is always positive and the Legendre test is satisfied no matter what $y(x)$ is chosen.

For a weak relative maximum, naturally, an inequality opposite in sense to (22.1) must hold. We see from the positivity of (22.2) that no curve can possibly yield a maximum for the distance problem. This is consistent with common sense since there is no *longest* path between two points. Similarly, some problems possess no minimizing curve and this explains why we occasionally insert a qualifying clause such as "if a minimizing curve exists."

23. The Second Variation and the Second Derivative

There is an obvious similarity between the Legendre condition and the second derivative condition for minima of ordinary calculus, but the analogy can be overplayed. (For example, Legendre incorrectly felt that the satisfaction of Eq. (20.1) and strict inequality in (22.1) would guarantee weak relative minimality.)

If $F_{y'y'} < 0$ when evaluated at some point on a candidate curve which satisfies Eq. (20.1), then one *can* find a better perturbed curve lying within any given weak neighborhood of the candidate curve. This means that the Legendre condition is necessary for weak relative minimality. However, it cannot be argued that if $F_{y'y'} > 0$ (strict inequality) one *cannot* find a better perturbed curve, as one might suspect by analogy with ordinary calculus. This is because $F_{y'y'}$ is not really the second variation $V_2[y, \eta]$ (see Eq. (19.4)), but rather only enters into it.

The second variation must be nonnegative if inequality (19.2) is to hold for all sufficiently small $|\epsilon|$ when $y(x)$ satisfies the Euler-Lagrange equation, thereby making the first variation zero. The second variation takes the form of a definite integral over the range of the independent variable x. A correct and powerful necessary condition for weak relative minimality over variations of the type (18.1) is that this integral, which involves $y(x)$, the perturbing function $\eta(x)$, and the derivatives of these functions, be nonnegative when evaluated in terms of the solution function $y(x)$ and any admissible $\eta(x)$. (This condition is quite analogous to the second derivative being nonegative for the minimum of a function.) In this form, however, it is a useless condition since it involves all admissible functions $\eta(x)$ and is not verifiable by any practical method.

24. The Jacobi Necessary Condition

For a 50-year-period in the late 18th and early 19th centuries, it was hoped that a net built of the Euler-Lagrange and Legendre conditions (with a slight modification in the case of equality in (22.1)) would be necessary and sufficient for weak relative minimality. Then Jacobi re-examined the Legendre condition and showed that it was not always effective in distinguishing relative minima.

Jacobi further examined the second variation integral (19.4) associated with perturbations of the form (18.1). He sought a condition guaranteeing the nonnegativity of the second variation. His study led to a statement about the zeros of a solution function $v(x)$ of a differential equation, called *Jacobi's equation*. Jacobi's linear second-order differential equation for $v(x)$ is

$$(F_{v'v'})v''(x) + [(d/dx)F_{v'v'}]v'(x) + [(d/dx)F_{vv'} - F_{vv}]v(x) = 0,$$

$$(24.1)$$

where the coefficients of $v(x)$, $v'(x)$, and $v''(x)$ are known functions of x determined by the particular integrand $F(x, y, y')$ and the particular solution curve $y = y(x)$ of the Euler-Lagrange equation.

To apply Jacobi's condition to a problem with a fixed right-hand end point, one finds a solution $v(x)$ of Eq. (24.1) that is zero at the right-hand end point x_1 of the interval of integration but is not identically zero. Then, if that solution does not take on the value zero at any point in the closed interval $[x_0, x_1]$ except x_1, it can be concluded that the strengthened Legendre condition

$$F_{v'v'} > 0 \qquad (24.2)$$

in $[x_0, x_1]$ guarantees that any curve $y = g(x)$ given by (18.1) will be no better than $y = y(x)$ for sufficiently small $|\epsilon|$. Consequently, satisfaction of the Euler-Lagrange and strengthened Legendre conditions and the Jacobi condition concerning the zeros of a solution of (24.1) are sufficient to assure weak relative minimality. A point other than x_1, if such exists, at which the solution $v(x)$ assumes the value zero, is called a *conjugate point*.

Jacobi further showed that if, associated with a candidate curve $y = y(x)$, there exists a conjugate point in the open interval (x_0, x_1), the curve cannot possibly be a minimizing curve, even if the Euler-Lagrange and strengthened Legendre conditions are satisfied. This proves that the Jacobi condition, asserting that the solution curve contain no conjugate point, is necessary for minimality.

25. Example

Application of the Jacobi condition to a minimum arc-length problem proceeds as follows. Suppose we seek the curve of minimum length between the points $(0, 0)$ and $(1, 1)$. The Euler-Lagrange equation suggests we study the straight line

$$y = x \tag{25.1}$$

as a possible solution. Equation (22.2) shows that the Legendre test is passed. The associated Jacobi equation (24.1) is

$$2^{-3/2} v''(x) + 0 \cdot v'(x) + 0 \cdot v(x) = 0, \tag{25.2}$$

since F_{yy} and $F_{yy'}$ are zero and $F_{y'y'}$ is constant along the curve (25.1). The solution of this equation takes the form of the straight line

$$v(x) = c_1 x + c_2. \tag{25.3}$$

Letting $v(1) = 0$ as required, and taking $v'(1) = k$, we obtain

$$v(x) = kx - k. \tag{25.4}$$

Unless $k = 0$, this curve takes the value zero only at $x = 1$. But $k = 0$ is prohibited, because then the curve $v = v(x)$ would be identically zero. Since the solution takes on the value zero in the interval $[0, 1]$ only at the point $x = 1$, we conclude that the Jacobi test is passed.

26. Focal Point

For a problem with a variable admissible right-hand end point (see Section 8), the required terminal value of the solution $v(x)$ of (24.1) is a certain nonzero number determined by the terminal condition of the problem. For such a problem, a point x where $v(x) = 0$ is called a *focal point* and it is necessary for weak relative minimality that no focal point exist in the interval of interest.

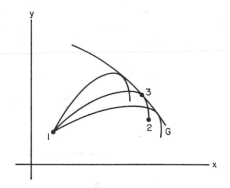

FIG. II.11

27. Geometric Conjugate Points

The strictly analytic investigation of the second variation has its geometric counterpart. Let us define the term *extremal curve* (or *extremal*) to mean a curve $y = y(x)$ that is admissible, that has continuous first and second derivatives, and that satisfies the Euler-Lagrange differential equation (20.2). By means of the theory of differential equations, it can be shown that through a fixed point, called 1 in Fig. II.11, there passes, in general, a one-parameter family of extremals. If such a family has an envelope G, then a point of contact of an extremal with the envelope is called a point conjugate to 1 on that extremal. In this figure, point 3 is conjugate to 1 on curve 12. Geometrically, Jacobi's necessary condition can now be stated: On a minimizing extremal curve connecting points 1 and 2, and with $F_{y'y'} \neq 0$ at each point on it, there can be no point 3 conjugate to 1 between 1 and 2. Except for certain exceptional cases, it can be shown that there is a one-to-one correspondence between zeros of Jacobi's differential equation as discussed earlier and geometric conjugate points as defined above.

28. The Weierstrass Necessary Condition

Research by Weierstrass performed a half century after Jacobi's work led to a major crisis in classical variational theory. We shall present this development in the terminology of weak and strong neighborhoods. Actually, these terms were unknown at the time and are the outgrowth of the observations of Weierstrass.

The analysis of earlier mathematicians had shown that, given a function $y(x)$ and a weak neighborhood of the function, a new function lying in the neighborhood of $y(x)$ and yielding a smaller value of the criterion functional (14.1) could be constructed by a weak variation of the type (18.1), unless $y(x)$ satisfied the Euler-Lagrange, Legendre, and Jacobi conditions. Hence, satisfaction of these conditions is necessary for a function to yield a weak relative minimum. Furthermore, it was known that, suitably strengthened, the above conditions are sufficient to assure that there exists a weak neighborhood of $y(x)$ in which no other curve gives as small a functional value as $y(x)$. Consequently $y(x)$, if it satisfies the strengthened conditions, yields a weak relative minimum.

Weierstrass showed that even though $y(x)$ yielded a weak relative minimum, it might be impossible to find any *strong* neighborhood of $y(x)$ in which $y(x)$ was unimprovable. To do this he constructed a method of perturbing $y(x)$ into a new function $g(x)$ such that $g(x)$ could be made to lie within any given strong neighborhood of $y(x)$ and yet failed to lie within any weak neighborhood N_ϵ for sufficiently small $|\epsilon|$. If such a perturbation yields a reduced value of the functional in all strong neighborhoods, yet fails to lie within the weak neighborhood in which $y(x)$ yields a weak relative minimum, the function $y(x)$ furnishes a weak relative minimum but not a strong relative minimum.

Having shown such a situation can indeed exist, Weierstrass gave a condition that a curve $y = y(x)$, yielding a strong relative minimum, must satisfy. The Weierstrass condition is therefore necessary for strong relative minimality and, consequently, necessary for absolute minimality.

In Fig. II.12, let $y = y(x)$ be the candidate arc, and let points 1 and 2 on the arc contain no point of discontinuity of y' between them. Let the curve $y = Y(x)$ be some arbitrary curve through point 1 with Y' evaluated at point 1 not equal to y' evaluated at point 1. Let point 3 be a movable point on $y = Y(x)$ and let δ be the arc-length along $y = Y(x)$

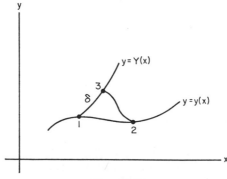

FIG. II.12

between points 1 and 3. Let the arc from 3 to 2 be generated by a one-parameter rule and coincide with $y = y(x)$ when point 3 coincides with 1. If the part of the curve $y = y(x)$ between 1 and 2 is replaced by the arc $\overset{\frown}{13}$ followed by the arc $\overset{\frown}{32}$, this construction generates, for $|\delta|$ sufficiently small, a deformation of $y = y(x)$ lying within any given strong neighborhood of $y = y(x)$. The deformed curve has a discontinuous derivative at point 1.

If ϵ_1 equals the difference between the right-hand derivatives Y' and y' evaluated at point 1, the deformed curve fails to lie within any weak neighborhood N_ϵ of $y(x)$ for $\epsilon < \epsilon_1$, no matter how small $|\delta|$ might be.

Let a function $E(x, y, y', Y')$ be defined by

$$E(x, y, y', Y')$$
$$= F(x, y, Y') - F(x, y, y') - (Y' - y')F_{y'}(x, y, y'). \tag{28.1}$$

Weierstrass showed that if, given a curve $y = y(x)$, the function $E(x, y, y', Y')$ fails to satisfy the inequality

$$E \geq 0 \tag{28.2}$$

for some $Y' \neq y'$, then there exist deformations lying within any given strong neighborhood of $y(x)$ which yield smaller values of the functional (14.1) than the value of $y(x)$. The *Weierstrass necessary condition*, designed to prohibit this possibility, can be stated: At every element (x, y, y') of a minimizing arc, the condition

$$E(x, y, y', Y') \geq 0 \tag{28.3}$$

must be satisfied for every admissible set (x, y, Y') different from (x, y, y').

Since the Weierstrass condition directly concerns minimality, rather than stationarity as did the Euler-Lagrange condition, it entails no further supporting statements analogous to the Legendre and Jacobi conditions that support the Euler-Lagrange stationarity condition. If we add the Weierstrass condition to our net, any function that fails to satisfy it cannot yield a strong relative minimum and, as a result, cannot yield an absolute minimum, and we have another necessary condition. As we shall show below by example, an occasional function satisfying the Euler-Lagrange, Legendre, and Jacobi conditions may be excluded by the Weierstrass condition; thus, we are closing down upon the answer.

The inclusion in the set of curves satisfying (28.3) of curves for which the equation

$$E = 0 \tag{28.4}$$

holds for some element (x, y, y') and for some $Y' \neq y'$, may let in an unwanted curve which is not even a relative minimum, but (28.3) suffices as a necessary condition. A condition demanding that E be strictly greater than zero might exclude the answer but can be used to construct sufficient conditions. Questions concerning the multitude of possible situations where $E = 0$ remain unanswered, and therefore a useful set of conditions that are both necessary and sufficient has not been found.

29. Example

As an illustration of the necessity of the Weierstrass condition, consider the problem: Choose a curve $y = y(x)$ connecting the points (0, 0) and (1, 1) and minimizing the functional $J[y]$ given by

$$J[y] = \int_0^1 y'^3 \, dx. \tag{29.1}$$

The unique solution of the integrated Euler-Lagrange equation (20.1) is the straight line $y = x$. The slope of the line is 1 and the above functional equals 1. As the reader can verify, along this curve both the Legendre condition and the Jacobi condition are satisfied, so no variation of the form (18.1) yields an improvement.

However,

$$E(x, y, y', Y') = Y'^3 - 1 - 3(Y' - 1) \tag{29.2}$$

for all (x, y, y') along the straight line connecting the origin and (1, 1). (Normally, E is a function of x but in this case it happens to be the same for all x.) The expression (29.2) is negative if $Y' < -2$, so the Weierstrass condition is not satisfied.

Consequently, there exist perturbations of the straight line $y = x$ that lie within any given strong neighborhood of $y = x$ and yield a smaller value of the criterion (29.1) than does $y = x$. Let us construct a specific example. The first segment of the perturbation is a straight line segment with slope less than -2, say -3, and connects the points (0, 0) and $(\delta, -3\delta)$. This corresponds to the arc $\overarc{13}$ in Fig. II.12. The second segment is a straight line connecting $(\delta, -3\delta)$ and (0.1, 0.1) and corresponds to arc $\overarc{32}$ of Fig. II.12. The third segment is part of the candidate curve $y = x$. The particular perturbed curve, for δ of about 0.06, is shown in Fig. II.13. At the point $x = \delta$, the curve $y = x$ and the perturbed curve differ by their maximum amount, 4δ, so the perturbed curve lies within the strong neighborhood $N_{4\delta}$ of $y = x$. This construction yields a curve

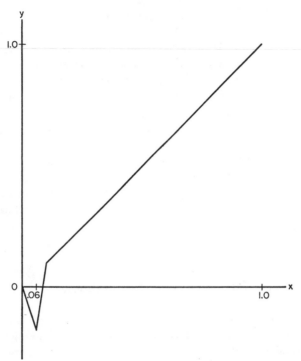

FIG. II.13

such that the criterion integral (29.1) equals $1 - 16\delta + o(\delta)$, which is less than 1 for all sufficiently small positive δ. Therefore, the problem has a relative minimum corresponding to the curve $y = x$ for weak variations of the type (18.1), but not for the strong variation of the Weierstrass type. Since the necessary condition that the integrated form of the Euler-Lagrange equation be satisfied admits only the straight-line solution that we have studied and the Weierstrass necessary condition prohibits that, we conclude that this problem has no strong relative minimum and the integrand can be made as small as desired.

As a further interesting example, the reader might investigate properties of the curve $y = x^2$ as a candidate for curve of minimum length connecting the origin and the point $(1, 1)$. For this curve, the Weierstrass E-function is strictly greater than zero for all (x, y, Y') not equal to (x, y, y') for all x. Hence, no Weierstrass deformation improves the result; yet, since the candidate curve fails to satisfy the Euler-Lagrange equation, there are clearly perturbations of the form (18.1) that yield improvements. The Weierstrass condition by itself is necessary but not sufficient for a strong relative minimum.

30. Discussion

It should be remarked here that the Legendre necessary condition (22.1) is a simple corollary of the Weierstrass necessary condition. Since neither the Euler-Lagrange equation nor the Jacobi condition can be deduced from the Weierstrass construction, the fact that the Legendre condition does follow from it is somewhat unexpected. However, this situation is easily understood in the dynamic programming derivations of these conditions to follow in the next chapter.

We have now mentioned the four most important conditions that must be satisfied by any curve that yields a strong relative minimum of a definite integral functional. Before continuing to a brief discussion of sufficiency theory, let us touch upon other necessary conditions that relate to specific forms of the problem statement.

31. Transversality Conditions

There is a class of conditions associated with the end points of a problem. If the terminal points of the curve sought are specified explicitly, then no additional conditions exist, nor are any needed to solve a problem. But, as mentioned in Section 8, there may be freedom in the choice of end points; perhaps one seeks the shortest path from a given point (specified end point) to a given curve (the exact point on the curve is not specified and is to be picked optimally). Then one can deduce properties of the solution curve at the unspecified end point that are necessary if the curve is to be better than neighboring curves with neighboring end points. These necessary conditions are called *transversality conditions*.

The general result states that if the terminal condition for a problem is the intersection of the solution curve $y = y(x)$ with a given terminal curve

$$y = h(x) \tag{31.1}$$

which has a continuous and finite derivative, then the minimizing curve must satisfy the equation

$$F + (h' - y')F_{y'} = 0 \tag{31.2}$$

where F, $F_{y'}$, h', and y' are evaluated at the point of termination; see Fig. II.14.

If the terminal curve is the vertical line $x = x_1$, the transversality condition is

$$F_{y'}\mid_{x=x_1} = 0. \tag{31.3}$$

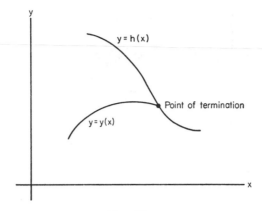

FIG. II.14

The transversality condition (31.3) that holds in the special case where the terminal abscissa is specified but the terminal ordinate is free is called a *natural boundary condition*.

For the minimum-distance example, expression (31.2) becomes

$$(1 + y'^2)^{1/2} + (h' - y')[y'/(1 + y'^2)^{1/2}] = 0, \qquad (31.4)$$

from which it follows that

$$y' = -1/h'. \qquad (31.5)$$

This shows that the curve of minimum arc-length connecting a point and a continuous curve must be orthogonal to the terminal curve at the point of their intersection; otherwise, a better path exists.

32. Corner Conditions

When we presented the differentiated form of the Euler-Lagrange equation (20.2), we noted that this equation was to hold between points of discontinuity in the derivative of the solution function, and that points where the solution function has a discontinuous derivative are called corners. The complete solution may consist of segments, each satisfying the Euler-Lagrange equation between corners. For the shortest-distance problem, the Euler-Lagrange equation implies that minimizing curves are straight lines between corners. A possible minimum arc-length curve that satisfies the above necessary condition is shown in Fig. II.15. One can further deduce, from the integrated Euler-Lagrange equation (20.1),

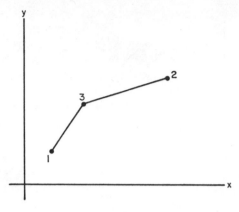

FIG. II.15

conditions that must be satisfied at a corner such as 3 in the figure if the composite curve is to be unimprovable within a neighborhood. These conditions, called *Weierstrass-Erdmann corner conditions*, state that at any corner point (x_0, y_0) of a minimizing curve, the relations

$$F_{y'} \mid_{x_0^-} = F_{y'} \mid_{x_0^+} \tag{32.1}$$

and

$$(F - y'F_{y'}) \mid_{x_0^-} = (F - y'F_{y'}) \mid_{x_0^+} \tag{32.2}$$

must be satisfied, where $\mid_{x_0^-}$ means evaluated in terms of the left-hand limit of y' at the corner point (x_0, y_0), and $\mid_{x_0^+}$ means evaluated in terms of the right-hand limit at the corner.

The reader can easily verify that for the minimum-distance integrand F given by

$$F(x, y, y') = (1 + y'^2)^{1/2} \tag{32.3}$$

condition (32.1) cannot be satisfied by two distinct values of y'. Consequently, there can be no corners.

33. Relative Summary

In summary of what has been said thus far, there are four major conditions that are necessary for a curve to furnish a strong relative minimum for a variational problem. Three of these, the Euler-Lagrange equation, the Legendre condition, and the Jacobi condition, follow from the study of the first and second variations associated with a perturbation of the form (18.1) of the curve $y = y(x)$. The perturbations lie within a weak neighborhood of $y = y(x)$. The fourth condition, attributed to Weierstrass, is deduced from the consideration of an entirely different type of deformation which yields curves which lie within a strong neighborhood of $y = y(x)$ but no sufficiently small weak ones. Further conditions depend upon the restrictions placed, in the statement of the problem, upon the terminal points of admissible solution curves.

Classically, necessary conditions are generally derived by considering the above two types of possible deformations (variations) of a curve which is a candidate for solution. They are contrived to prohibit the perturbations from yielding better values of the functional under investigation than the value yielded by the candidate. The straightforward analysis of perturbations of type (18.1) of a curve $y = y(x)$ leads to conditions involving definite integrals (the first and second variations) which contain the arbitrary function $\eta(x)$. Then, by various mathematical devices (one, for example, being integration by parts), the appearances of the arbitrary function $\eta(x)$ are eliminated and these conditions are converted to practical ones which must hold at each point of a minimizing curve. Due to this derivational route, little intuitive or geometric content is generally attributed to these conditions. One is content to demonstrate that without them all would not be well with the alleged extremal. Mathematically speaking, such an argument is convincing. But if new types of problems are to be posed and solved, and if the theory of the calculus of variations is to become a useful engineering tool, a better appreciation of the physical or geometric meaning of these conditions is desirable.

In the dynamic programming approach presented in this book, a viewpoint is adopted such that all comparisons are done locally by variations at a point. No arbitrary curves are introduced and the conclusions are immediately statements about the minimizing curve. Since no further manipulation is necessary, the results have geometrical or physical significance. While in the realm of classical variational problems the dynamic programming approach yields *no conclusions not attainable by standard methods*, it does produce new interpretations of results. This in itself would appear to be sufficient justification of the method, particularly in this computer era when variational problems have engineering significance. Almost every day variational problems are numerically solved and the solutions are implemented.

As we shall see in Chapter VII on stochastic and adaptive optimization problems, the dynamic programming viewpoint has the additional merit of allowing new nonclassical problems to be formulated and treated.

34. Sufficient Conditions

For engineering purposes, necessary conditions are more important than sufficient conditions. There are several reasons. Since the set of curves satisfying a valid sufficient condition may be vacuous, seeking a curve which satisfies a sufficient condition is akin to looking for a needle in a haystack which may not even contain a needle. This is a task not particularly appealing to a practical person with a pressing problem. Second, while necessary conditions are useful tests which can eliminate pretender curves, the violation of a sufficient condition by a curve proves little. Finally, various successive approximation algorithms that generate a sequence of curves converging through the space of nonminimizing curves toward a curve yielding a relative minimum can be formulated around necessary conditions.

It should be noted here that all the necessary conditions concern relative, not absolute, extrema. Most sufficient conditions that exist are suitably strengthened combinations of the four fundamental necessary conditions and are of three types. Some guarantee weak relative minimization; others promise strong relative minimization; yet others, if satisfied, assure absolute minimization. These latter, unfortunately, are of a type that are rarely verifiable in practice. In dismissing conditions of the latter type as impractical, we relinquish all hope of isolating curves that yield anything provably'better than relative minima. Such is the lamentable, but unavoidable, fate of practical applied variational theory.

The following is a typical set of sufficient conditions for a weak relative minimum. A curve without corners connecting points 1 and 2 and having the properties that

(1)   it satisfies the Euler-Lagrange equation,
(2) $F_{y'y'} > 0$ at every element (x, y, y') of it,
(3)   it contains no point 3 conjugate to point 1,

furnishes a weak relative minimum for the problem with integrand F and end points 1 and 2. (Note that strict inequality is required in (2) and that the end-point 2 cannot be conjugate to point 1 in Condition (3).)

If the further condition

(4)   at every element (x, y, y') in a neighborhood of those elements of the curve, the condition $E(x, y, y', Y') > 0$ is satisfied for every admissible set (x, y, Y') with $Y' \neq y'$

holds, the curve furnishes a strong relative minimum. (The function $E(x, y, y', Y')$ is defined in Eq. (28.1). Note that strict inequality is required.)

35. Hamilton-Jacobi Theory

Another classical development that deserves mention is the Hamilton-Jacobi theory. Hamilton deduced, from the differential equations satisfied by minimizing curves, the partial differential equation for a function $S(x, y)$:

$$S_x = F(x, y, z) - S_y z. \qquad (35.1)$$

Here, F is the integrand of the original variational problem with y' replaced by z, and z is given implicitly in terms of x, y, and S_y by the relation

$$F_{y'}(x, y, z) = S_y. \qquad (35.2)$$

The function yielding, at the point (x, y), the minimum value of the integral of F from a fixed initial point to the variable point (x, y) can be identified as a solution function of these equations.

The Hamilton-Jacobi theory shows how a sufficiently general solution of the partial differential equation (35.1) can be used to determine extremal curves for the variational problem with integrand F.

An equation pair quite similar to the above, with an inessential sign change throughout, will appear early in the next chapter. Whereas classically, with the exception of the approach of Carathéodory (1935), the Hamilton-Jacobi equation (35.1) represents the culmination of a long derivative beginning with the Euler-Lagrange equation, it will appear *at the beginning* of our dynamic programming development. It will be seen in Chapter III that the above equations, (35.1) and (35.2), follow directly from the fundamental principle of dynamic programming—the principle of optimality—discussed in its discrete form in Chapter I.

The necessary conditions, such as the Euler-Lagrange equation, will be deduced *from it*. In a sense we shall, in subsequent chapters, be traveling the classical road in the opposite direction—a direction we hope the reader will agree is natural and comfortable. But, we stress again, it is no more or less scenic until, in Chapter VII, we stray into nonclassical terrain.

36. Other Problem Formulations

The problem of minimizing a definite integral that we have been discussing is often referred to in the literature as the *simplest problem* of the calculus of variations. It has many generalizations. Most natural is the generalization of dimension. Rather than consider an independent variable x, a dependent function $y(x)$, and its derivative $y'(x)$, we can study an integrand depending on x, a set of n unknown functions $y_1(x)$, ..., $y_n(x)$, and their n respective derivatives. This problem leads to n simultaneous Euler-Lagrange equations as well as to certain changes in the other necessary conditions.

A second interesting and useful modification is the introduction of additional relations, called *side conditions*, to be satisfied by admissible curves. What is called an *isoperimetric* problem requires that the definite integral of F be minimized while at the same time a second definite integral

$$\int_{x_0}^{x_1} G(x, y, y') \, dx, \tag{36.1}$$

dependent upon the function $y(x)$ and its derivative, takes on a specified value, c. Consequently, the set of admissible curves is limited to those curves such that

$$\int_{x_0}^{x_1} G(x, y, y') \, dx = c. \tag{36.2}$$

A problem may have other types of side conditions. For example, if, in the multidimensional problem mentioned above, n functions $y_i(x)$, $i = 1$, ..., n, are sought, a typical side condition might specify some relation

$$G(x, y_1, \ldots, y_n, y_1', \ldots, y_n') = 0 \tag{36.3}$$

which is to hold among these functions and, perhaps, their derivatives at each point of the vector solution curve. If constraints such as (36.3) are specified, the problem is no longer of the "simple" type, but rather bears the name *problem of Lagrange*.

Admissible $y(x)$, or $y'(x)$, may be bounded at each value of x by inequality constraints such as

$$h_1(y(x)) \leq g_1(x) \tag{36.4}$$

or

$$h_2(y'(x)) \leq g_2(x) \tag{36.5}$$

or

$$h_3(y(x), y'(x)) \leq g_3(x), \tag{36.6}$$

where the functions h and g are specified. Motivated by the dynamic programming viewpoint, we shall in later chapters call the value of y corresponding to a given x the *state* and y' the *decision*. Then, inequality (36.4) represents a state-variable constraint, inequality (36.5) a decision-variable constraint, and inequality (36.6) a mixed state and decision constraint. We shall speak much more of these types of contraints in Chapter V, since they arise in many practical applications of the theory.

Another problem statement that will occupy us in Chapter IV, and subsequently, is the following: A *control function*

$$u(t), \qquad t \geq t_0, \tag{36.7}$$

determines a set of n functions $x_i(t)$, $i = 1, \ldots, n$, defined for time $t \geq t_0$ by the differential equations

$$\dot{x}_i(t) = f_i(x_1, \ldots, x_n, t, u) \qquad i = 1, \ldots, n, \tag{36.8}$$

with initial conditions

$$x_i(t_0) = x_{i_0}, \qquad i = 1, \ldots, n. \tag{36.9}$$

Any set of functions $x_i(t)$ corresponding to some control function $u(t)$ is called a *trajectory*. The control function $u(t)$ is to be chosen such that a given function of the x_i and t,

$$\Phi(x_1, \ldots, x_n, t), \tag{36.10}$$

takes on its minimum value when it is evaluated at some time T, where T is determined implicitly as the first time a set of terminal conditions

$$\Psi_j(x_1, \ldots, x_n, t) = 0 \qquad j = 1, \ldots, p \leq n \tag{36.11}$$

is satisfied.

Such a problem is called a *terminal control problem* since the criterion is a function Φ, evaluated at the terminal time T. This differs from the previously discussed problems where the criterion was a definite integral. In classical terminology, the above problem is an example of a *problem of Mayer*. (See Chapter I, Section 10 where we introduced a discrete version of this problem.) A terminal control problem can be recast by a variable change into a problem involving a definite integral with side conditions such as we have mentioned above, so it is not essentially new. However, such a transformation muddies the intuitive waters and we shall handle the above form of the problem separately and extensively.

Finally, the very general *problem of Bolza* involves both an integral and a terminal criterion in combination. Again, such a problem can be transformed by a variable change into either of the above types of problems.

37. Example of a Terminal Control Problem

As an example of a problem of the Mayer type, we can reformulate the minimum arc-length problem. Let us imagine that we are navigating a

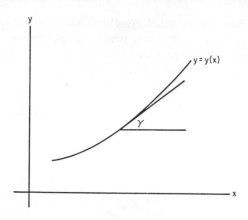

FIG. II.16

particle, moving at a constant velocity v, between two fixed points, the origin and $(1, 1)$. Since, with fixed velocity, time of travel is proportional to distance traveled, the minimum-time path is also the path of minimum length. We let x and y replace x_1 and x_2 in the above general formulation, and let the steering angle $\gamma(t)$, where γ is the angle between the x-axis and the velocity vector of the particle, play the role of the control function $u(t)$. A trajectory given parametrically by $x = x(t)$ and $y = y(t)$ can be represented in the (x, y)-plane by a curve $y = y(x)$, such as the one shown in Fig. II.16. Equations (36.8) take the form

$$\dot{x} = v \cos \gamma \qquad \dot{y} = v \sin \gamma \qquad (37.1)$$

and the initial conditions (36.9) are

$$x(0) = 0 \qquad y(0) = 0. \qquad (37.2)$$

Since the function to be minimized is the terminal time, for expression (36.10) we have

$$\Phi(x, y, t) = t \qquad (37.3)$$

and the stopping conditions (36.11) become

$$\Psi_1(x, y, t) = x - 1 = 0 \qquad \Psi_2(x, y, t) = y - 1 = 0. \qquad (37.4)$$

As the reader will observe in the example, while the criterion (36.10) and terminal conditions (36.11) are written as quite general functions, in application they are often conditions on individual state variables.

38. Necessary Conditions for the Problem of Mayer

It has been our policy in this chapter to mention classical results that we shall develop later from the dynamic programming viewpoint. Regarding the above problem of Mayer, there exists a very important necessary condition, called the *multiplier rule*, which corresponds to the Euler-Lagrange equation of the simplest problem. A set of n undetermined *Lagrange multiplier functions*

$$\lambda_i(t) \qquad i = 1, \ldots, n, \tag{38.1}$$

is introduced to incorporate the n differential relations (36.8). Then, variations about a candidate trajectory are considered just as for the simplest problem. It is necessary, if there exist neighboring admissible trajectories,* that the first variation must be equal to zero in order to preclude neighboring improvement. Mathematically, this condition involves the multiplier functions $\lambda_i(t)$, and takes the form: Corresponding to a minimizing control $u(t)$ and associated trajectory, there exists a set of n multiplier functions, $\lambda_i(t)$, and p numbers, ν_j, such that the multiplier functions satisfy the differential equations

$$\dot{\lambda}_i(t) = -\sum_{j=1}^{n} \lambda_j(t)\,(\partial f_j/\partial x_i) \qquad i = 1, \ldots, n, \tag{38.2}$$

with terminal conditions

$$\lambda_{i|T} = \frac{\partial \Phi}{\partial x_i}\bigg|_T - \sum_{j=1}^{p} \nu_j \frac{\partial \Psi_j}{\partial x_i}\bigg|_T \qquad i = 1, \ldots, n$$

$$\sum_{j=1}^{n} \lambda_j f_{j|T} = \sum_{j=1}^{p} \nu_j \frac{\partial \Psi_j}{\partial t}\bigg|_T - \frac{\partial \Phi}{\partial t}\bigg|_T, \tag{38.3}$$

and such that the minimizing control $u(t)$ satisfies, at each time t, the equation

$$\sum_{j=1}^{n} \lambda_j(\partial f_j/\partial u) = 0. \tag{38.4}$$

The analog of the Legendre condition requires that

$$\sum_{j=1}^{n} \lambda_j(\partial^2 f_j/\partial u^2) \geq 0. \tag{38.5}$$

---

* A problem is called normal if the minimizing trajectory can be surrounded by neighboring admissible trajectories. We treat only normal problems in this book.

Yet another necessary condition, corresponding to the Weierstrass condition, states that at each point of a minimizing trajectory the control minimizes the expression

$$\sum_{j=1}^{n} \lambda_j f_j \tag{38.6}$$

over all admissible controls.

The Jacobi condition also has an analog for the problem of Mayer, which we shall develop in Chapter IV, Sections 13–16, but it is too complex to be included here.

39. Analysis of the Example Problem

For the minimum-time example introduced in Section 37, there are two state variables, x and y. The equations (38.2) become

$$\dot{\lambda}_x = 0 \qquad \dot{\lambda}_y = 0, \tag{39.1}$$

where x and y replace the subscripts 1 and 2. Hence, the $\lambda_i(t)$ are constant functions of time, c_1 and c_2, and condition (38.4), which determines the control $\gamma(t)$ in terms of the $\lambda_i(t)$, states

$$- c_1 v \sin \gamma + c_2 v \cos \gamma = 0, \tag{39.2}$$

or, equivalently,

$$\tan \gamma = c_2/c_1 . \tag{39.3}$$

Hence, the steering angle is a constant function of time. The constant steering angle γ that produces a trajectory intersecting the terminal point $(1, 1)$ can be shown to yield a minimizing, rather than a maximizing, trajectory.*

40. Two-Point Boundary Value Problems

One of the first steps in the solution of a variational problem is the determination of a curve satisfying the Euler-Lagrange or multiplier equa-

---

* To study the problem thoroughly would require a discussion of corner conditions. These conditions will be derived in Chapter IV.

tions with associated boundary conditions. Some of the conditions are explicitly stated in the specification of the problem and others are transversality conditions imputed by means of analysis. Usually some conditions concern the initial point of the solution curve and others concern the terminal point. After a curve satisfying the above conditions has been found, other tests can be applied to determine whether it is the solution or an imposter.

The solution of a set of differential equations with boundary conditions specified at each of two different points is no simple matter numerically. For this reason, it was not until some 15 years after the introduction of the high-speed digital computer that the solution of practical variational problems became fairly widespread. Even today one finds a plethora of computational algorithms proposed and much is still unknown about the relative merits of each.

The difficulty associated with problems with mixed boundary conditions stems from the methods available for the numerical solution of differential equations. Almost all methods assume that a full set of boundary conditions is known at one point and then proceed to generate, quite efficiently, the solution emanating from that point. These methods are rather impotent when less than a full set of boundary conditions is specified at each of a set of points.

41. A Well-Posed Problem

In this section we shall consider a fairly general problem of the Mayer type and show that, speaking conceptually, the conditions given in Section 38 lead to a reasonable differential equation problem with the appropriate number of specified conditions to determine a solution. Such a problem is termed *well-posed*. First, however, let us consider a very simple problem.

As an example of a well-posed problem with mixed boundary conditions, suppose we seek the solution $y(x)$ of the differential equation

$$d^2y/dx^2 = 0, \tag{41.1}$$

such that

$$y(0) = 0 \qquad y(1) = 1. \tag{41.2}$$

The general solution of (41.1) is a straight line $ax + b$. One and only one straight line connects the points $(0, 0)$ and $(1, 1)$ since the two terminal conditions determine the parameters a and b.

The problem of finding the solution of (41.1) passing through the point

(0, 0) is not well-posed since an infinite number of such straight lines exist. Neither is the problem of finding the solution of (41.1) which passes through (0, 0) and (1, 1) and has slope 2 at the point (0, 0). No such straight line exists since too much has been required of only two parameters.

A well-posed nonlinear differential equation problem may possess several solutions rather than a unique one, but it should not have, in general, an infinite number of solutions with a different solution corresponding to each value of an unspecified parameter.

We now turn to a rather general situation. We use the fact that the solution of a variational problem can be characterized in terms of differential equations and mixed boundary conditions. We adopt the view that certain unspecified initial conditions are to be determined in such a way that the resulting trajectory will satisfy the specified terminal conditions. We do not discuss in this volume just how to go about determining the appropriate initial conditions in practice.

Let us assume that in the problem statement we are given a set of n differential equations

$$\dot{x}_i(t) = f_i(x_1, \ldots, x_n, t, u) \qquad i = 1, \ldots, n, \qquad (41.3)$$

with given initial conditions, specified at time t_0,

$$x_i(t_0) = x_{i_0} \qquad i = 1, \ldots, n. \qquad (41.4)$$

The optimal control $u(t)$ is to yield a trajectory satisfying a set of terminal conditions

$$\Psi_j(x_1, \ldots, x_n, t) = 0 \qquad j = 1, \ldots, p \leq n, \qquad (41.5)$$

and minimizing a given function

$$\Phi(x_1, \ldots, x_n, t) \qquad (41.6)$$

evaluated at the terminal time.

As we saw in Section 38, variational analysis leads to the conclusion that, corresponding to the optimal trajectory, there exists a set of n multiplier functions $\lambda_i(t)$, and p numbers ν_j, satisfying the differential equations

$$\dot{\lambda}_i(t) = - \sum_{j=1}^{n} \lambda_j(t) \, (\partial f_j / \partial x_i) \qquad i = 1, \ldots, n, \qquad (41.7)$$

with terminal conditions

$$\lambda_{i|_T} = (\partial \Phi / \partial x_i)|_T - \sum_{j=1}^{p} \nu_j (\partial \Psi_j / \partial x_i)|_T \qquad i = 1, \ldots, n \qquad (41.8)$$

and

$$\sum_{j=1}^{n} \lambda_j f_{j|T} = \sum_{j=1}^{p} \nu_j (\partial \Psi_j / \partial t)|_T - (\partial \Phi / \partial t)|_T, \qquad (41.9)$$

and the optimal control function $u(t)$ satisfies the equation

$$\sum_{j=1}^{n} \lambda_j (\partial f_j / \partial u) = 0. \qquad (41.10)$$

Suppose we wish to solve such a problem on a digital computer. The values of the multipliers $\lambda_i(t)$ are unknown at time t_0 but must satisfy, at the terminal time, conditions (41.8) and (41.9), which also involve the states x_i. The state variables x_i are known at t_0 but at the terminal time only certain relations (41.5) among them are specified. Simultaneous numerical integration of the sets of differential equations (41.3) and (41.7), as mentioned above, requires that the values of x_i and λ_i be known at one particular time.

We can, if we wish, guess the unknown n numbers $\lambda_i(t_0)$. Then the control $u(t)$ can be determined from (41.10) and the differential equations (41.3) and (41.7) can be used to step x and λ forward to time $t_0 + \Delta t$. Now, Eq. (41.10) determines $u(t_0 + \Delta t)$ and the process continues.

We terminate this numerical integration process when one of the terminal conditions (41.5) is satisfied. Now we examine the other $p - 1$ terminal constraints given by (41.5). If they are not all satisfied, we do not have an admissible trajectory. Hence, we see that our initial guess of the n missing numbers $\lambda_i(t_0)$ must at least be such as to yield a trajectory satisfying $p - 1$ terminal conditions. This can be done and $n - (p - 1)$ degrees of freedom remain in our initial choices. We must also satisfy terminal conditions (41.8) and (41.9). Since the terminal states and the terminal values of the multiplier functions are known after the determination of a trajectory by numerical integration, (41.8) and (41.9) represent $n + 1$ equations for the p unknown constants ν_j. With $p \leq n$, these equations are overdetermined and will not, in general, have a solution, since less than $n + 1$ variables cannot be found in general to satisfy $n + 1$ equations. However, we noted above that we have $n - p + 1$ degrees of freedom left in the choice of the initial values of the multipliers $\lambda_i(t_0)$. These $n - p + 1$ free initial values of multipliers plus p terminal ν_j give us $n + 1$ quantities to be chosen. This exactly matches the $n + 1$ terminal conditions (41.8) and (41.9). Our over-all problem, then, is to determine $n + p$ quantities (n initial values of multiplier functions and p terminal numbers ν_j), that satisfy $n + p$ conditions ($p - 1$ conditions (41.5) at that time when some arbitrarily chosen one of them is satisfied, and $n + 1$ terminal conditions (41.8) and (41.9)). Since the number of unknowns equals the number of conditions, the problem is well posed.

42. Discussion

The reader who has no prior familiarity with the optimization of trajectories may find the immediately preceding results and examples mystifying due to the introduction and manipulation of Lagrange multiplier functions. We shall not elaborate further here, but ask his temporary indulgence. Several chapters will be devoted to the elucidation of the above results.

The important thing for the reader to note here is that the above results are stated in terms of Lagrange multiplier functions artificially introduced to include the constraining differential equations. In dynamic programming no such device is required.

43. Computational Solution

Since we have devoted this chapter to classical results, we might mention "classical" techniques for the numerical solution of variational problems, and the two-point boundary value problem that results from variational analysis. We use quotation marks because the whole area is relatively new and in flux, and the established techniques are all recent.

There are two fundamentally different types of approaches, though both are iterative. One proceeds by numerically treating differential equations with associated boundary conditions that approximate the true equations and boundary conditions for the variational problem. At each iteration, the solution of the approximating problem is produced. The second method attempts to converge on the solution through a sequence of curves, each of which solves no particular problem, but yields a smaller value of the functional to be minimized than did its predecessor.

The method described in Section 41, where unknown initial values are guessed and the guesses are modified in the hope of fulfilling required terminal conditions, is an example of the first type of approach. Each computed curve yields a stationary value of the criterion among the set of curves yielding the particular terminal states of the computed curve (see Breakwell (1959)). Another method, still of type one, is an extension of Newton's method and linearizes the dynamical and variational differential equations and terminal conditions about a nominal set of values. The linear differential equation problem is solved exactly. The true dynamical and variational differential equations are successively relinearized about the previous solution, and when convergence occurs it is very rapid (see Hestenes (1949)). This method is called quasi-linearization by Bellman and Kalaba (1964), who have sought to popularize it.

Approaches of the second type, which attempt to successively decrease the criterion value until a curve yielding a relative minimum is found, are called gradient methods (see Kelley (1962)), or methods of steepest ascent (see Bryson and Denham (1962)). These methods avoid certain problems involving instability that are inherent in the first type of approach, and are in rather general use at present. Gradient methods can be generalized, at great additional computational labor, to include second-order effects (see Kelley *et al.* (1963)). Convergence, when it occurs, is more rapid for second-order methods. The steepest ascent method of Bryson is developed, using dynamic programming concepts, in Appendix III of Bellman and Dreyfus (1962).

44. Summary

We began this chapter with a discussion of the simplest problem of the calculus of variations. This problem involved the choice of a scalar or vector function that minimized a definite integral functional. Admissible solution functions satisfied certain continuity and end point restrictions, but no other constraining side relations. Four conditions that must be satisfied by the minimizing curve were presented and illustrated. These four necessary conditions are called the Euler-Lagrange condition, the Legendre condition, the Weierstrass condition, and the Jacobi condition. They all followed from the requirement that variations of a minimizing curve must not yield a value of the criterion functional that is smaller than the value associated with the minimizing curve. The first, second, and fourth condition are necessary for weak relative minimality as well as, naturally, strong relative minimality and absolute minimality. The third condition, that of Weierstrass, is necessary for strong relative minimality and hence for absolute minimality, but is not necessary for weak relative minimality. Further conditions that must be satisfied at corners (points at which the solution has a discontinuous derivative) were presented, as well as transversality conditions related to the specification of the admissible end points of the problem. We indicated that the primary difficulty in the classical derivations was the conversion of intuitive statements, concerning definite integrals involving the minimizing curve and a perturbation of that curve, into statements concerning properties that hold at each point of a minimizing curve. These properties involve neither a definite integral nor the perturbed curve. The first portion of the chapter was concluded with a relative summary in Section 33.

After a very brief mention of sufficiency theory and of the Hamilton-Jacobi theory, we turned our attention to various generalizations of the problem statement, with emphasis on the terminal control problem. This problem finds many practical applications in the areas of automation and control. As in the case of the simplest problem, there are four fundamental necessary conditions. The principal novelty of this problem is the appearance of auxiliary Lagrange multiplier functions in the characterization of the solution.

All the important classical necessary conditions that we have developed are satisfied by any curve yielding a strong relative minimum of the criterion functional. The portion of the classical theory that concerns itself with properties satisfied at each point of the minimizing curve, cannot distinguish a curve yielding the absolute minimum from those yielding relative minima, of which there might be many, just as no local condition can separate an argument yielding the absolute minimum of a function from those arguments yielding relative minima. Very little is said in the classical variational theory about properties that are uniquely those of the absolutely minimizing curve.

In the subsequent chapters we shall reconsider the above variational problems from the dynamic programming point of view and reproduce various results of the classical theory. We shall emphasize the geometrical and physical interpretations that are afforded by the dynamic programming approach.

References to Standard Texts

Shown below are references to three standard texts on the calculus of variations which contain details of the derivations of results that we have cited. We denote by [A] the book

Akhiezer, N. I., "The Calculus of Variations" (Aline H. Frink, transl.). Ginn (Blaisdell), Boston, Massachusetts, 1962;

by [B] the book

Bliss, G. A., "Lectures on the Calculus of Variations." Chicago Univ. Press, Chicago, 1959;

and by [G] the book

Gelfand, I. M., and S. V. Fomin, "Calculus of Variations" (Richard A. Silverman, transl. and ed.). Prentice-Hall, Englewood Cliffs, New Jersey, 1963.

References [A] and [G] are translations of very readable recent Russian works. Reference [B] represents the culmination of many years of enthusiastic variational research by professors and students at the University of Chicago and is a classic in the field.

The Euler-Lagrange Equation [Section 20]

    [A]   pp. 3–14.
    [B]   pp. 10–12.
    [G]   pp. 8–15.

The Legendre Condition [Section 22]

    [A]   pp. 68–69.
    [B]   pp. 20–23.
    [G]   pp. 101–105.

The Jacobi Necessary Condition [Section 24]

    [A]   pp. 69–81.
    [B]   pp. 24–36.
    [G]   pp. 105–115.

The Weierstrass Necessary Condition [Section 28]

    [A]   pp. 64–67.
    [B]   pp. 20–23.
    [G]   pp. 146–149.

Transversality Conditions [Section 31]

    [A] pp. 93–98.
    [B] p. 162.
    [G] pp. 59–61.

Corner Conditions [Section 32]

    [A] pp. 12–14.
    [B] pp. 12–13.
    [G] pp. 61–63.

Hamilton-Jacobi Theory [Section 35]

    [A] pp. 81–89.
    [B] pp. 70–75.
    [G] pp. 88–93.

Necessary Conditions for the Problem of Mayer [Section 38]

    [A] pp. 117–124.
    [B] pp. 199–203.

CHAPTER III

The Simplest Problem

1. Introduction

The problem of finding a curve $y = y(x)$ that minimizes a functional $J[y]$ given by

$$J[y] = \int_{x_0}^{x_1} F(x, y, y') \, dx, \tag{1.1}$$

where the integrand is a specified function of $y(x)$, the derivative $y'(x)$, and the independent variable x, is called the *simplest problem* in the calculus of variations. This problem will occupy us initially.

Both $y(x)$ and its derivative $y'(x)$ may be vector functions; i.e., one may seek a set of scalar functions $y_1(x), \ldots, y_n(x)$ minimizing a scalar integral

$$\int_{x_0}^{x_1} F(x, y_1, \ldots, y_n, y_1', \ldots, y_n') \, dx . \tag{1.2}$$

If $y(x)$ is a vector function, and if it is stipulated that further relations of the form

$$G(x, y_1, \ldots, y_n, y_1', \ldots, y_n') = 0 \tag{1.3}$$

must be satisfied for all x by admissible solution functions, one has a more general problem called the *problem of Lagrange*. The Lagrange problem can appear in several other forms that can be transformed into each other by suitable changes of variable. One of the forms of this more general problem is called the *problem of Mayer*. A particular problem of the Mayer type, called the *terminal control problem*, will occupy us to a considerable extent in subsequent chapters.

We shall study the simplest problem by means of the method of dynamic programming. We shall proceed in a formal fashion, assuming whatever is necessary to maintain as simple and intuitive a flow of presentation as possible.

We begin by considering the problem of finding a curve $y = y(x)$, with specified initial point (x_0, y_0) and final point (x_1, y_1), that minimizes a given definite integral functional $J[y]$ given by

$$J[y] = \int_{x_0}^{x_1} F(x, y, y') \, dx. \tag{1.4}$$

Such a problem is said to have *fixed end points*. We conceptually divide the problem into two parts: an initial stage, and the remaining problem. Reasoning as in Chapter I, we deduce a recurrence relation and proceed formally to obtain a fundamental partial differential equation as the limiting form of this recurrence relation when the length of the initial stage becomes vanishingly small.

It would appear that, with suitable assumptions, our derivational steps could be rigorously justified; as yet, this has not been done. In a paper written jointly with L. D. Berkovitz (Berkovitz and Dreyfus (1964)) and summarized in Section 34 of this chapter, we developed the fundamental partial differential equation rigorously by a slightly different procedure, still in the spirit of dynamic programming, and justified some of the formal results of this chapter.

2. Notation

We wish to explain certain of our notation prior to undertaking our mathematical development. As the reader already realizes from Chapter I, on discrete dynamic programming, in order to solve a particular problem with specified initial and final conditions, we imbed it in a general family of problems. There are two ways of accomplishing this. Generally in what follows, we use what we called in Chapter I the backward recursive method. Each member of the family of problems has a different initial point, but requires the satisfaction of the same terminal conditions. Conclusions are then reached for an arbitrary initial point about properties that the optimal curve satisfies at that point. Since any point of the solution curve for a particular problem can be regarded as the initial point of a new problem, any property holding at a general initial point must hold at each point of the entire optimal curve for any particular problem. For this reason, if we call the initial point (x, y), we obtain results, in terms of x, y, and the derivative y' evaluated at the point (x, y), which are to hold at each point of an optimal curve. Such results will agree in form with those of the classical theory that were presented in Chapter II. But if we are to designate our initial point as (x, y), we had best call by other names the *dummy* variable of integration x of expression (1.4) and the solution curve $y = y(x)$ that is sought. Therefore, we take the problem to be stated in (ξ, η)-space, rather than (x, y)-space, with (x, y) now specifying the coordinates of an initial point in (ξ, η)-space. In these terms, our problem is to find the admissible curve $\eta = \eta(\xi)$, $\xi_0 \leq \xi \leq \xi_1$, satisfying $\eta(\xi_0) = \eta_0$ and $\eta(\xi_1) = \eta_1$, that minimizes the functional $J[\eta]$ given by

$$J[\eta] = \int_{\xi_0}^{\xi_1} F(\xi, \eta, \eta') \, d\xi, \tag{2.1}$$

where $\eta' = d\eta/d\xi$.

3. The Fundamental Partial Differential Equation

Let the problem just stated have initial point (x, y), where $x \leq \xi_1$, rather than initial point (ξ_0, η_0). The problem is then to find the admissible curve $\eta = \eta(\xi)$, $x \leq \xi \leq \xi_1$, with $\eta(x) = y$ and $\eta(\xi_1) = \eta_1$, that minimizes the functional $J[\eta]$ given by

$$J[\eta] = \int_{x}^{\xi_1} F(\xi, \eta, \eta') \, d\xi. \tag{3.1}$$

We introduce the auxiliary function $S(x, y)$, called the *optimal value function*, by means of the definition

$$S(x, y) = \min_{\{P\}} \left[\int_{x}^{\xi_1} F(\xi, \eta, \eta') \, d\xi \right] \tag{3.2}$$

where the set P contains all admissible curves $\eta = \eta(\xi)$ emanating from the initial point (x, y) and satisfying the terminal conditions of the problem. That is, $S(x, y)$ is the minimum attainable value of the definite integral criterion (3.1).*

We reason just as we did for discrete processes. Given $x < \xi_1$, we first pick a small increment $\Delta\xi$ such that $x + \Delta\xi \leq \xi_1$. We then consider as candidates for the minimizing curve only those admissible curves emanating

---

* For some initial points for certain problems, it may be possible to make the value function arbitrarily small, or there may exist a lower bound to attainable values which can be approached by suitable choices of curves, but which cannot be attained. In our treatment, however, we shall restrict ourselves to problems and initial points such that the minimum value of the criterion exists and can be attained.

from (x, y) that are arbitrary over the small interval $[x, x + \Delta\xi]$ and which, over the remaining interval $[x + \Delta\xi, \xi_1]$, are optimal for the new problem with its initial point identical with the terminal point of the curve chosen over the initial small interval. By the principle of optimality, the best of these candidate curves will be the absolutely minimizing curve for the problem.

We begin our derivation by justifying two approximations. Even if the absolutely minimizing curve for the original problem has a discontinuous derivative at some point ξ_2, for any given $x < \xi_2$ one can take $\Delta\xi$ so small that $x + \Delta\xi < \xi_2$. Then, the optimal curve has a continuous right-hand derivative η' over $[x, x + \Delta\xi]$ and we need only consider arbitrary curves $\eta = \eta(\xi)$ over $[x, x + \Delta\xi]$ that have continuous derivatives. If η' is continuous in the interval $[x, x + \Delta\xi]$, and if F is continuous in its arguments, we can replace the value of the contribution of $\eta = \eta(\xi)$ to the criterion (3.1) over the interval $[x, x + \Delta\xi]$, namely,

$$\int_x^{x+\Delta\xi} F(\xi, \eta, \eta') \, d\xi, \tag{3.3}$$

by the approximation

$$F(x, y, y') \, \Delta\xi + o(\Delta\xi), \tag{3.4}$$

where y' denotes the derivative $d\eta/d\xi$ of $\eta = \eta(\xi)$ evaluated at the point (x, y), and $o(\Delta\xi)$ means terms in $\Delta\xi$ which, after division by $\Delta\xi$, approach zero as $\Delta\xi$ approaches zero. This is the first approximation we need. Another approximation is the following: A function $\eta(\xi)$ such that $\eta(x) = y$ and η' is continuous in $[x, x + \Delta\xi]$ will have, corresponding to the abscissa $\xi = x + \Delta\xi$, the ordinate value η given by the equation

$$\eta(x + \Delta\xi) = y + y' \, \Delta\xi + o(\Delta\xi), \tag{3.5}$$

where $y' = \eta'(x)$. That is, the straight line with slope y' is a good approxi-

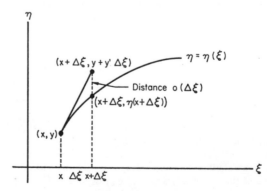

FIG. III.1

mation over a sufficiently small interval, to the actual continuous curve with initial slope y' (see Fig. III.1).

We can proceed using these approximations. The minimum value of the criterion integral (3.1) for a problem with initial point (x, y) is less than or equal to any attainable value. By definition, $S(x, y)$ is the minimum value and, by the approximations above, the value given by the expression

$$F(x, y, y') \, \Delta \xi + o \, (\Delta \xi) + S(x + \Delta \xi, y + y' \, \Delta \xi + o \, (\Delta \xi)) \qquad (3.6)$$

can be attained. We obtain this value if, over the initial interval $[x, x + \Delta \xi]$, we choose a continuously differentiable curve with slope y' at its initial point, and then choose, over the remaining interval, the optimal curve emanating from the terminal point of the curve chosen over the initial interval.

We have, then, the inequality

$$S(x, y) \leq F(x, y, y') \, \Delta \xi + o \, (\Delta \xi) + S(x + \Delta \xi, y + y' \, \Delta \xi + o(\Delta \xi)) \qquad (3.7)$$

holding for all choices of initial y'. If the slope y' at the point (x, y) is chosen so as to minimize the sum on the right-hand side of (3.7), we obtain equality in (3.7), since the set of candidate curves includes the optimal curve. This yields the equation

$$S(x, y) = \min_{y'}[F(x, y, y') \, \Delta \xi + o(\Delta \xi) + S(x + \Delta \xi, y + y' \, \Delta \xi + o(\Delta \xi))].$$

$$(3.8)$$

Different values of y' will generally minimize the right-hand side of (3.8) for different initial points (x, y).

Equation (3.8) is analogous to Eq. (4.1) of Chapter I for the discrete problem. The choice of direction y' in the current problem corresponds to the choice of a U or D decision, the expression (3.4) replaces the arc-numbers, $\Delta \xi$ is the discrete stage x-increment which equalled 1 in Chapter I, and $y' \, \Delta \xi + o(\Delta \xi)$ is analogous to the state increment that equalled either $+1$ or -1 in Chapter I. In both examples, and in almost all multistage decision processes, the state increment is a function of the initial decision, while the optimal value of the functional for the remaining problem, after the first decision is implemented, depends on the state increment.

If the second partial derivatives of $S(x, y)$ exist and are bounded, we can expand the right-hand term of Eq. (3.8) about the point (x, y) and write*

$$S(x, y) = \min_{y'}[F(x, y, y') \, \Delta \xi + o(\Delta \xi) + S(x, y) + S_x \, \Delta \xi$$

$$+ S_y y' \, \Delta \xi + o(\Delta \xi)]. \qquad (3.9)$$

---

* A function subscripted by one of its arguments denotes the conventional partial derivative.

Subtracting $S(x, y)$ from both sides of (3.9) and letting $\Delta\xi$ approach zero yields the equation

$$0 = \min_{y'}[F(x, y, y') + S_x + S_y y'] \,. \tag{3.10}$$

This is the fundamental partial differential equation that is satisfied by the optimal value function $S(x, y)$.

Note that a function $y'(x, y)$, the value of which at each point (x, y) minimizes the bracketed expression on the right-hand side of (3.10), is associated with a solution $S(x, y)$ of Eq. (3.10). This function associates with each point (x, y) the value at that point of the derivative η' of the optimal curve $\eta = \eta(\xi)$ connecting (x, y) with the terminal point. We call this function the *optimal policy function*. It corresponds to the set of arrows associated with vertices in the examples of Chapter I. If the function $S(x, y)$ is known, its partial derivatives are also known and the value of the optimal y' at any particular point is easily determined by minimizing a function of the one variable y'. Also, if $y'(x, y)$ is known everywhere, the value of $S(x, y)$ at any particular point is determined by evaluation of the criterion integral (3.1) in terms of the curve determined by the optimal policy function. Hence, either the optimal value function or the optimal policy function may be considered the solution to the problem.

4. A Connection with Classical Variations

Since the fundamental partial differential equation will appear repeatedly during the remainder of this volume, it is essential that we analyze various of its geometric and algebraic aspects. These considerations will aid us in characterizing the proper boundary conditions for the equation and in developing the various necessary conditions, implied by the fundamental equation, that will occupy us for the remainder of this chapter.

We begin by establishing a possible conceptual connection with the classical viewpoint. In Chapter II, on the classical variational theory, two types of perturbations of candidate curves were considered. The special type used to derive the Euler-Lagrange equation perturbed the entire candidate curve in the direction of another, arbitrary curve. The variation used by Weierstrass perturbed the candidate curve over only a small portion of its length, the rest of the curve remaining unchanged. The dynamic programming approach involves what can be considered a variation, but one of a type quite different from either of the above. Over a small initial interval, the candidate curve is perturbed arbitrarily as long as it remains admissible.

The remainder of the curve is defined to be optimal for the remaining problem so that each perturbation in the initial interval produces a dependent deformation of the remaining curve. While we do not know these deformations explicitly until we have solved the problem in complete generality, they are conceptually well defined.

5. A Partial Differential Equation of the Classical Type

The fundamental partial differential equation, when written in the form

$$0 = \min_{y'}[F(x, y, y') + S_x + S_y y'], \tag{5.1}$$

is not a partial differential equation of the type encountered in most texts, involving as it does a minimization operation. Conceptually, we can convert it to the usual form by realizing that, corresponding to any given point (x, y) and value of the partial derivative S_y, there exists a value of y' that minimizes the expression in brackets in (5.1). In theory, we can solve for the minimizing y' and write

$$y' = y'(x, y, S_y). \tag{5.2}$$

Substitution of this result into Eq. (5.1) eliminates the minimization and the explicit appearances of y' and we obtain, in place of Eq. (5.1), the equation

$$0 = F(x, y, y'(x, y, S_y)) + S_x + S_y y'(x, y, S_y). \tag{5.3}$$

We now have a first-order partial differential equation of the classical type where a given combination of two independent variables, x and y, and the partial derivatives of an unknown function of these variables, equals zero. We pay a price for conventionality, however, since Eq. (5.1) is linear in the explicit appearances of the partial derivatives of S, while Eq. (5.3) is generally nonlinear. Examples of the conversion from form (5.1) to (5.3) will be found in Sections 12–14.

6. Two Kinds of Derivatives

In the discussion above, we conceived of the (x, y)-space of possible initial points for a given variational problem and we characterized two functions whose values depend upon the initial point, the optimal value function $S(x, y)$, and the optimal policy function $y'(x, y)$. When we adopt this point of view, the variables x and y are independent of each other. One may speak of the effect on the value of the dependent variable S, or upon y', at a particular point (x, y) of a small change in x with y held fixed, or a small change in y with x held fixed. The symbols S_x, S_y, y'_x, and y'_y denote these conventional types of partial derivatives. A change in x or y means that we are changing the initial point and considering a new variational problem.

At other times it is convenient to recognize that the value of y', at a point (x, y), that is yielded by the solution of the fundamental equation (5.1) is the optimal value at the point (x, y) of $d\eta/d\xi$, where $\eta = \eta(\xi)$ is the solution curve for the *particular* variational problem with initial point (x, y). If we restrict our attention to this particular problem and its solution, the value of $d\eta/d\xi$ renders η dependent upon ξ. Should we wish to consider each point of the optimal solution curve for this particular problem as the initial point of a new variational problem, the ordinate y of the initial point with abscissa $x + \Delta\xi$ depends on the initial point (x, y) of the original problem and the optimal y' at the point (x, y). In this sense, the ordinate y of the new initial point is dependent on the abscissa x when evaluated along a *particular* optimal curve through initial-condition space. Let us consider the rate of change of $S(x, y)$ with respect to a change in x where y is regarded as dependent upon x through a given differential equation relationship

$$dy/dx = \bar{y}'(x, y), \tag{6.1}$$

where $\bar{y}'(x, y)$ may be the optimal policy function or any other function. We shall use the symbol $(dS/dx)_{\bar{y}'}$ for this derivative, where the denominator of the symbol indicates the variable to be considered independent and the subscript indicates the rule through which the other arguments of S depend upon x.

By the chain rule for differentiation, we have the equation

$$(dS/dx)_{\bar{y}'} = S_x + S_y\bar{y}' \tag{6.2}$$

which relates the two types of derivatives that we have defined.

7. Discussion of the Fundamental Partial Differential Equation

Returning now to Eq. (5.1), we see that it is equivalent to two statements. First, if y' is optimal, it must be chosen so as to minimize the expression

$$F(x, y, y') + (dS/dx)_{y'}. \tag{7.1}$$

Furthermore, when $y'(x, y)$ is the optimal policy function, we have the equation

$$F(x, y, y') + (dS/dx)_{y'} = 0. \qquad (7.2)$$

Let us examine these two results for meaning.

Consider a problem with fixed initial point (x_0, y_0) and fixed terminal point (ξ_1, η_1). Suppose that the minimizing curve $\eta = \bar{\eta}(\xi)$ for this problem has been determined, and the number $S(x_0, y_0)$ is the value of the integral of $F(\xi, \bar{\eta}, \bar{\eta}')$. Let us now consider a variable point (x, y) moving along the minimizing curve. For any such point we have

$$\int_{x_0}^{x} F(\xi, \bar{\eta}, \bar{\eta}') \, d\xi + \int_{x}^{\xi_1} F(\xi, \bar{\eta}, \bar{\eta}') \, d\xi = S(x_0, y_0) . \qquad (7.3)$$

The second term on the left-hand side of Eq. (7.3) equals, by definition, $S(x, y)$, where $y = \bar{\eta}(x)$. Consequently, we have the equation

$$S(x, y) - S(x_0, y_0) = -\int_{x_0}^{x} F(\xi, \bar{\eta}, \bar{\eta}') \, d \qquad (7.4)$$

which holds for all (x, y) on the minimizing curve. Since $S(x_0, y_0)$ is a fixed number, differentiation of (7.4) with respect to the variable intermediate abscissa x, with y dependent upon x through the optimal y', gives

$$(dS/dx)_{y'} = -F(x, y, y') \qquad (7.5)$$

This is Eq. (7.2). If we return to Section 5 of Chapter I, we see that Eq. (7.4) above is equivalent to *Property 1* if we take (x_0, y_0) to be the co-ordinates of the initial point of an arc, (x, y) to be the coordinates of its end point, and the integral of F taken between x_0 and x to be the value of the included arc. We see then, that Eq. (7.2) is the differential form of Property 1 of discrete and finite problems.

The incremental contribution to the value of the functional $J[\eta]$ that we are minimizing (a contribution that we shall call a cost) associated with the curve connecting the point (x, y) with a nearby point $(x + \Delta x, y + \bar{y}' \Delta x)$, for any $\bar{y}'$, is, to first order,

$$F(x, y, \bar{y}) \, \Delta x. \qquad (7.6)$$

The incremental decrease in the optimal value of the criterion functional associated with starting at the nearby point $(x + \Delta x, y + \bar{y}' \Delta x)$ rather than the point (x, y), a decrease that we shall call a saving, is

$$S(x, y) - S(x + \Delta x, y + \bar{y} \, \Delta x). \qquad (7.7)$$

We deduced in Eq. (7.4) that, along the optimal path, the cost equals the saving. Clearly, along any path other than the optimal path the cost exceeds the saving; i.e.,

$$F(x, y, \bar{y}') \, \Delta x - S(x, y) + S(x + \Delta x, y + \bar{y}' \, \Delta x) \geq 0. \qquad (7.8)$$

Dividing by Δx and letting $\Delta x \to 0$, we obtain the inequality

$$F(x, y, \bar{y}') + (dS/dx)_{\bar{y}'} \geq 0. \qquad (7.9)$$

From inequality (7.9) and Eq. (7.5), we see that the optimal y' minimizes the left-hand side of (7.9). This is relation (7.1), and, in the discrete problem of Chapter I, is called *Property 2*. The above two properties combined yield the equation

$$0 = \min_{y'}[F(x, y, y') + S_x + S_y y']. \qquad (7.10)$$

This is the fundamental partial differential equation, deduced by a discrete application of the principle of optimality and a passage to a limit in Section 3. We have shown here, for those who distrust the limiting process used in Section 3, that two rather intuitive statements about the continuous problem lead to the same fundamental equation.

8. Characterization of the Optimal Policy Function

We mentioned in Section 5 that the minimizing y' in Eq. (5.1) could be expressed as a function of x, y, and S_y, and that by eliminating the explicit appearance of y' the nonclassical partial differential equation (5.1) could be converted into a nonlinear, but classical, type of equation. We wish to point out here an alternative route. We shall show that the partial derivatives of the optimal value function can be eliminated from Eq. (5.1) in favor of those of the optimal policy function $y'(x, y)$. A partial differential equation that is satisfied by the optimal policy function $y'(x, y)$ is then obtained. To carry out this program we must assume that F is continuously differentiable with respect to y', that the optimal y' is finite, and that y' is not constrained in the statement of the problem. Then, a necessary condition for the minimization in Eq. (5.1) is that the partial derivative with respect to y' of the expression in brackets on the right-hand side equal zero.* This

---

* We shall discuss problems in later chapters where admissible y' are restricted as part of the problem statement. If y' is optimal in a bounded region, the derivative need not be zero at the optimal value of y'.

consideration allows us to deduce from Eq. (5.1) the two equations

$$F_{y'}(x, y, y') + S_y = 0 \tag{8.1}$$

and

$$F(x, y, y') + S_x + S_y y' = 0 \tag{8.2}$$

Solution of (8.1) and (8.2) for S_x and S_y yields

$$S_y = -F_{y'} \tag{8.3}$$

and

$$S_x = -F + F_{y'} y'. \tag{8.4}$$

We now assume that $S(x, y)$ has continuous second partial derivatives, and we take the partial derivative of Eq. (8.3) with respect to x and of Eq. (8.4) with respect to y. We then equate the second cross-partial derivatives S_{xy} and S_{yx}. Recognizing, as we perform those steps, that y' is a function of x and y, we obtain the partial differential equation*

$$F_{xy'} + F_{y'y'} y'_x = F_y + F_{y'} y'_y$$
$$- (F_{yy'} + F_{y'y'} y'_y)y' - F_{y'} y'_y. \tag{8.5}$$

Regrouping terms, we obtain the first-order quasi-linear partial differential equation

$$F_{y'y'} y'_x + F_{y'y'} y'y'_y + (F_{xy'} + F_{yy'} y' - F_y) = 0 \tag{8.6}$$

that is satisfied by the optimal policy function $y'(x, y)$.

Equation (8.6) is called quasi-linear because it can be written in the form

$$P(x, y, y') y'_x + Q(x, y, y')y'_y + R(x, y, y') = 0 \tag{8.7}$$

which is linear in the highest-order partial derivatives of the solution function $y'(x, y)$. A quasi-linear equation need not be linear in the solution function itself. There is a special theory, called the theory of characteristics, for such equations. We shall treat Eq. (8.6) further in Section 19.

9. Partial Derivatives along Optimal Curves

We have noted that if, at a given initial point (x, y), the value of S_y is known, the minimization operation in Eq. (5.1) allows the determination of the value of y', the derivative $d\eta/d\xi$ of the optimal curve emanating from that point. Suppose that we follow the optimal curve to a nearby point by

---

* The symbol y'_x denotes the conventional partial derivative, with respect to the variable x, of the function $y'(x, y)$.

moving in the indicated direction y'. That point may now be considered the initial point of a new problem. If we knew S_y at this new point, we could deduce y' at the new point and by continuing this process could generate the entire optimal curve emanating from the given initial point (x, y). It is natural, then, to ask what is the value of

$$(dS_y/dx)_{y'},$$

where y' is the optimal policy, at a point (x, y). We shall also ask this question about S_x.

The following reasoning leads to the answers to these questions. By the chain rule for differentiation, we have the results

$$(dS_x/dx)_{y'} = S_{xx} + S_{xy}y' \tag{9.1}$$

and

$$(dS_y/dx)_{y'} = S_{xy} + S_{yy}y'. \tag{9.2}$$

Partial differentiation of Eq. (8.2) with respect to x, recognizing that the optimal y' depends on x, yields the equation

$$F_x + F_{y'}\,(\partial y'/\partial x) + S_{xx} + S_{xy}y' + S_y\,(\partial y'/\partial x) = 0. \tag{9.3}$$

Similarly, partial differentiation of Eq. (8.2) with respect to y yields

$$F_y + F_{y'}\,(\partial y'/\partial y) + S_{xy} + S_{yy}y' + S_y\,(\partial y'/\partial y) = 0. \tag{9.4}$$

If the assumptions made prior to Eq. (8.1) are valid, the terms in Eqs. (9.3) and (9.4) involving the partial derivatives of y' can be dropped due to Eq. (8.1),* and the equations

$$S_{xx} + S_{xy}y' = -F_x \tag{9.5}$$

and

$$S_{xy} + S_{yy}y' = -F_y \tag{9.6}$$

follow. These equations, in conjunction with Eqs. (9.1) and (9.2), yield

$$(dS_x/dx)_{y'} = -F_x \tag{9.7}$$

and

$$(dS_y/dx)_{y'} = -F_y. \tag{9.8}$$

The differential equations (9.7) and (9.8) answer our questions. Along an optimal curve emanating from the point (x, y), the quantities S_x and S_y vary

---

* At a point of discontinuous y' along the optimal curve, this product of a zero term by an infinite term requires special attention. An argument by Berkovitz and Dreyfus, that we have sketched in Section 34, shows that S_x and S_y are continuous across a manifold of discontinuous y' if optimal curves cross the manifold. Consequently, the product of interest is either zero or finite at such a corner, and can be neglected. In Chapter VI we shall study cases where optimal curves follow, rather than cross, a manifold of discontinuous y'. Then, it turns out that the product term cannot be neglected.

with x in accordance with the differential equations (9.7) and (9.8). If the correct numerical value of S_y is known at a particular initial point (x, y), the minimization operation of Eq. (5.1), which determines the optimal y' at that point, and Eq. (9.8), which allows us to reapply Eq. (5.1) as x increases, determine the complete optimal curve originating from the particular initial point.

Pontryagin and his associates (1962) have presented an interesting modification of the above derivation. Assume that S has continuous second partial derivatives and that F has continuous first partial derivatives with respect to x and y. Consider the fundamental equation

$$0 = \min_{y'}[F(x, y, y') + S_x + S_y y'] \tag{9.9}$$

that is satisfied by $S(x, y)$ and $y'(x, y)$. For some fixed (x, y), say (x_0, y_0), suppose that y'_0 minimizes the expression

$$F(x_0, y_0, y') + S_x \big|_{x_0, y_0} + S_y \big|_{x_0, y_0} y'. \tag{9.10}$$

Let us set y' equal to y'_0 and consider the function of x and y

$$F(x, y, y'_0) + S_x + S_y y'_0. \tag{9.11}$$

By (9.9), for any point (x, y) the minimizing y' renders the bracketed expression equal to zero. Consequently, the particular number y'_0 renders expression (9.11) greater than or equal to zero for all (x, y). But at the point (x_0, y_0), expression (9.11) equals zero by (9.9). We can conclude, then, that

$$\min_{(x, y)}[F(x, y, y'_0) + S_x + S_y y'_0] = 0 \tag{9.12}$$

and that a minimizing (x, y) is (x_0, y_0). Since (9.11) is continuously differentiable in x and y, due to the assumptions about S and F, we have the results, at the point (x_0, y_0) which may be taken to be any point,

$$F_x(x_0, y_0, y'_0) + S_{xx}(x_0, y_0) + S_{xy}(x_0, y_0) y'_0 = 0, \tag{9.13}$$

$$F_y(x_0, y_0, y'_0) + S_{xy}(x_0, y_0) + S_{yy}(x_0, y_0) y'_0 = 0. \tag{9.14}$$

These equations are the same as Eqs. (9.5) and (9.6) that we previously obtained from Eqs. (9.3) and (9.4) by using Eq. (8.1).

10. Boundary Conditions for the Fundamental Equation: I

We have defined the optimal value function $S(x, y)$ and deduced a partial differential equation that $S(x, y)$ satisfies. But until we specify boundary conditions on $S(x, y)$, we face the difficulty that there can be many functions that satisfy the fundamental equation that do not necessarily satisfy the definition of the optimal value function.

To review, the optimal value function is defined to be just what its name implies: Associated with a given integrand $F(\xi, \eta, \eta')$, a particular initial point (x, y), and given terminal conditions on admissible curves $\eta = \eta(\xi)$, there is a curve, $\eta = \bar{\eta}(\xi)$ with $\bar{\eta}(x) = y$, which satisfies the terminal conditions and minimizes the integral of $F(\xi, \eta, \eta')$. We denote by $S(x, y)$ the value of the integral of $F(\xi, \eta, \eta')$ yielded by the minimizing curve.

The proper boundary conditions on $S(x, y)$ will be seen to depend on the terminal conditions on admissible curves specified in the problem statement. As we have already seen, the form of the fundamental equation does not depend upon the terminal condition of the particular problem.

If admissible curves are those that terminate at any point on the vertical line $\xi = \xi_1$, where ξ_1 is specified, then

$$S(\xi_1, y) = 0 \tag{10.1}$$

for all y. This is because, in this case, the minimum value of the functional $J[\eta]$ given by

$$J[\eta] = \int_{\xi_1}^{\xi_1} F(\xi, \eta, \eta') \, d\xi, \tag{10.2}$$

equals zero, the upper and lower limits of integration being identical. The boundary condition (10.1) determines, in general, a unique solution of the fundamental equation. For the discrete version of this result, see Property 3 of Section 9, Chapter I.

If the terminal condition is that ξ and η are related by an equation

$$\eta = g(\xi), \tag{10.3}$$

which defines a terminal curve in (ξ, η)-space, then

$$S(x, y) = 0 \tag{10.4}$$

for all x and y such that

$$y = g(x). \tag{10.5}$$

As above, this is because, when x and y are related by (10.5), the initial points are also terminal points. Here, again, the boundary condition (10.4) determines, in general, a unique solution of the fundamental equation.

11. Boundary Conditions: II

The case where admissible curves must terminate at a specified final point (ξ_1, η_1) differs considerably from the cases we have examined. A condition uniquely determining the particular solution of the fundamental equation (5.1) that satisfies the definition of the optimal value function can be stated quite simply in a form that is not the usual one associated with boundary conditions for partial differential equations. The nonclassical condition is as follows: Recalling that a solution $S(x, y)$ implies a policy function $y'(x, y)$, it is necessary that the particular solution function $S(x, y)$ we seek have an associated policy function $y'(x, y)$ that produces curves, from all initial points (x, y) lying in the region of definition of S, that pass through the specified terminal point. This condition determines the desired particular solution of the fundamental equation (5.1) to within an additive constant. The condition that $S(\xi_1, \eta_1) = 0$, determines the constant. But this is only an indirect characterization of the particular solution of (5.1) that satisfies the definition of the optimal value function.

In order to produce a more conventional boundary condition directly on the solution of Eq. (5.1) so that only the optimal value function satisfies the equation, we reason differently. Since $\eta(\xi_1)$ is specified to be η_1, initial points with x equal to ξ_1 and with y equal to any value of η other than η_1 are inadmissible. And, since the optimal value function is defined along the line $x = \xi_1$ only at the point $y = \eta_1$, at which point it equals zero, the optimal value function $S(x, y)$ has no well-defined partial derivative with respect to y at the point (ξ_1, η_1).

If one considers the optimal curve $\eta = \bar{\eta}(\xi)$ connecting any particular admissible initial point with the terminal point (ξ_1, η_1), and if any point (x, y) on that curve is examined, one discovers that S_y is defined at each such (x, y) point with the exception of the terminal point. It is seen that S_y, evaluated at a sequence of points that approach the terminal point along the curve $\eta = \bar{\eta}(\xi)$, remains bounded and approaches a limit. We shall show what this limiting value of S_y associated with a particular optimal curve terminating at (ξ_1, η_1) must be if $S(x, y)$ is to be the optimal value function for a problem with a specified terminal point. The limiting value of S_y will be different for each different optimal curve coming into the fixed point from differing initial points.

A necessary condition (under the assumptions of Section 8) in order that y' minimize the bracketed expression on the right-hand side of Eq. (5.1) is that the partial derivative with respect to y' of the bracketed expression equal zero. Performing this differentiation yields Eq. (8.1), namely

$$F_{y'} + S_y = 0. \tag{11.1}$$

This relation must be satisfied at each initial point (x, y), with the exception of the point (ξ_1, η_1). Further, for initial point (x_0, y_0), $x_0 < \xi_1$, very near the terminal point (ξ_1, η_1), the optimal curve to the end point must closely approximate the straight line with slope

$$\eta' = (\eta_1 - y_0)/(\xi_1 - x_0) \tag{11.2}$$

which connects the initial and terminal points. Hence, although S_y is undefined at (ξ_1, η_1), we have seen that it is defined at (x_0, y_0) near (ξ_1, η_1), and also that $F_{y'}$ can be evaluated at (x_0, y_0) with y'_0 given approximately by (11.2). If a function $S(x, y)$ satisfying (5.1) is to be the particular solution that satisfies the definition of the optimal value function, the sum

$$F_{y'} + S_y, \tag{11.3}$$

with each term evaluated as described above, must approach zero as (x_0, y_0) approaches (ξ_1, η_1). This test will be illustrated by example in Section 13.

The verification of this sort of boundary condition is cumbersome in a two-dimensional space and, if the problem is stated in an n-dimensional space with a p-dimensional terminal manifold, apparently hopeless. In this case, we must fall back on the nonclassical conditions that S must satisfy the fundamental equation, must be identically zero on the terminal manifold, and all optimal curves emanating from points (x, y) in the region of definition of S and determined by the optimal policy function associated with S must intersect the terminal manifold.

12. An Illustrative Example—Variable End Point

We return to the minimum arc-length problem that we met in Chapter II in order to illustrate the results developed above. Suppose, first, that we seek the curve $\eta = \eta(\xi)$ of minimum length joining a point (x, y), $x \le 1$, and the line $\xi = 1$. The functional $J[\eta]$ to be minimized by the choice of $\eta(\xi)$ is given by

$$J[\eta] = \int_x^1 (1 + \eta'^2)^{1/2}\, d\xi. \tag{12.1}$$

We have the constraint at the initial point that

$$\eta(x) = y, \tag{12.2}$$

while, at the terminal line $\xi = 1$, $\eta(1)$ is free.

The fundamental partial differential equation (5.1) in the (x, y) initial condition space is

$$0 = \min_{y'}[(1 + y'^2)^{1/2} + S_x + S_y y'], \tag{12.3}$$

with boundary condition

$$S(1, y) = 0 \tag{12.4}$$

given by Eq. (10.1). The value of y' that absolutely minimizes the bracketed expression on the right-hand side of Eq. (12.3) is finite only if $|S_y| < 1$. If $|S_y| > 1$, an unbounded y' can be chosen, yielding the value $-\infty$ for the expression

$$(1 + y'^2)^{1/2} + S_x + S_y y'. \tag{12.5}$$

Assuming $|S_y| < 1$, and using calculus to express the minimizing y' in terms of x, y, and S_y, we obtain, by setting equal to zero the derivative with respect to y' of the bracketed expression on the right-hand side of Eq. (12.3), the equation

$$[y'/(1 + y'^2)^{1/2}] + S_y = 0. \tag{12.6}$$

Solving Eq. (12.6) for y', we obtain

$$y' = -S_y/(1 - S_y^2)^{1/2}. \tag{12.7}$$

Substitution of this result in (12.3) and simplification produces the nonlinear (but conventional) partial differential equation

$$0 = (1 - S_y^2)^{1/2} + S_x. \tag{12.8}$$

This is the conversion process we discussed in abstract in Section 5. Since this is not a text on the solution of partial differential equations, we shall not solve (12.8) directly, but the reader can easily verify that the function $S(x, y)$, given by

$$S(x, y) = 1 - x, \tag{12.9}$$

satisfies (12.8) with boundary condition (12.4). The solution is unique. To obtain the optimal policy function $y'(x, y)$, we substitute S_y determined from Eq. (12.9) in Eq. (12.7) and obtain

$$y'(x, y) = 0. \tag{12.10}$$

A moment of reflection should convince the reader that the optimal curve $\eta = \eta(\xi)$ connecting the point (x, y), $x < 1$, with the line $\xi = 1$ is indeed a straight line with zero slope as implied by (12.10), and that the value of the functional (12.1) is indeed $1 - x$, as stated by Eq. (12.9).

13. A Further Example—Fixed Terminal Point

If the solution curve sought is required to pass through the final point $(1, 0)$, rather than merely reach the line $\xi = 1$, we would have a different situation. The optimal value function still must satisfy Eq. (12.8), but the boundary condition is either the implicit one of Section 11, or it involves limiting conditions on points very near the terminal point.

From the definition of $S(x, y)$ and the fact that the curves of minimum length are straight lines, we anticipate that $S(x, y)$ must be given by the formula for the distance between (x, y) and $(1, 0)$; i.e.,

$$S(x, y) = ((1 - x)^2 + y^2)^{1/2}. \tag{13.1}$$

The reader can verify that $S(x, y)$ given by (13.1) is indeed a solution of Eq. (12.8). By the substitution of S_y, obtained by the partial differentiation of Eq. (13.1), into formula (12.7), we find the optimal policy function $y'(x, y)$ is given by

$$y'(x, y) = -y/(1 - x). \tag{13.2}$$

Differential equation (13.2) has general solution

$$1 - x = cy, \tag{13.3}$$

which is a family of curves through $(1, 0)$. Consequently, the implicit form of the boundary condition on $S(x, y)$ is satisfied and $S(x, y)$ is indeed the optimal value function.

One can verify the equivalent explicit terminal condition (11.3)—namely, that the value of the expression

$$F_{y'} + S_y \tag{13.4}$$

approaches zero as (x_0, y_0) approaches the terminal point (ξ_1, η_1), if y' in $F_{y'}$ is replaced by

$$(\eta_1 - y_0)/(\xi_1 - x_0). \tag{13.5}$$

Expression (13.5) is the slope of the straight line from (x_0, y_0) to (ξ_1, η_1). Performing the indicated calculation, we see from Eq. (13.1) that

$$S_y(x_0, y_0) = y_0/((1 - x_0)^2 + y_0^2)^{1/2}, \tag{13.6}$$

while

$$F_{y'}(x_0, y_0, y'_0) = y'_0/(1 + y'^2_0)^{1/2}. \tag{13.7}$$

Substitution of expression (13.5) with $\xi_1 = 1$ and $\eta_1 = 0$ for y'_0 gives

$$F_{y'}(x_0, y_0, y'_0) = \frac{-y_0/(1 - x_0)}{(1 + [y_0^2/(1 - x_0)^2])^{1/2}} = \frac{-y_0}{((1 - x_0)^2 + y_0^2)^{1/2}}. \tag{13.8}$$

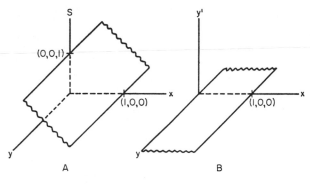

FIG. III.2

We see, in this case, that expression (13.4) exactly equals zero for any (x_0, y_0) since (13.5) gives the correct optimal slope everywhere rather than an approximation to it near the end point. In the more general situation where optimal curves are not straight lines, the sum of expressions (13.6) and (13.8) approaches zero only when (x_0, y_0) approaches (ξ_1, η_1).

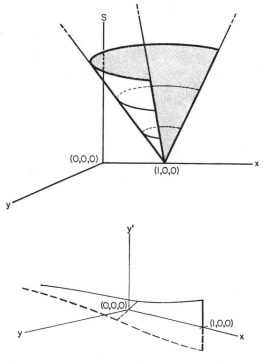

FIG. III.3

To reiterate, the implicit condition that the optimal policy function, implied by the optimal value function, yields curves that satisfy the terminal conditions is an intuitive and correct, but rather nonclassical, type of boundary condition. The equivalent explicit boundary condition directly on $S(x, y)$, illustrated above, is less intuitively satisfying but a little more in the spirit of classical partial differential equation theory.

In Figs. III.2 and III.3 we sketch a portion of the optimal value and optimal policy functions for the two versions of the minimum-distance problem discussed above. We do so to emphasize the fact that we are considering geometric quantities with geometric as well as algebraic properties.

We caution the reader that the complete analytic solution of problems, such as we have produced above, is rare and our concern will be much more for what can be deduced from the partial differential equation characterization of the solution than for analytic solution. However, simple and completely solvable problems make good illustrative examples since the conclusions can easily be verified by other means.

14. A Higher-Dimensional Example

As a final example, in order to illustrate the generalization of these ideas to problems of higher dimensions, let us seek the path of minimum arc-length connecting a given point with a curve in three-dimensional space. The functional J is given by

$$J[\eta(\xi), \zeta(\xi)] = \int_x^{\xi_1} (1 + \eta'^2 + \zeta'^2)^{1/2} \, d\xi, \qquad (14.1)$$

and we seek a pair of functions $\eta(\xi)$ and $\zeta(\xi)$ such that, initially, when $\xi = x$,

$$\eta(x) = y, \qquad \zeta(x) = z. \qquad (14.2)$$

and terminally,

$$\xi + \eta + \zeta = 1, \qquad \xi + 2\eta - \zeta = 1. \qquad (14.3)$$

The latter pair of equations determines a terminal straight line in (ξ, η, ζ)-space.

The fundamental partial differential equation for the optimal value function $S(x, y, z)$, is

$$0 = \min_{y', z'} [(1 + y'^2 + z'^2)^{1/2} + S_x + S_y y' + S_z z']. \qquad (14.4)$$

The necessary conditions that are implied by the minimization under the assumptions of Section 8 are

$$0 = F_{y'} + S_y \quad \text{and} \quad 0 = F_{z'} + S_z. \tag{14.5}$$

These equations can be used to eliminate y' and z' from (14.4). This step yields the partial differential equation

$$(1 - S_y{}^2 - S_z{}^2)^{1/2} + S_x = 0. \tag{14.6}$$

We seek a solution of (14.6) that is zero along the line given by

$$x + y + z = 1, \quad x + 2y - z = 1. \tag{14.7}$$

Rather than attempt to solve Eq. (14.6) by formal analytical steps, we shall merely verify an assumed solution. The function

$$S(x, y, z) = \left(\frac{5}{14} - \frac{10}{14} x - \frac{12}{14} y - \frac{6}{14} z + \frac{5}{14} x^2 \right.$$

$$\left. + \frac{10}{14} y^2 + \frac{13}{14} z^2 + \frac{12}{14} xy + \frac{6}{14} xz - \frac{4}{14} yz \right)^{1/2}, \tag{14.8}$$

obtained from a formula of analytic geometry giving the distance between the point (x, y, z) and the line given by Eqs. (14.7), satisfies Eq. (14.6) and is zero at points on the line (14.7). The algebra involved in verifying the final condition (i.e., that the optimal trajectory from any initial point, as determined by computing y' and z' by Eqs. (14.5) using the values of the partial derivatives obtained from Eq. (14.8), intersects the curve (14.7)) appears to be prohibitive, and is left to any doubting readers.

15. A Different Method of Analytic Solution

We shall develop in this section, and illustrate in the next section, a technique for the analytic solution of certain dynamic programming problems. The scheme that we produce is identical with the Hamilton-Jacobi theory of classical mechanics, although our derivation is quite different from classical ones. This and the next section may be omitted with no loss of continuity.

The present method differs considerably from the usual dynamic programming technique of the previous sections where a specific function satisfying the fundamental partial differential equation and appropriate boundary conditions was sought. As we have seen, if such a function, called the optimal value function, is known analytically, then differentiation and the solution of simultaneous equations determines the derivative, at each point, of the optimal curve emanating from that point. Integration is then required, in the usual dynamic programming method, to determine the curve itself.

We shall show in this section that if one can find an analytic solution of the fundamental partial differential equation containing a sufficient number of arbitrary constants, one can, in theory, determine stationary curves themselves merely by differentiations and the solution of simultaneous equations.

To demonstrate the method, let us investigate a rather general problem. Consider the $(n + 1)$-dimensional space χ of points (ξ, η), where ξ is a scalar and η is a vector of dimension n. Let M denote an $(n + 1 - p)$-dimensional manifold in χ specified by the simultaneous equations

$$\begin{matrix} g_1(\xi, \eta) = 0 \\ \vdots \\ g_p(\xi, \eta) = 0 \end{matrix} \qquad 1 \le p \le n + 1. \qquad (15.1)$$

Consider the set C of all those curves $\eta = \eta(\xi)$, where $\eta(\xi)$ is any n-dimensional continuous vector function, that connect any point m of M to a fixed point in χ given by

$$\xi = \xi_f$$

$$\begin{matrix} \eta_1 = \eta_{1f} \\ \vdots \\ \eta_n = \eta_{nf} \end{matrix} \qquad (15.2)$$

We wish to find that member curve of the set C which minimizes the definite integral

$$\int_{\xi_m}^{\xi_f} F(\xi, \eta(\xi), \eta'(\xi)) \, d\xi, \qquad (15.3)$$

where ξ_m denotes the ξ-coordinate of the point of intersection of the curve with M. Both the initial point on M and the curve $\eta = \eta(\xi)$ emanating from that point are to be determined.

We begin the new method of solution by defining a function $S(x, y, X, Y)$, where y and Y are vectors and x and X are scalars, by

$S(x, y, X, Y) =$ the minimum attainable value of the definite integral of $F(\xi, \eta(\xi), \eta'(\xi))$ evaluated in terms of any admissible curve $\eta = \eta(\xi)$ connecting the initial point $\xi = X$, $\eta = Y$ on M, and terminal point $\xi = x, \eta = y$.

The function S satisfies the partial differential equation*

$$0 = \min_{y'}[F(x, y, y') - S_x - S_y y'] \tag{15.4}$$

by the principle of optimality applied at the terminal point (x, y). It also satisfies the partial differential equation

$$0 = \min_{Y'}[F(X, Y, Y') + S_X + S_Y Y'] \tag{15.5}$$

by the application of the principle of optimality at the initial point (X, Y). By the definition of S, we have the further condition on S that

$$S(X, Y, X, Y) = 0. \tag{15.6}$$

Suppose, as in earlier sections, that we use the first-order condition implied by the minimization in (15.4) and (15.5) to solve for y' and Y', obtaining

$$y' = g(x, y, S_y), \qquad Y' = g(X, Y, -S_Y) . \tag{15.7}$$

We then replace (15.4) and (15.5) by the partial differential equations of conventional form

$$0 = F(x, y, g(x, y, S_y)) - S_x - S_y g(x, y, S_y) \tag{15.8}$$

and

$$0 = F(X, Y, g(X, Y, -S_Y)) + S_X + S_Y g(X, Y, -S_Y). \tag{15.9}$$

Now, suppose that we have found a function $S_1(x, y, \alpha)$ satisfying (15.8), where α is a vector of arbitrary constants of the same dimension as y. We call such a function a *sufficiently general* solution of (15.8) since it will, in what follows, serve our purposes. (The most general solution of a partial differential equation like (15.8) involves arbitrary functions.) Then, one can easily verify that

$$S_1 + \beta \tag{15.10}$$

where β is a constant, also satisfies (15.8). Let us choose

$$\beta = -S_1(X, Y, \alpha) . \tag{15.11}$$

As a result, the function

$$S_2(x, y, X, Y, \alpha) = S_1(x, y, \alpha) - S_1(X, Y, \alpha) \tag{15.12}$$

clearly satisfies both Eq. (15.8) and the boundary condition (15.6) for any value of the constant vector α. We shall choose α so that it depends upon

---

* The notation $S_y y'$ denotes $\sum_{i=1}^{n} S_{y_i} y_i'$.

the initial point, but not the terminal point, of the specific problem. Let the symbol S_{2X} denote the partial derivative of the function S_2 with respect to X. Since S_{2X} (with α held fixed) equals $-S_{2x}$ and, similarly, S_{2Y} equals $-S_{2y}$, and also $S_{2\alpha}$ evaluated at $x = X$ and $y = Y$ equals zero, it follows that Eq. (15.9) is satisfied, when evaluated at the point $x = X$ and $y = Y$, by S_2.

By using the n conditions on S_2,

$$0 = F_{y'} - S_{2y} , \tag{15.13}$$

implied by the minimization in (15.4), and by evaluating these equations at $x = X$, $y = Y$, we can, in theory, solve for the n constants α in terms of X, Y, Y', obtaining then the solution function of (15.8) in the form

$$S_3(x, y, X, Y, Y') . \tag{15.14}$$

Now that the constants α have been explicitly expressed in terms of X, Y, Y', we can write the n equations,

$$0 = F_{Y'}(X, Y, Y') + S_{3Y} , \tag{15.15}$$

implied by the minimization in (15.5). The system of equations (15.15) allows us, in theory, to solve for each component of y as a function of x, X, Y, Y', and we have the n equations

$$y_1 = y_1(x, X, Y, Y')$$
$$\cdot$$
$$\cdot \tag{15.16}$$
$$\cdot$$
$$y_n = y_n(x, X, Y, Y')$$

for a curve $y = y(x)$ that emanates from the fixed initial point (X, Y) with slope Y' and yields a stationary value of the integral of F to any point (x, y) on the curve. This form of the result is usually the final goal of the Hamilton-Jacobi method when used in classical mechanics. However, we seek a stationary curve from a point to be optimally determined on an initial manifold to a fixed final point, so we must continue the analysis.

If the initial point (X, Y) on M is optimal, the initial point must satisfy the first-order local condition that, for fixed final point, the value of S_3 must be stationary with respect to perturbations in the initial point chosen such that the perturbed point remains on M. Recalling that the initial manifold M is of dimension $n + 1 - p$, we now impose the condition that $n + 1 - p$ independent directional derivatives of S_3, taken with respect to the initial point and spanning the manifold M, must be zero. In particular, this must be true when evaluated at the point $x = X$, $y = Y$. These relationships (there will be zero such relationships if the initial point is explicitly specified, since then $p = n + 1$) allow us to solve for $n + 1 - p$ of the Y' in terms of $x, y, X, Y, Y'_1, \ldots, Y'_{p-1}$, where Y'_i denotes the ith component of the vector Y'. The components of Y' viewed as independent are not necessarily the first $p - 1$.

The condition that solution curves pass through the specified terminal point (ξ_f, η_f) allows the $p - 1$ independent components of Y' and any $n + 1 - p$ components of Y to be expressed in terms of $\xi_f, \eta_f, x, X, Y_1, \ldots, Y_{p-1}$, where $Y_1, \ldots, Y_{p-1}$ are not necessarily the first $p - 1$ components of Y. Consequently, we have

$$y_1 = y_1(x, X, Y_1, \ldots, Y_{p-1}, \xi_f, \eta_f)$$
$$\cdot$$
$$\cdot \qquad\qquad\qquad\qquad (15.17)$$
$$\cdot$$
$$y_n = y_n(x, X, Y_1, \ldots, Y_{p-1}, \xi_f, \eta_f) \,.$$

Evaluated at the initial point (X, Y), these are $n + 1 - p$ independent equations for $X, Y_1, \ldots, Y_n$. These equations, in conjunction with Eqs. (15.1) of the initial manifold, allow us to solve for the $n + 1$ quantities $X, Y_1, \ldots, Y_n$ in terms of (ξ_f, η_f), and then (15.17) becomes

$$y_1 = y_1(x, \xi_f, \eta_f)$$
$$\cdot$$
$$\cdot \qquad\qquad\qquad\qquad (15.18)$$
$$\cdot$$
$$y_n = y_n(x, \xi_f, \eta_f) \,.$$

This result asserts that those general terminal points (x, y) satisfying (15.18) lie on the particular stationary curve connecting M with the point (ξ_f, η_f). Stationary curves in the (ξ, η)-problem-space are then given by

$$n_1 = y_1(\xi, \xi_f, \eta_f)$$
$$\cdot$$
$$\cdot \qquad\qquad\qquad\qquad (15.19)$$
$$\cdot$$
$$\eta_n = y_n(\xi, \xi_f, \eta_f)$$

obtained by letting $x = \xi$ and $y = \eta$ in (15.18).

If all the above steps can be carried out and yield unique solutions, and if minimizing curves exist, Eqs. (15.19) represent the minimizing curve joining the initial manifold M and the terminal point (ξ_f, η_f).

The most interesting aspects of the above development are: (1) only a sufficiently general solution of the fundamental partial differential equation need be found, rather than either the most general solution or the very specific solution of the previous sections; and (2) the method yields directly the equation of a stationary curve rather than an expression for the derivative of a stationary curve at each of its points.

16. An Example

Suppose that we seek the curve of minimum length in (ξ, η, ζ)-space connecting the one-dimensional initial manifold M given by

$$\xi = 0 \qquad \zeta = 0 \tag{16.1}$$

(i.e., the η-axis) with the point (ξ_f, η_f, ζ_f), where $\xi_f \geq 0$.

The fundamental partial differential equations (15.4) and (15.5) are, in this case,

$$0 = \min_{y', z'}[(1 + y'^2 + z'^2)^{1/2} - S_x - S_y y' - S_z z'] \tag{16.2}$$

and

$$0 = \min_{Y', Z'}[(1 + Y'^2 + Z'^2)^{1/2} + S_X + S_Y Y' + S_Z Z']. \tag{16.3}$$

The minimization in (16.2) implies the two equations

$$0 = \frac{y'}{(1 + y'^2 + z'^2)^{1/2}} - S_y ,$$

$$0 = \frac{z'}{(1 + y'^2 + z'^2)^{1/2}} - S_z , \tag{16.4}$$

with a similar result implied by (16.3). Solution for y', z', Y', and Z' and substitution in (16.2) and (16.3) yield the forms (15.8) and (15.9) of the fundamental equations

$$S_x{}^2 + S_y{}^2 + S_z{}^2 = 1 \tag{16.5}$$

and

$$S_X{}^2 + S_Y{}^2 + S_Z{}^2 = -1. \tag{16.6}$$

The function

$$S_1(x, y, z, \alpha, \beta) = ((x - \alpha)^2 + (y - \beta)^2 + z^2)^{1/2} \tag{16.7}$$

represents a sufficiently general solution of (16.5) since it contains two undetermined constants. The function S_2 of Eq. (15.12) becomes

$$S_2(x, y, z, X, Y, Z, \alpha, \beta) = ((x - \alpha)^2 + (y - \beta)^2 + z^2)^{1/2}$$
$$- ((X - \alpha)^2 + (Y - \beta)^2 + Z^2)^{1/2} \tag{16.8}$$

which, if α and β are considered functions of X, Y, and Z, satisfies Eq. (16.5) identically and (16.6) when $x = X$, $y = Y$, and $z = Z$.*

By (15.13) we obtain

$$0 = \frac{Y'}{(1 + Y'^2 + Z'^2)^{1/2}} - \frac{Y - \beta}{((X - \alpha)^2 + (Y - \beta)^2 + Z^2)^{1/2}}$$

$$0 = \frac{Z'}{(1 + Y'^2 + Z'^2)^{1/2}} - \frac{Z}{((X - \alpha)^2 + (Y - \beta)^2 + Z^2)^{1/2}} \qquad (16.9)$$

which, solving for α and β, yield

$$\alpha = X - (Z/Z'), \qquad \beta = Y - Y'(Z/Z'). \qquad (16.10)$$

Hence, S_3 takes the form

$$S_3(x, y, z, X, Y, Z, Y', Z')$$
$$= \{[x - X + (Z/Z')]^2 + [y - Y + Y'(Z/Z')]^2 + z^2\}^{1/2}$$
$$\qquad\qquad - (Z/Z')(1 + Y'^2 + Z'^2)^{1/2}. \qquad (16.11)$$

Equations (15.15) are

$$0 = \frac{Y'}{(1 + Y'^2 + Z'^2)^{1/2}}$$

$$- \frac{y - Y + Y'(Z/Z')}{([x - X + (Z/Z')]^2 + [y - Y + Y'(Z/Z')]^2 + z^2)^{1/2}}$$

and

$$0 = \frac{Z'}{(1 + Y'^2 + Z'^2)^{1/2}}$$

$$+ \frac{[x - X + (Z/Z')](Z')^{-1} + [y - Y + Y'(Z/Z')](Y'/Z')}{([x - X + (Z/Z')]^2 + [y - Y + Y'(Z/Z')]^2 + z^2)^{1/2}}$$

$$- \frac{(1 + Y'^2 + Z'^2)^{1/2}}{Z'}. \qquad (16.12)$$

---

* It is interesting to note that no choice of the constants α and β as functions of X, Y, and Z yields the optimal value function for this problem, which is

$$S = ((x - X)^2 + (y - Y)^2 + (z - Z)^2)^{1/2}.$$

Yet, the method works. The sufficiently general solution used in this method of solution need not contain the relevant optimal value function as a special case.

Rather than put these equations immediately in the form (15.16), we now use the local stationarity condition that was discussed after Eq. (15.16). For the initial manifold M of this example, we have the condition

$$S_{3Y}\Big|_{\substack{x=X \\ y=Y \\ z=Z}} = 0, \tag{16.13}$$

which yields the result

$$Y' = 0. \tag{16.14}$$

Substituting this result into Eqs. (16.12) and solving yields

$$y = Y, \quad z = (x - X)Z' + Z. \tag{16.15}$$

Requiring that the solution curve go through the particular final point (ξ_f, η_f, ζ_f) determines Y and Z' in terms of the terminal point, yielding

$$y = \eta_f, \quad z = (x - X)(\zeta_f - Z)/(\xi_f - X) + Z. \tag{16.16}$$

The fact that the first equation above and Eqs. (16.1) must be satisfied at the initial point (X, Y, Z), produces the equations

$$Y = \eta_f, \quad 0 = X, \quad \text{and} \quad 0 = Z. \tag{16.17}$$

We now solve the system (16.17) for the three quantities X, Y, and Z in terms of ξ_f, η_f, and ζ_f. (This step is trivial in this particular example.) Substituting this result into (16.16) produces the stationary curve

$$y = \eta_f, \quad z = (\zeta_f/\xi_f)\, x, \tag{16.18}$$

through the terminal point (ξ_f, η_f, ζ_f). We see that the terminal points (x, y, z) satisfying (16.18) lie on the stationary curve connecting the manifold (16.1) with the point (ξ_f, η_f, ζ_f). In (ξ, η, ζ)-space, the stationary curve is given by

$$\eta = \eta_f, \quad \zeta = (\zeta_f/\xi_f)\, \xi. \tag{16.19}$$

A separate argument based on uniqueness is necessary to show absolute minimality.

The new method presented in these sections is of greater theoretical than practical interest. While it usually is easier to find a sufficiently general solution of a partial differential equation than the specific solution satisfying given boundary conditions, the partial differential equations associated with most problems are too complex to be solved in either form, and numerical methods are required. For computational purposes, it should be noted, the usual dynamic programming method appears preferable since computers are designed to cope with specific functions rather than with functions containing arbitrary constants.

17. From Partial to Ordinary Differential Equations

The solution of the fundamental equation containing the absolute minimization operation has much to recommend it since it produces absolutely minimizing curves within the region of solution and, at one stroke, solves the problem for an entire range of possible initial conditions. However, such a stroke is rarely forthcoming—analytically because of the perversity of nonlinear partial differential equations, and numerically due to the prohibitive computational time and the space required to construct a tabular solution of a partial differential equation when there are more than three independent state variables.*

Rather than attempt the solution of nonlinear partial differential equations, we shall, in this volume, generally turn to the study of certain ordinary differential equations that are deduced from the fundamental partial differential equation (we began this program in Section 9). In taking this more narrow view, we sacrifice absolute minimality in favor of relative minimality. Furthermore, if numerical methods are required (and they almost always are), we must settle for the solution of a particular problem with particular initial conditions.

18. The Euler-Lagrange Equation

We have deduced the fundamental partial differential equation

$$0 = \min_{y'}[F(x, y, y') + S_x + S_y y'] \tag{18.1}$$

that is satisfied by the optimal value function. Under the assumptions that $F_{y'}$ is continuous, that no constraints are imposed upon admissible y' in the statement of the problem, and that the optimal value of y' is finite, we have shown that Eq. (18.1) implies the two equations

$$0 = F(x, y, y') + S_x + S_y y' \tag{18.2}$$

and

$$0 = F_{y'}(x, y, y') + S_y . \tag{18.3}$$

Equation (18.3) asserts that for given numerical values of x, y, S_x, and S_y, the derivative with respect to y' of the expression in brackets in (18.1) must be zero when y' minimizes the bracketed quantity.

---

* Some techniques that are useful in the direct numerical treatment of the fundamental partial differential equation are developed in Bellman and Dreyfus (1962).

In Section 9, we reduced the problem from one in partial differential equation theory to one in the ordinary differential equation domain. We observed that knowledge of S_y at a point (x, y) allows one to determine the optimal value of y' at that point. Furthermore, evaluated along a particular optimal curve $\eta = \bar{\eta}(\xi)$, the partial derivatives S_x and S_y satisfy the ordinary differential equations

$$(dS_x/dx)_{y'} = -F_x \tag{18.4}$$

and

$$(dS_y/dx)_{y'} = -F_y, \tag{18.5}$$

where S and F are viewed as functions of the one independent variable x along the particular optimal curve $\eta = \bar{\eta}(\xi)$ and where y' denotes $\bar{\eta}'$. We can conclude then, that associated with an optimal curve there exist functions $S_x(x)$ and $S_y(x)$ satisfying differential equations (18.4) and (18.5) such that the derivative y' of the optimal curve minimizes, for each value of x, the expression

$$F + S_x + S_y y'. \tag{18.6}$$

Furthermore, the minimum value of expression (18.6) is zero. The statement that the derivative of the solution curve minimizes an expression involving the auxiliary functions $S_x(x)$ and $S_y(x)$, which in turn satisfy certain differential equations, corresponds in form with the conclusions we shall draw in subsequent chapters when we study more difficult problems. For the simplest problem, however, a simpler form of this result can be derived.

Assuming that $\bar{\eta}'(\xi)$ is continuous on an interval, total differentiation of (18.3), regarding y and y' as dependent upon x through the condition that y' be optimal, yields

$$0 = (dF_{y'}/dx)_{y'} + (dS_y/dx)_{y'}. \tag{18.7}$$

This result, combined with (18.5), accomplishes the elimination of S_y from our results. We obtain the ordinary second-order differential equation

$$(dF_{y'}/dx)_{y'} - F_y = 0. \tag{18.8}$$

This equation is the Euler-Lagrange differential equation (see Eq. (20.2) in Chapter II). If $F_{y'y} \neq 0$, Eq. (18.8) can be written in the form

$$y'' + \frac{F_{yy'}}{F_{y'y'}} y' + \frac{F_{xy'} - F_y}{F_{y'y'}} = 0. \tag{18.9}$$

If we integrate (18.5) between x_0 and x, regarding y and y' as dependent upon x, we obtain the result

$$S_y(x) - S_y(x_0) = -\int_{x_0}^{x} F_y \, dx . \qquad (18.10)$$

Elimination of S_y by means of Eq. (18.3) yields the equation

$$F_{y'} = \int_{x_0}^{x} F_y \, dx + c , \qquad (18.11)$$

which is the integrated form of the Euler-Lagrange condition, Eq. (20.1).

19. A Second Derivation of the Euler-Lagrange Equation

A second derivation of the Euler-Lagrange result stems from the quasi-linear partial differential equation

$$F_{y'y'}(\partial y'/\partial x) + y'F_{y'y'}(\partial y'/\partial y) + (F_{xy'} + F_{yy'}y' - F_y) = 0 \qquad (19.1)$$

that is satisfied by the optimal policy function (see Eq. (8.6)). We assume that $F_{y'y'} \neq 0$, and rewrite Eq. (19.1) as

$$\frac{\partial y'}{\partial x} + y'\frac{\partial y'}{\partial y} = -\left(\frac{F_{xy'} + F_{yy'}y' - F_y}{F_{y'y'}}\right). \qquad (19.2)$$

We noted in Section 6 that, given any function $f(x, y)$ of two variables where the second variable is dependent upon the first through a differential equation relationship

$$dy/dx = \bar{y}'(x, y), \qquad (19.3)$$

we can write, by the chain rule,

$$\left(\frac{df}{dx}\right) = \frac{\partial f}{\partial x} + \frac{\partial f}{\partial y}\bar{y}' . \qquad (19.4)$$

Let the function $f(x, y)$ of Eq. (19.4) be the optimal policy function $y'(x, y)$. The value of this function at the point (x, y) is the derivative of the optimal curve emanating from the point (x, y). Along an optimal curve, the rule relating y to x is

$$dy/dx = y'(x, y), \qquad (19.5)$$

where $y'(x, y)$ is the optimal policy function. Taking $\bar{y}'(x, y)$ in (19.4) as

the optimal policy function, Eq. (19.4) becomes

$$\left(\frac{dy'}{dx}\right)_{y'} = \frac{\partial y'}{\partial x} + \frac{\partial y'}{\partial y} y'. \tag{19.6}$$

The left-hand side of Eq. (19.6) is the derivative, taken along an optimal curve, of the derivative of the optimal curve. Hence, it equals y'', the second derivative of the minimizing curve. By Eq. (19.6), we see that the left-hand side of Eq. (19.2) equals y''. Therefore, we can rewrite (19.2) as

$$y'' = -(F_{xy'} + F_{yy'}y' - F_y)/F_{y'y'}. \tag{19.7}$$

When this second-order differential equation is written as

$$y'' + (F_{yy'}/F_{y'y'})y' + (F_{xy'} - F_y)/F_{y'y'} = 0, \tag{19.8}$$

we see, by comparison with (18.9), that we have again deduced the Euler-Lagrange equation.

Equation (19.8) follows immediately from (19.2) by means of the theory of characteristics. We prefer the above formal derivation, however, to the *ad hoc* invocation of a powerful but perhaps unfamiliar theory. While most types of partial differential equations relate the rate of change in the solution function in one direction to the rates of change in other directions, **a** quasi-linear equation relates the rate of change of the solution function in a particular direction at each point to nothing more than the coordinates of the point and the value of the solution at that point. The curves along which the solution can be extended in this manner are given by ordinary differential equations and are called *characteristic curves*. Since the direction, at a given point, in which we can deduce the rate of change of y', if we are given the value of y' at that point, turns out to be given by y', we conclude that the characteristic curves of the partial differential equation (19.2) are curves satisfying the Euler-Lagrange equation for the variational problem with integrand F.

In summary, we have shown how the problem of finding optimal curves by the solution of a partial differential equation leads to a problem involving the ordinary differential equations (18.4) and (18.5) in the auxiliary functions $S_x(x)$ and $S_y(x)$, and a minimization operation on expression (18.6). We then showed, from two points of view, that the auxiliary functions could be eliminated from the result in the case of the simplest problem. We obtained in this way, the Euler-Lagrange differential equation.

In a region in which the fundamental equation is valid, under certain other conditions stated earlier, the satisfaction of the Euler-Lagrange equation is a condition that is necessarily satisfied by the optimal curve. Suppose that Eq. (18.2) held but that (18.3) was not satisfied at the point

(x_0, y_0) on a candidate curve with derivative y'_0 at that point. Then, for sufficiently small Δx, consider the curve consisting of an initial segment with derivative Y'_0 over the interval $[x_0, x_0 + \Delta x]$, where Y'_0 yielded a smaller value of expression (18.6) than y'_0 and $|Y'_0 - y'_0|$ was sufficiently small, and a remaining segment that was optimal for the remaining problem with initial point $(x_0 + \Delta x, y_0 + Y'_0 \Delta x + o(\Delta x))$. This curve could be made to lie within any given weak neighborhood of the candidate curve and yield a better value of the criterion functional. Consequently, Eqs. (18.2) and (18.3), which yield the Euler-Lagrange equation, are necessary conditions for a weak relative minimum.

20. The Legendre Necessary Condition

According to the fundamental partial differential equation (18.1), the optimal value of y' at the initial point (x, y) should be chosen so as to minimize the expression

$$F + S_x + S_y y' . \tag{20.1}$$

In previous sections we used the fact that, for fixed x, y, S_x, and S_y, and under certain assumptions, the derivative of expression (20.1) with respect to y' must equal zero when evaluated in terms of a minimizing value of y'. The further necessary condition of ordinary differential calculus that the second derivative of expression (20.1) with respect to y' must be nonnegative in order that y' yield a minimum value of expression (20.1) rather than a maximum value, is

$$F_{y'y'} \geq 0 . \tag{20.2}$$

This condition, which must hold at each point of an optimal curve since each point can be considered the initial point of a new problem, is the Legendre condition stated as Eq. (22.1) of Chapter II.

21. The Weierstrass Necessary Condition

For expression (20.1) to take on its minimum value at a particular y', we have asserted that its first derivative with respect to y', with x, y, S_x, and S_y fixed, must equal zero, and its second derivative must be nonnegative. These conditions are necessary for y' to yield a relative minimum of expression (20.1). For the expression to take on its absolute minimum, as it must, we can write the following condition: For all Y' other than the optimal y', the inequality

$$F(x, y, Y') + S_x + S_y Y' \geq F(x, y, y') + S_x + S_y y' \qquad (21.1)$$

must hold. Canceling the S_x terms and using the first-order necessary condition for a minimum (18.3) to replace S_y by $-F_{y'}$, we conclude that the inequality

$$F(x, y, Y') - F(x, y, y') - (Y' - y') F_{y'}(x, y, y') \geq 0 \qquad (21.2)$$

must be satisfied for every admissible set (x, y, Y') different from (x, y, y') along an optimal curve. Defining

$$E(x, y, y', Y') = F(x, y, Y') - F(x, y, y')$$

$$- (Y' - y') F_{y'}(x, y, y'), \qquad (21.3)$$

we can write the condition (21.2), which is necessary for absolute minimality of expression (20.1) at each point, as

$$E(x, y, y', Y') \geq 0. \qquad (21.4)$$

This is the Weierstrass necessary condition—see Eq. (28.3) of Chapter II

If Eq. (18.2) holds and if the Weierstrass condition is violated at a point (x, y) where the derivative of a candidate curve equals y', a new curve that has a quite different derivative, call it Y', at (x, y) but is optimal from $(x + \Delta x, y + Y' \Delta x + o(\Delta x))$ to the end point, will yield a superior value of the functional criterion. For Δx sufficiently small, this new curve will lie within any given strong neighborhood, but no sufficiently small weak one of the candidate curve. The Weierstrass condition is therefore necessary for strong relative minimality.

We have seen that Eq. (18.2) and the relative minimality with respect to y' of expression (20.1) at each point of a candidate curve imply that the curve yields a weak relative minimum in the sense of Chapter II. Absolute minimality of expression (20.1) at each point of a candidate curve implies strong relative minimality. Since the absolute minimality of expression (20.1) at a point implies relative minimality at that point, we see that the Weierstrass condition implies the Legendre condition. It does not imply the Euler-Lagrange equation, however, since Eq. (18.2) (as well as the stationarity condition (18.3) that is implied, in general, by absolute minimality of expression (20.1)) was used in the derivation of the Euler-Lagrange equation.

Although these results were derived classically from various considerations, they follow from *one* fundamental principle in dynamic programming. While we have shown that the fundamental partial differential equation implies that the Euler-Lagrange, Legendre, and Weierstrass necessary conditions must hold along an optimal curve, we have not shown that these necessary conditions imply the fundamental equation. Indeed, they obviously do not do so, since the necessary conditions concern a particular curve and the fundamental equation holds in an entire region of the space of possible initial points. Consequently, these conditions are necessary, but not sufficient, for determining absolutely minimizing curves.

22. The Jacobi Necessary Condition

We have deduced a fundamental partial differential equation and shown that it implies three conditions that curves yielding relative minima of the criterion functional must satisfy. To derive the fundamental equation, we assumed the existence and boundedness of the second partial derivatives of the optimal value function (see the remarks preceding Eqs. (3.9)). We now deduce a test for the boundedness of these second partial derivatives. This test can be related to the Jacobi condition of the classical theory that was discussed in Chapter II.

We shall devote seven sections (Sections 22–28) to the study of the Jacobi condition and shall present several examples. We feel that our analysis, which differs radically from the classical approach, sheds considerable intuitive light on what is classically a rather shadowy subject and therefore merits the space we allot to it. The Jacobi condition itself is probably of less practical significance than any of the previous three necessary conditions, and we emphasize that it is the novelty of our approach and interpretations, rather than the practical value of the conclusions, that motivates our detailed treatment.

In almost all cases, the arguments leading to the fundamental partial differential equation will be valid for problems of very short duration—i.e., problems with initial and terminal points that are close together. Hence, Eq. (18.1) will be valid in the neighborhood of the terminal point. However, some problems have the property that as versions of longer duration are considered, a point is encountered at which the structure of the solution suddenly changes dramatically. This is a point, in our notation, where a second partial derivative of S becomes unbounded. We shall seek such points by assuming that Eq. (18.1) is valid in the neighborhood of the terminal point and then by using Eq. (18.1) to determine if and when a second partial derivative of S becomes unbounded.

The minimization in Eq. (18.1) implies, under assumptions noted earlier, that the identity

$$0 = F_{y'} + S_y \qquad (22.1)$$

holds for all points (x, y) at which S is defined. Partial differentiation of this identity with respect to y in order to determine S_{yy} yields

$$0 = F_{yy'} + F_{y'y'} \, (\partial y'/\partial y) + S_{yy} . \qquad (22.2)$$

We see that if F has bounded second partial derivatives, S_{yy} will be bounded, unless $\partial y'/\partial y$ is unbounded and $F_{y'y'}$ is nonzero.

In what follows, we assume that F has bounded second-partial derivatives and $F_{y'y'} \neq 0$ when evaluated in terms of a particular curve without corners which satisfies the three necessary conditions derived in earlier sections. We derive a differential equation that can be used to determine $(\partial y'/\partial y) \, (x)$ at points along that curve. At any point where $(\partial y'/\partial y)$ becomes infinite, we must relinquish our conclusions about the relative optimality of the curve, since the neglecting of terms involving higher derivatives of S in the passage from Eq. (3.9) to (3.10) may be invalid.

The condition that $(\partial y'/\partial y) \, (x)$ never becomes infinite turns out to be equivalent to the Jacobi condition of the classical calculus of variations. A point where $(\partial y'/\partial y) \, (x)$ becomes infinite is called a *conjugate point* in the classical theory if the terminal point (ξ_1, η_1) is specified in the original statement of the problem. It is called a *focal point* if the terminal point is variable.

We shall study only the boundedness of S_{yy}, since consideration of the other partial derivatives yields the same result.

We assume that $S(x, y) \in C^3$ in some region including the terminal point. Consequently, in that region, Eq. (18.1) is valid. As we have seen before, Eq. (18.1) implies the two equations

$$0 = F + S_x + S_y y' \qquad (22.3)$$

and

$$0 = F_{y'} + S_y . \qquad (22.4)$$

Let us define an *Euler curve** to be an arc without corners satisfying the Euler-Lagrange, Weierstrass, and Legendre conditions. We shall use Eqs. (22.3) and (22.4) to determine the function $(\partial y'/\partial y) \, (x)$ evaluated along an Euler curve.

Since (22.4) holds identically for all initial points, we can take the partial derivative with respect to y of (22.4) to obtain, as before,

$$0 = F_{yy'} + F_{y'y'} \, (\partial y'/\partial y) + S_{yy} . \qquad (22.5)$$

This equation gives $(\partial y'/\partial y) \, (x)$ in terms of S_{yy}. To eliminate S_{yy}, we take

---

* This technical term will be used quite often in our discussion of the Jacobi condition.

the partial derivative of the identity (22.3) with respect to y, obtaining

$$0 = F_y + S_{xy} + S_{yy}y', \qquad (22.6)$$

where the terms involving $\partial y'/\partial y$ are eliminated by use of Eq. (22.4). We then take the full derivative of (22.5) and the partial derivative of (22.6). This yields, using the notation of Section 6,

$$0 = \left(\frac{d}{dx}\left(F_{yy'} + F_{y'y'}\frac{\partial y'}{\partial y}\right)\right)_{y'} + S_{xyy} + S_{yyy}y' \qquad (22.7)$$

and

$$0 = F_{yy} + F_{yy'}(\partial y'/\partial y) + S_{xyy} + S_{yyy}y' + S_{yy}(\partial y'/\partial y) . \qquad (22.8)$$

Equations (22.7) and (22.8) combined, yield

$$0 = \left(\frac{d}{dx}\left(F_{yy'} + F_{y'y'}\frac{\partial y'}{\partial y}\right)\right)_{y'} - F_{yy} - F_{yy'}\frac{\partial y'}{\partial y} - S_{yy}\frac{\partial y'}{\partial y} . \qquad (22.9)$$

Substituting for S_{yy} by means of Eq. (22.5), we accomplish the elimination of S from the result. This yields

$$0 = \left(\frac{d}{dx}\left(F_{yy'} + F_{y'y'}\frac{\partial y'}{\partial y}\right)\right)_{y'} - F_{yy} + F_{y'y'}\left(\frac{\partial y'}{\partial y}\right)^2 . \qquad (22.10)$$

This is a Riccati-type differential equation that yields $(\partial y'/\partial y)$ (x) at each point of an Euler curve, along which the various terms involving F are evaluated, if $(\partial y'/\partial y)$ (x) is known at any one point.

The expression $(\partial y'/\partial y)$ (x) is infinite, when evaluated at the terminal point $x = \xi_1, y = \eta_1$. The behavior of $(\partial \eta'/\partial \eta)$ (ξ_1) can be determined by the following argument. Let us write $\eta(\xi_1)$ as a power series expanded about the point x, where $\xi_1 - x$ is small. This yields

$$\eta(\xi_1) = \eta(x) + \eta'(x)(\xi_1 - x) + o(\xi_1 - x) . \qquad (22.11)$$

Taking the partial derivative of (22.11) with respect to $\eta(x)$, we obtain the equation

$$\partial\eta(\xi_1)/\partial\eta(x) = 1 + (\partial\eta'/\partial\eta)(x)(\xi_1 - x) + o(\xi_1 - x) . \qquad (22.12)$$

Since $\eta(\xi_1)$ is specified, the left-hand side of Eq. (22.12) equals zero, yielding the result

$$(\partial\eta'/\partial\eta)(x) = -(\xi_1 - x)^{-1} + o(1) . \qquad (22.13)$$

Replacing $\eta(x)$ by y and $\eta'(x)$ by y', Eq. (22.13) defines the limiting behavior of $(\partial y'/\partial y)(x)$ as x approaches ξ_1.

It follows from (22.13) that in order to determine $(\partial y'/\partial y)(x)$, we seek a solution of (22.10) with the limiting behavior (22.13) at the terminal point.

Any point x prior to ξ_1 at which $(\partial y'/\partial y)(x)$ again becomes unbounded is a conjugate point. At such a point S_{vv} is unbounded.

Another form of the above result follows from the transformation

$$(\partial y'/\partial y)(x) = v'(x)/v(x) \tag{22.14}$$

applied to (22.10). This converts (22.10) into the linear differential equation in $v(x)$,

$$(F_{y'y'})v''(x) + \left(\frac{d}{dx} F_{y'y'}\right)_{y'} v'(x) + \left(\left(\frac{d}{dx} F_{yy'}\right)_{y'} - F_{yy}\right)v(x) = 0,$$

$$\tag{22.15}$$

which is the conventional form of the Jacobi differential equation (see Eq. (24.1) of Chapter II).

Since $(\partial y'/\partial y)(x)$ was infinite at ξ_1 and we sought an earlier point where it became unbounded, we require in Eq. (22.15) that $v(\xi_1) = 0$ and seek an earlier point where it is zero. Such a point, if one exists, will be a conjugate point, provided $v(x)$ is not identically zero.* Because (22.15) is linear, this proviso guarantees that $v'(x)$ does not equal zero at any point at which $v(x)$ equals zero.

23. Discussion of the Jacobi Condition

Let us investigate further the meaning of a conjugate point by considering a one-parameter family of Euler curves $\eta = \eta(\xi)$ through the terminal point (ξ_1, η_1). Such a family normally exists since the general solution of the second-order Euler-Lagrange differential equation involves two arbitrary constants, and one constant can be sacrificed to satisfy the terminal condition $\eta(\xi_1) = \eta_1$. Let

$$\eta(a, \xi) \tag{23.1}$$

be this family, and $\eta'(a, \xi)$ be its derivative. At the particular point (x, y) (denoting η' at that point by y'), we have

$$\frac{\partial y'}{\partial y}(x) \frac{\partial y}{\partial a}(x) = \frac{\partial y'}{\partial a}(x) \tag{23.2}$$

or

$$\frac{\partial y'}{\partial y}(x) = \frac{(\partial y'/\partial a)(x)}{(\partial y/\partial a)(x)}. \tag{23.3}$$

---

* If $v(x)$ were identically zero, the variable change (22.14) would be meaningless.

Since the numerator in Eq. (23.3) is the derivative of the denominator, we see that we can identify $v(x)$ of the transformation (22.14) as $\partial y/\partial a$, to within a constant multiple. Hence, $\partial y/\partial a$ satisfies Jacobi's equation (22.15) (a fact observed first by Jacobi), and equals zero at a conjugate point.

We have characterized a conjugate point in terms of the Jacobi differential equation and have argued that the nonexistence of a conjugate point on an Euler curve implies the boundedness of the second partial derivatives of the optimal value function. This boundedness property renders our derivation of the fundamental equation valid. We can conclude, then, that the satisfaction of the Jacobi condition as well as the Euler-Lagrange, Legendre, and Weierstrass conditions (with strict inequality in the latter two conditions) is sufficient to guarantee that an arc without corners furnishes a strong relative minimum (among curves with specified endpoints) of a given definite integral functional. Actually, the Jacobi condition is proved by classical analysis to be a necessary condition. A dynamic programming argument that shows that the unboundedness, at an interior point of an Euler curve, of a second partial derivative of the optimal value function necessarily implies that the curve can be improved by choosing a new curve that lies within a strong neighborhood of the original one, is lacking at the present time.

24. Neighboring Optimal Solutions

We have seen that if a nontrivial solution $v(x)$ of Jacobi's equation (22.15) that is zero at ξ_1 is known, then $v'(x)/v(x) = (\partial y'/\partial y)(x)$, the change in the derivative of the Euler curve at the point (x, y) associated with a change in initial y value. This result yields a practical means of deducing, from one particular optimal curve, by the use of the solution of the Jacobi equation, information about neighboring optimal solutions. Similar results are known for the more general Mayer problem and will be discussed in Section 17 of Chapter IV.

25. An Illustrative Example

Let us apply our results to the minimum arc-length problem. Suppose we seek the curve $\eta = \eta(\xi)$ of minimum arc-length connecting the point (x, y), $x < 1$, with the end point $(1, 0)$. The first three necessary conditions lead us to examine the straight line between the points. The Riccati equation

(22.10) for the arc-length integrand

$$F(\xi, \eta, \eta') = (1 + \eta'^2)^{1/2} \qquad (25.1)$$

is given by

$$\frac{d}{dx}\left[(1 + y'^2)^{-3/2}\frac{\partial y'}{\partial y}(x)\right] + (1 + y'^2)^{-3/2}\left[\frac{\partial y'}{\partial y}(x)\right]^2 = 0. \qquad (25.2)$$

Since y' is a constant along a straight-line solution, we can divide Eq. (25.2) by the nonzero constant term $(1 + y'^2)^{-3/2}$ and obtain

$$\frac{d}{dx}\frac{\partial y'}{\partial y}(x) + \left(\frac{\partial y'}{\partial y}(x)\right)^2 = 0. \qquad (25.3)$$

This equation has general solution

$$\frac{\partial y'}{\partial y}(x) = \frac{1}{x - \xi_1 + k^{-1}} \qquad (25.4)$$

where $k = (\partial y'/\partial y)(\xi_1)$ and, in this case, $\xi_1 = 1$. We have seen in Eq. (22.13), for a fixed terminal point, that $(\partial y'/\partial y)(\xi_1)$ is unbounded, so the particular solution of the form (25.4) that gives $(\partial y'/\partial y)(x)$ is

$$(\partial y'/\partial y)(x) = (x - 1)^{-1}. \qquad (25.5)$$

This expression is infinite for no value of x other than $x = 1$, so no point conjugate to the end point $(1, 0)$ exists on the straight line that we are examining. This is reasonable since we know that for a fixed terminal point, small changes in the initial point always result in small changes in the slope of the straight line to the terminal point.

In fact, Eq. (25.5) can be derived directly in this case. For initial point (x, y) and terminal point $(1, 0)$, the optimal curve (straight line) has slope, at the point (x, y), given by

$$y'(x, y) = y/(x - 1). \qquad (25.6)$$

Therefore,

$$(\partial y'/\partial y)(x) = (x - 1)^{-1}, \qquad (25.7)$$

which confirms result (25.5)

26. Determination of Focal Points

We have concerned ourselves, up to this point, with the equations that are used in the determination of conjugate points. These are initial points, given a variational problem with fixed final point, such that a small perturbation of the point leads to a large change in the slope of the Euler curve emanating from the point. If the given variational problem has a variable terminal point, rather than a specified one, the effect of a perturbation of the initial point on the slope of the Euler curve emanating from the point will differ from the effect for a problem with a fixed terminal point, since perturbing the initial point will generally also affect the terminal point. Given a problem with a variable terminal point and an Euler curve that satisfies the requisite terminal transversality conditions,* a point on the curve at which $\partial y'/\partial y$ is unbounded is called a *focal point*.

We now develop a general procedure for determining the correct terminal value of S_{yy} for a problem with a variable, rather than a fixed, terminal point. Then, Eq. (22.5) can be used—once the terminal value of S_{yy} is known—to obtain the terminal value of $(\partial y'/\partial y)(x)$ needed for the analysis, via Eq. (22.10), to determine a focal point.

First, suppose that the terminal abscissa ξ_1 is fixed but $\eta(\xi_1)$ is unspecified. Then, from Eq. (22.5) and the fact that $S(x, y)$ (and therefore S_y and S_{yy}) is identically zero along the terminal line $x = \xi_1$, we conclude that

$$(\partial y'/\partial y)(\xi_1) = -F_{yy'}(\xi_1)/F_{y'y'}(\xi_1) . \tag{26.1}$$

This is a finite initial condition for the backward integration of the Riccati equation (22.10). Our form of the result differs from the conventional one. Classically, a nonzero terminal value of $v(x)$ is used in the integration of (22.15).

The determination of the proper terminal value for the solution function of the Riccati equation (22.10) or for the Jacobi equation (22.15) becomes more complicated in the case of a variable terminal point which is required to lie on a given curve $\eta = g(\xi)$. We begin our study of this situation by noting that partial differentiation of Eq. (22.3) with respect to x, using (22.4) to eliminate $\partial y'/\partial x$ terms, yields

$$0 = F_x + S_{xx} + S_{xy}y', \tag{26.2}$$

and, doing likewise with respect to y, yields

$$0 = F_y + S_{xy} + S_{yy}y', \tag{26.3}$$

where (x, y, y') are evaluated along the particular Euler curve under investigation. Since, for a given Euler curve, the terminal value of x, y, and y' are known, the above represents two equations for the unknown terminal values of S_{xx}, S_{xy}, and S_{yy}. Now, recall that, by definition,

$$S(x, y) = 0 \tag{26.4}$$

---

* These conditions are discussed in detail in Section 29.

along the terminal curve

$$y = g(x). \tag{26.5}$$

By total differentiation of (26.4), where y depends upon x by (26.5), we obtain the equation

$$S_x + S_y g' = 0 \tag{26.6}$$

where g' is the slope of the terminal curve (26.5) at the point of termination of the Euler curve. Differentiating (26.6) again, with y dependent upon x by (26.5), gives

$$S_{xx} + 2S_{xy}g' + S_{yy}g'^2 + S_y g'' = 0. \tag{26.7}$$

By Eq. (22.4), S_y may be replaced by $-F_{y'}$. We have now obtained a third equation relating the unknown quantities S_{xx}, S_{xy}, and S_{yy}. Equation (26.7), together with Eqs. (26.2) and (26.3), can be used to determine S_{yy} and then $\partial y'/\partial y$ at the end point.

27. Example

As an example we shall consider a minimum arc-length problem. The integrand is

$$F(\xi, \eta, \eta') = (1 + \eta'^2)^{1/2} \tag{27.1}$$

and we take the terminal curve to be given by the equation

$$\xi = (1 - \eta^2)^{1/2} \tag{27.2}$$

defining a semicircle with center at the origin and radius 1.

If the Euler curve under investigation is the straight line

$$\eta = c\xi, \tag{27.3}$$

the terminal point at which curve (27.2) and curve (27.3) intersect is $((1 + c^2)^{-1/2}, c(1 + c^2)^{-1/2})$.

Evaluated at this point, we have the relations

$$g' = -x/y = -c^{-1}, \tag{27.4}$$

$$g'' = -(x^2 + y^2)/y^3 = -(1 + c^2)^{3/2} c^{-3}, \tag{27.5}$$

$$y' = c, \tag{27.6}$$

$$F_{y'} = c(1 + c^2)^{-1/2} \tag{27.7}$$

$$F_x = F_y = F_{yy'} = 0, \tag{27.8}$$

and

$$F_{y'y'} = (1 + c^2)^{-3/2}.$$ (27.9)

The three equations from Section 26 to be solved simultaneously are

$$S_{xx} + cS_{xy} = 0,$$ (27.10)

$$S_{xy} + cS_{yy} = 0,$$ (27.11)

and

$$S_{xx} - (2/c) S_{xy} + (S_{yy}/c^2) = -(1 + c^2)/c^2.$$ (27.12)

Solution yields

$$S_{yy} = -(1 + c^2)^{-1}.$$ (27.13)

From Eq. (22.5), we have the relation

$$\partial y'/\partial y = (1 + c^2)^{-1} (1 + c^2)^{3/2} = (1 + c^2)^{1/2}$$ (27.14)

holding at the terminal point where curve (27.3) intersects curve (27.2).

Using this result in Eq. (25.4), which gives the function $(\partial y'/\partial y)(x)$ in terms of the terminal point ξ_1—here $(1 + c^2)^{-1/2}$—and $(\partial y'/\partial y)(\xi_1)$— here $(1 + c^2)^{1/2}$—we obtain

$$(\partial y'/\partial y)(x) = 1/[x - (1 + c^2)^{-1/2} + (1 + c^2)^{-1/2}] = x^{-1}.$$ (27.15)

This function becomes unbounded at $x = 0$, which, therefore, is a focal point for the particular problem under examination.

28. Discussion of the Example

Figure III.4 shows a portion of the terminal semicircle and the family of Euler curves which are straight lines orthogonal to it. We see that the Euler curves all intersect each other at the focal point $\xi = 0$.

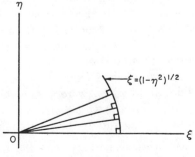

Fɪɢ. III.4

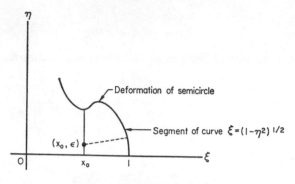

$$\text{Segment of curve } \xi = (1-\eta^2)^{1/2}$$

FIG. III.5

Let us examine the particular Euler straight line $\eta = 0$ (the ξ-axis). By drawing a small semicircle with center at $(x_0, 0)$, $0 < x_0 < 1$, and radius $(1 - x_0)$, we see that all points other than $(1, 0)$ on the circumference of the small semicircle lie within the large terminal semicircle of radius 1 shown in Fig. III.4. Consequently, to reach the terminal semicircle at any point other than $(1, 0)$ requires a line of length greater than $(1 - x_0)$. We see, then, that for initial point $(x_0, 0)$ with abscissa x_0 between 0 and 1, the curve $\eta = 0$ is optimal. For initial point $(0, 0)$ the small semicircle so constructed coincides with the terminal semicircle shown in the figure so all radial straight lines, including the line $\eta = 0$, are equal-valued and are relative minima.* For initial points on the ξ-axis to the left of the origin, which we have shown by Eq. (27.15) to be a focal point, the constructed semicircle has a radius larger than the terminal one, so the point $(1, 0)$ is the worst possible terminal point. In this case, the straight line to $(1, 0)$ is the longest shortest-arc-length curve reaching the terminal semicircular arc. This explains why curves with focal points on them are not optimal although they may satisfy the first three necessary conditions.

Notice that if we had been studying the curve $\eta = 0$ as candidate for optimal curve and the terminal curve were as shown in Fig. III.5, we would have obtained the same result as above, since the value of $\partial y'/\partial y$ at the point $(1, 0)$ is unaffected by deforming the terminal curve at points a finite distance away from $(1, 0)$. Suppose that the initial point were $(x_0, 0)$ and at that point the vertical line is of the same length as the horizontal one. The absolutely minimizing curve from (x_0, ϵ), $\epsilon > 0$, to the terminal curve is the vertical line; and $\partial y'/\partial y$, were y' the slope of the absolutely minimizing curve, would be infinite at $(x_0, 0)$. But our analysis, once we convert the fundamental partial differential equation to ordinary differ-

---

* This is a special situation. Generally, it can be shown that a curve emanating from a point that is conjugate (or focal) to the endpoint does *not* yield even a relative minimum.

ential equations, is local rather than global and the Jacobi condition concerns only those Euler curves that belong to the same family. The relative extremal shown by the dotted line in Fig. III.5, rather than the vertical line, is the object of investigation when the Jacobi condition is applied, and, with respect to it, the point $(x_0, 0)$ is not a focal point.

One can use Fig. III.4 to see why it is that $(\partial y'/\partial y)(0)$ is unbounded. Consider the straight line between $(0, 0)$ and $(1, 0)$. Imagine a point $(x_0, 0)$, $0 \leq x_0 \leq 1$, moving backward from $(1, 0)$ towards $(0, 0)$. For each value of x_0, perturb the η-coordinate 0, by a fixed small amount ϵ, upward from the ξ-axis. Then draw the straight line from the origin through the point (x_0, ϵ) to the terminal semicircle. The segment of this line between (x_0, ϵ) and the terminal semicircle is the Euler curve from the point to the semicircle. The difference $\Delta y'$ between the slope of the line so constructed and the slope, zero, of the ξ-axis, divided by Δy (which equals ϵ), approximates $(\partial y'/\partial y)(x_0)$. When $x_0 = 1$, the slope of the new Euler curve is, to first order, $\epsilon/1$; hence, $\Delta y' = \epsilon$ and

$$(\partial y'/\partial y)(1) = \Delta y'/\Delta y = \epsilon/\epsilon = 1 \qquad (28.1)$$

(see Eq. (27.15)). When $x_0 = \frac{1}{2}$, the Euler curve from $(\frac{1}{2}, \epsilon)$ to the terminal semicircle has slope $\epsilon/\frac{1}{2} = 2\epsilon$ and

$$(\partial y'/\partial y)(\tfrac{1}{2}) = 2\epsilon/\epsilon = 2. \qquad (28.2)$$

When $x_0 = \epsilon$, the Euler curve has slope 1 and

$$(\partial y'/\partial y)(\epsilon) = \epsilon^{-1}. \qquad (28.3)$$

Hence, when $x_0 = 0$,

$$(\partial y'/\partial y)(0) = \infty. \qquad (28.4)$$

Note that these results check with Eq. (27.15) for the solution $(\partial y'/\partial y)(x)$ of the Riccati equation (25.3).

The reader should verify that the optimal value function for the minimum arc-length problem with terminal semicircle (27.2) is given by

$$S(x, y) = 1 - (x^2 + y^2)^{1/2} \qquad (28.5)$$

for all initial points (x, y), such that

$$x \geq 0, \qquad x^2 + y^2 \leq 1. \qquad (28.6)$$

By partial differentiation of (28.5), we obtain the result

$$S_{yy}(x, y) = -x^2/(x^2 + y^2)^{3/2}. \qquad (28.7)$$

Hence, $S_{yy} = -x^2$ at points on the terminal semicircle (this checks with

Eq. (27.13) which holds for the case $x = (1 + c^2)^{-1/2})$ and is unbounded at the origin.

29. Transversality Conditions

We discussed in Sections 10 and 11 the global boundary conditions on the optimal value function $S(x, y)$ that correspond to various versions of the original problem statement. We now translate these into local statements about properties that must hold at the terminal point of a particular curve if it is to be optimal. We have already considered this situation to some extent in our development of the Jacobi condition.

We observed in Section 10 that if ξ_1, the terminal value of the independent variable ξ, is fixed, but $\eta(\xi_1)$, the value of the dependent variable, is free, we have the result, for all y,

$$S(\xi_1, y) = 0. \tag{29.1}$$

Hence,

$$S_y(\xi_1, y) = 0, \tag{29.2}$$

and, by Eq. (18.3),

$$F_{y'}(\xi_1, y, y') = 0 \tag{29.3}$$

at the terminal point (ξ_1, y). This is called the *natural boundary condition* that corresponds to unrestricted terminal ordinate. It relates the terminal slope to the point of termination of the optimal curve.

If admissible curves terminate on the curve

$$\eta = h(\xi), \tag{29.4}$$

we have

$$S(x, y) = 0 \tag{29.5}$$

for all x and y related by

$$y = h(x). \tag{29.6}$$

Since the ratio of the change in the value of $S(x, y)$ to the change in x, if y depends on x through Eq. (29.6) for the terminal curve, is zero at a terminal point satisfying (29.6), we have the equation

$$S_x + S_y h' = 0 \tag{29.7}$$

holding at the terminal point. This becomes, upon elimination of S_x by Eq. (18.2),

$$F + S_y y' - S_y h' = 0 \tag{29.8}$$

where y' is the terminal slope of the solution curve and h' is the slope of the terminal curve (29.4) at the point of termination of the solution curve. Using Eq. (18.3) to eliminate S_y, we obtain the equation

$$F + (h' - y') F_{y'} = 0. \tag{29.9}$$

This is a classical *transversality condition* for this problem (see Eq. (31.2) of Chapter II).

Let us now consider problems with variable initial point. If the initial point has specified ξ-coordinate ξ_0, but free η-coordinate, we know that the optimal curve must originate from the point where the optimal value function takes on its minimum over points on the line

$$x = \xi_0. \tag{29.10}$$

Hence, if S_y is continuous, the equation

$$S_y(\xi_0, y) = 0 \tag{29.11}$$

is a necessary condition for the optimality of the initial point (ξ_0, y). This yields, by Eq. (18.3), the necessary condition

$$F_{y'}(\xi_0, y, y') = 0 \tag{29.12}$$

relating the initial point with the derivative of the optimal curve at that point.

For a problem with the initial point restricted to lie on a curve of the form (29.4), the minimization of the optimal value function along the initial curve yields result (29.9). To first order, the condition that a function be identically zero along a given curve (the variable terminal-point condition) does not differ from the condition that its first derivative be zero at a point on the curve (the variable initial-point condition). The second-order conditions differ, as we shall see in the next section.

We consider now a more general problem where one seeks to minimize the definite integral of a function F that depends on the independent variable ξ, on n functions $\eta_i(\xi)$, $i = 1, \ldots, n$, and on their derivatives $\eta_i'(\xi)$. Suppose that p terminal equations, $p \leq n + 1$, of the form

$$\Psi_j(\xi, \eta_1, \ldots, \eta_n) = 0, \quad j = 1, \ldots, p, \tag{29.13}$$

are specified. To deduce transversality conditions we reason as follows: The derivative of $S(x, y_1, \ldots, y_n)$, evaluated at the terminal point of an optimal curve and taken with the η_i dependent upon ξ in such a way that Eqs. (29.13) remain satisfied, must be zero. Hence,

$$0 = S_x + \sum_{i=1}^{n} S_{y_i} g_i', \tag{29.14}$$

when the numbers $g_i{}'$ are such that

$$\frac{\partial \Psi_j}{\partial x} + \sum_{i=1}^{n} \frac{\partial \Psi_j}{\partial y_i} g_i{}' = 0, \quad j = 1, \ldots, p. \tag{29.15}$$

This result can be written, under suitable assumptions on the independence of the Eqs. (29.13), in terms of p undetermined constant Lagrange multipliers ν_i, $i = 1, \ldots, p$, as: Associated with a given optimal curve there must exist p constants ν_i, $i = 1, \ldots, p$, such that the terminal values of S_x and S_{y_i} are given by

$$S_x + \sum_{i=1}^{p} \nu_i \frac{\partial \Psi_i}{\partial x} = 0 \tag{29.16}$$

and

$$S_{y_i} + \sum_{i=1}^{p} \nu_i \frac{\partial \Psi_i}{\partial y_j} = 0, \quad j = 1, \ldots, n. \tag{29.17}$$

The partial derivatives of the optimal value function can be eliminated from (29.16) and (29.17) by means of Eqs. (18.2) and (18.3) to obtain

$$-F + \sum_{i=1}^{n} y_i{}' F_{y_i{}'} + \sum_{i=1}^{p} \nu_i \frac{\partial \Psi_i}{\partial x} = 0 \tag{29.18}$$

and

$$-F_{y_i{}'} + \sum_{i=1}^{p} \nu_i \frac{\partial \Psi_i}{\partial y_j} = 0, \quad j = 1, \ldots, n. \tag{29.19}$$

30. Second-Order Transversality Conditions

We turn now to second-order transversality conditions. As we saw in Chapter I, if a problem is so stated that the initial point is not uniquely specified but can be freely chosen from a specified set of points, such as the points on a given curve, and if we choose to use the backward characterization of optimality with boundary conditions specified at the terminal end, a further condition necessary for minimality is that $S(x, y)$ take on, at the optimal initial point, its minimum value over the specified set of admissible initial points. When the set of admissible initial points is the line

$$x = \xi_0, \tag{30.1}$$

we have seen how a necessary condition for the minimality of $S(x, y)$ at the point (ξ_0, y) on curve (30.1) yields condition (29.11). The second-order necessary condition for minimality is that at the initial point (ξ_0, y), the inequality

$$S_{yy}(\xi_0, y) \geq 0 \tag{30.2}$$

must hold. This inequality can be reexpressed in terms of the given integrand F by using Eq. (22.5). This yields the necessary condition

$$-F_{yy'} - F_{y'y'}\,(\partial y'/\partial y) \geq 0 \tag{30.3}$$

where x, y, y', and $\partial y'/\partial y$ are to be evaluated at the initial point of the optimal-candidate curve. We saw in Section 22 that $(\partial y'/\partial y)(x)$ satisfies the Riccati differential equation (22.10) with terminal value determined by Eqs. (22.13), (26.1), or as discussed after Eq. (26.7), depending upon the terminal conditions of the problem.

As we saw in Section 29, if the initial point of the minimizing curve must lie on a curve given by $\eta = h(\xi)$, we have the stationarity condition for the initial point that the derivative, with y dependent upon x by $y = h(x)$, of the optimal value function must equal zero when evaluated at the initial point. Hence,

$$S_x + S_y h' = 0. \tag{30.4}$$

This equation yielded Eq. (29.9) after elimination of S_x and S_y. Furthermore, the second derivative of S with y dependent upon x through the relation $y = h(x)$ must be nonnegative when evaluated at the initial point if the initial point minimizes the optimal value function over all initial points. This observation leads to the inequality

$$S_{xx} + 2S_{xy}h' + S_{yy}h'^2 + S_y h'' \geq 0 \tag{30.5}$$

that holds at the initial point. Using Eqs. (22.5), (26.2), and (26.3) to eliminate the second partial derivatives of S, we obtain, in place of (30.5), the inequality

$$-(y' - h')^2 F_{y'y}(\partial y'/\partial y) - (y' - h')^2 F_{yy'} - F_x + y'F_y - 2h'F_y - F_y h'' \geq 0,$$
$$\tag{30.6}$$

that must hold at the initial point of the minimizing curve emanating from a variable initial point lying on a specified initial curve. The number $\partial y'/\partial y$ is obtained by the solution of Eq. (22.10) with the appropriate terminal condition as discussed in earlier sections. If the other necessary conditions held and (30.6) did not, we would have chosen the particular initial point on $\eta = h(\xi)$ from which emanated the maximum-valued curve among those curves emanating from neighboring points on $\eta = h(\xi)$ and minimizing the integral of F, given the initial point.

31. Example

To illustrate the second-order transversality result, let us consider the problem of finding the curve of minimum arc-length connecting the two circular arcs

$$\text{A:} \quad \xi^2 + \eta^2 = (\tfrac{1}{2})^2 \tag{31.1}$$

$$\text{B:} \quad \xi^2 + \eta^2 = 1. \tag{31.2}$$

We shall study the straight line

$$\eta = \xi \tag{31.3}$$

connecting the point $(2^{-3/2}, 2^{-3/2})$ on A with the point $(2^{-1/2}, 2^{-1/2})$ on B, as shown in Fig. III.6. By Eq. (27.15),

$$\partial y'/\partial y \,|_{x=2^{-3/2}} = 2^{3/2} \tag{31.4}$$

for this situation. Furthermore, when $x = 2^{-3/2}$,

$$y' = 1, \tag{31.5}$$

$$h' = -1, \tag{31.6}$$

$$F_{y'} = 2^{-1/2}, \tag{31.7}$$

$$F_{y'y'} = 2^{-3/2} \tag{31.8}$$

$$F_{yy'} = F_x = F_y = 0, \tag{31.9}$$

and

$$h'' = -2^{5/2} . \tag{31.10}$$

Hence, condition (30.6) becomes

$$-(2^2)(2^{-3/2})(2^{3/2}) - (2^{-1/2})(-2^{5/2}) \geq 0. \tag{31.11}$$

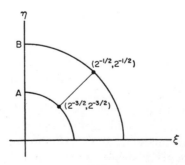

FIG. III.6

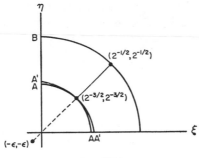

F_IG. III.7

The left-hand side of inequality (31.11) equals exactly zero. This means that, to second order, optimal curves from nearby initial points on A yield neither a better nor a worse value. It is obvious from the figure that this result is correct.

If the initial-condition circle A were changed to the circle

$$A': \quad (\xi + \epsilon)^2 + (\eta + \epsilon)^2 = (\tfrac{1}{2} + \sqrt{2}\epsilon)^2 , \qquad (31.12)$$

shown in Fig. III.7 for $\epsilon > 0$, all results above, up to Eq. (31.10), would remain valid. The new result is that at $x = 2^{-3/2}$,

$$h'' = - 2/(2^{-3/2} + \epsilon) . \qquad (31.13)$$

For $\epsilon > 0$, this change increases the value of the negative second term of (31.11) and the result is that the sum on the left of (31.11) is negative and the necessary condition (30.6) is violated. It is obvious from Fig. III.7 that all initial points on A' near $(2^{-3/2}, 2^{-3/2})$ are better starting points and that the curve under study is the minimum-length curve from the locally worst initial point rather than the best.

The opposite situation develops if $\epsilon < 0$. Then, $(2^{-3/2}, 2^{-3/2})$ turns out to be, locally, the best initial point on A'.

32. The Weierstrass-Erdmann Corner Conditions

It is shown by Berkovitz and Dreyfus, by a method sketched in Section 34 of this chapter, that under certain rather general conditions the optimal value function has continuous first partial derivatives. This result is shown also to hold at corner points, points of discontinuous derivatives of optimal curves, as long as a certain nontangency condition holds. Assuming this condition, these results concerning the continuity of S_x and S_y, in conjunction with Eqs. (18.2) and (18.3), allow us to draw conclusions about conditions that are satisfied at a corner of an optimal curve. By Eq. (18.3), the continuity of S_y across a corner implies

$$F_{y'}(x, y, y'^-) = F_{y'}(x, y, y'^+) \tag{32.1}$$

where y'^- is the left-hand derivative at the corner and y'^+ is the right-hand derivative.

The continuity of S_x implies, by Eq. (18.2) and the above result, the equation

$$F(x, y, y'^-) - F_{y'}(x, y, y'^-)y'^- = F(x, y, y'^+) - F_{y'}(x, y, y'^+)y'^+ . \tag{32.2}$$

These are the two Weierstrass-Erdmann corner conditions that must relate y'^- and y'^+ at a corner point of a curve if the curve is to be optimal.

33. Summary

We have now concluded the portion of this chapter in which the dynamic programming formalism is used to deduce, and interpret, various of the classical necessary conditions for the simplest problem of the calculus of variations.

We began by deducing the fundamental partial differential equation by means of a discrete application of the principle of optimality and of a limiting procedure. Our derivation required the assumption that the second partial derivatives of the optimal value function were bounded.

Satisfaction of the fundamental equation, under certain conditions on the regularity of optimal curves, is both a necessary and sufficient condition for optimality. It was shown that the fundamental equation implies that optimal curves satisfy the Euler-Lagrange differential equation, the Legendre condition, and the Weierstrass condition.

We then developed a connection between our assumption of the boundedness of the second partial derivatives of the optimal value function and the Jacobi condition. We illustrated geometric aspects of our result by means of several examples.

Next, problems with variable end points were considered and connections between the classical transversality conditions and stationarity conditions concerning the optimal value function were established. Second-order conditions for the minimality of the optimal value function over the set of admissible initial points led to second-order transversality conditions and further relationships with the second-order results that accompanied the Jacobi condition.

Finally, the continuity of the first partial derivatives of the optimal value function was shown to imply the Weierstrass-Erdmann corner conditions.

We see, then, that many of the necessary conditions of the calculus of variations can be deduced, not only from the classical study of optimal curves and variations of these curves, but also by the investigation of the optimal value function and its properties. While each of our derivations for the simplest problem stemmed from a property of the optimal value function, the final result was generally expressed in a form in which the optimal value function did not explicitly appear.

In the next section we shall summarize the contents of a paper by L. D. Berkovitz and the author which treats the simplest problem rigorously and establishes many of the results argued formally in this book. The conceptual approach, while very much in the spirit of dynamic programming, differs significantly from that of this book. Then, in the following two sections we shall study certain generalized problems. Our results for these problems explicitly contain an appearance of the optimal value function. The isoperimetric problem of Section 35 is not of the simple form since it involves a subsidiary condition on admissible curves and does not, strictly speaking, belong in this chapter. While problems with subsidiary conditions are the topic of subsequent chapters, the later problems are of the Mayer, or terminal control, type and do not involve a definite integral criterion. Consequently, we have chosen to append the isoperimetric problem with its integral criterion to this chapter.

34. A Rigorous Dynamic Programming Approach

A paper by Berkovitz and Dreyfus (1964) presents a rigorous development of many of the results of this chapter, and we shall summarize that paper here. We shall neither attempt to make mathematically explicit all assumptions nor go through tedious rigorous reasoning. Rather, we shall indicate the chronology and types of arguments employed, restricting ourselves to a two-dimensional simplification, in the hope of thereby making the reference more accessible to the interested reader.

The paper begins by defining the set R of points $(x, y)^*$ such that the optimal admissible curves from the initial point $\xi = x$, $\eta = y$ in R remain

---

* The original paper uses the notation (t, x) rather than (x, y), and x in the paper is an n-dimensional vector, whereas we shall consider y to be a scalar in this section. Furthermore, in the paper our optimal value function S is called W and the optimal policy function y' is called p. Other obvious notational disparities also exist.

in R. It is assumed that there exists an optimal policy function $y'(x, y)$ that is continuous in an open set Q contained in R.

Theorem 1, the proof of which we sketch below, establishes the formula

$$S_y(x, y) = \int_x^a F_y(\xi, \eta(\xi), \eta'(\xi))\, d\xi - F_{y'}(a, b, y'(a, b)) \quad (34.1)$$

at points (x, y) in Q where the point (a, b) lies in Q and is on the optimal curve $\eta = \eta(\xi)$ emanating from (x, y). In particular, when $(a, b) = (x, y)$ we have

$$S_y(x, y) = - F_{y'}(x, y, y'(x, y)) \quad (34.2)$$

which is result (8.1) of this chapter. If $F_{y'}$ and y' are continuous functions of their arguments, then Eq. (34.2) shows that S_y is a continuous function of x and y on Q.

Theorem 1 is proved by means of arguments that follow. Let $\eta = \eta(\xi)$ denote the optimal curve emanating from the point $\xi = x$, $\eta = y$. Consider the point $(x, y + h)$ and the curve $\eta = \bar{\eta}(\xi)$ emanating from that point with the properties that

(1) between $\xi = x$ and $\xi = a - u$, $\bar{\eta}(\xi)$ is obtained by displacing $\eta(\xi)$ a distance h in the η-direction;

(2) between $\xi = a - u$ and $\xi = a$, $\bar{\eta}(\xi)$ is the straight line connecting the points $(a - u, \eta(a - u) + h)$ and $(a, \eta\,(a))$;

(3) for $\xi > a$, $\bar{\eta}(\xi)$ coincides with $\eta(\xi)$.

The functions $\eta(\xi)$ and $\bar{\eta}(\xi)$ are represented in Fig. III.8. Let $u = h/\alpha$ where α is a positive constant. From the optimality of $\eta(\xi)$ we have

$$S(x, y) = \int_x^{a-u} F(\xi, \eta(\xi), \eta'(\xi))\, d\xi$$

$$+ \int_{a-u}^a F(\xi, \eta(\xi), \eta'(\xi))\, d\xi + S(a, \eta(a)). \quad (34.3)$$

Since $\bar{\eta}(\xi)$ is an admissible candidate for minimizing curve from $(x, y + h)$, we have

$$S(x, y + h) \leq \int_x^{a-u} F(\xi, \bar{\eta}(\xi), \bar{\eta}'(\xi))\, d\xi$$

$$+ \int_{a-u}^a F(\xi, \bar{\eta}(\xi), \bar{\eta}'(\xi))\, d\xi + S(a, \bar{\eta}(a)). \quad (34.4)$$

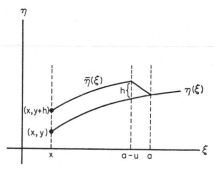

FIG. III.8

Subtracting (34.3) from (34.4) yields

$$S(x, y + h) - S(x, y) \le \int_{x}^{a-u} [F(\xi, \bar{\eta}(\xi), \bar{\eta}'(\xi)) - F(\xi, \eta(\xi), \eta'(\xi))] \, d\xi$$

$$+ \int_{a-u}^{a} [F(\xi, \bar{\eta}(\xi), \bar{\eta}'(\xi)) - F(\xi, \eta(\xi), \eta'(\xi))] \, d\xi. \quad (34.5)$$

Dividing both sides of inequality (34.5) by $h > 0$ and letting $h \to 0$ and $\alpha \to 0$, yields formula (34.1) with the equal sign in (34.1) replaced by a less-than-or-equal-to sign, and with $S_y(x, y)$ replaced by lim sup of the difference quotation.

The argument is then reversed. The optimal curve from $(x, y + h)$ is compared with the curve from (x, y) obtained by displacing the optimal curve downward a distance h over the interval $x \le \xi \le a - u$ and then connecting the displaced curve with the fixed optimal curve as in Fig. III.9. This leads to inequality (34.5) with the sense of the inequality reversed, and lim sup replaced by lim inf, and hence, to formula (34.1).

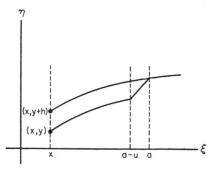

FIG. III.9

The result that

$$(dS/dx)_{y'} = -F,$$ (34.6)

where y' is the optimal policy, is then established, yielding the formula

$$0 = F + S_x + S_y y'.$$ (34.7)

This proves the continuity of S_x since S_y has been shown to be continuous in its arguments.

For any choice of y', it is then shown that

$$F + S_x + S_y y' \geq 0,$$ (34.8)

and, consequently, we have the fundamental equation

$$0 = \min_{y'}[F + S_x + S_y y'].$$ (34.9)

Next, the situation where $y'(x, y)$ is discontinuous along a curve C in (x, y)-space is investigated. The family of optimal curves may appear, in this case, as shown in Fig. III.10. A point (x_0, y_0) on C is considered. We denote by y'^- the left-hand slope of the optimal curve through (x_0, y_0), by y'^+ the right-hand slope, and by y'_c the slope of C at (x_0, y_0). We assume that the partial derivatives of S may be discontinuous across C and write S_x^- and S_y^- on the left of C and S_x^+ and S_y^+ on the right. The formulas

$$0 = F^- + S_x^- + S_y^- y'^- \leq F^+ + S_x^- + S_y^- y'^+,$$ (34.10)

$$0 = F^+ + S_x^+ + S_y^+ y'^+ \leq F^- + S_x^+ + S_y^+ y'^-,$$ (34.11)

and

$$S_x^- + S_y^- y'_c = S_x^+ + S_y^+ y'_c,$$ (34.12)

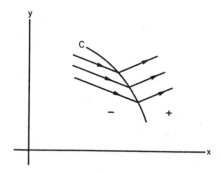

FIG. III.10

are easily established. By suitably combining the above inequalities we obtain

$$(S_x{}^+ - S_x{}^-) + (S_y{}^+ - S_y{}^-)y'_C = 0 ,\qquad(34.13)$$

$$(S_x{}^+ - S_x{}^-) + (S_y{}^+ - S_y{}^-)y'^- \geq 0 ,\qquad(34.14)$$

and

$$(S_x{}^+ - S_x{}^-) + (S_y{}^+ - S_y{}^-)y'^+ \leq 0 .\qquad(34.15)$$

If optimal curves cross the curve C and are not tangent to it, these three results imply the equations

$$S_x{}^+ = S_x{}^-\qquad(34.16)$$

and

$$S_y{}^+ = S_y{}^- ,\qquad(34.17)$$

therefore S_x and S_y have been shown to be continuous across such a curve C of discontinuous slope.

Finally, the reference paper shows rigorously that many classical necessary conditions and other results follow from the conclusions given here.

35. An Isoperimetric Problem

To illustrate quite a different application of the dynamic programming viewpoint, we consider what is called an isoperimetric problem. Such a problem has an integral constraint condition that admissible curves must satisfy.

The problem is to find a curve $\eta = \eta(\xi)$ that minimizes

$$\int_{(\xi_0,\eta_0)}^{(\xi_1,\eta_1)} F(\xi, \eta, \eta')\, d\xi ,\qquad(35.1)$$

and satisfies the additional constraint relation

$$\int_{(\xi_0,\eta_0)}^{(\xi_1,\eta_1)} G(\xi, \eta, \eta')\, d\xi = \xi_0 ,\qquad(35.2)$$

where G is a given function and ξ_0 is a given number.

The optimal value function is now defined to be the minimum value of (35.1) associated with the initial point (x, y), where admissible curves are subject to the constraint

$$\int_{(x,y)}^{(\xi_1,\eta_1)} G(\xi, \eta, \eta')\, d\xi = z,\qquad(35.3)$$

where z can be any number. The optimal value function depends, in this case, on x, y, and z, and we can write

$$S(x, y, z) \;=\; \min_{\{P\}} \int_{(x,y)}^{(\xi_1,\eta_1)} F(\xi, \eta, \eta') \, d\xi , \qquad (35.4)$$

where the set P contains all admissible curves connecting (x, y) with (ξ_1, η_1) and satisfying condition (35.3).

The basic recurrence relation is

$$S(x, y, z) \;=\; \min_{y'}[F(x, y, y') \, \Delta\xi + o(\Delta\xi)$$

$$+ \, S(x + \Delta\xi, y + y' \, \Delta\xi + o(\Delta\xi), z + z' \, \Delta\xi + o(\Delta\xi))] . \quad (35.5)$$

Passage to the limit yields

$$0 \;=\; \min_{y'}[F + S_x + S_y y' + S_z z'] , \qquad (35.6)$$

where z', by differentiation of Eq. (35.3), is given by

$$z' \;=\; -G(x, y, y') . \qquad (35.7)$$

The analog of Eq. (18.2) is

$$F + S_x + S_y y' - S_z G = 0 , \qquad (35.8)$$

and of (18.3) is

$$F_{y'} + S_y - S_z G_{y'} = 0 . \qquad (35.9)$$

Differentiation with respect to x of identity (35.9), with y and y' considered dependent on x through the optimal policy function $y'(x, y, z)$, yields

$$\left(\frac{d}{dx} F_{y'}\right)_{y'} + S_{xy} + S_{yy} y' - S_{yz} G - \left(\frac{d}{dx} S_z G_{y'}\right)_{y'} = 0 . \quad (35.10)$$

Partial differentiation of identity (35.8) with respect to y gives

$$F_y + F_{y'} \frac{\partial y'}{\partial y} + S_{xy} + S_y \frac{\partial y'}{\partial y} + S_{yy} y' - \left(G_y + G_{y'} \frac{\partial y'}{\partial y}\right) S_z - G S_{yz} = 0 .$$

$$(35.11)$$

Partial differentiation of identity (35.8) with respect to z yields

$$F_{y'} \frac{\partial y'}{\partial x} + S_{xz} + S_{yz} y' + S_y \frac{\partial y'}{\partial x} - S_{zz} G - S_z G_{y'} \frac{\partial y'}{\partial x} = 0 . \quad (35.12)$$

Equation (35.9) eliminates three terms of Eq. (35.12), and Eq. (35.7) can be used to replace $-G$ by z'. We see that

$$S_{xx} + S_{yz}y' + S_{zz}z' = 0 , \tag{35.13}$$

or

$$\left(\frac{d}{dx} S_z\right)_{y'} = 0 . \tag{35.14}$$

Consequently, when evaluated along an optimal curve, the equation

$$S_z = c , \tag{35.15}$$

where c is a constant, holds. Now, using Eq. (35.9) to eliminate the $\partial y'/\partial y$ terms in Eq. (35.11) and combining results (35.11) and (35.10), we obtain the equation

$$\left(\frac{d}{dx} F_{y'}\right)_{y'} - \left(\frac{d}{dx} S_z G_{y'}\right)_{y'} = F_y - G_y S_z . \tag{35.16}$$

Let us denote S_z by $-\lambda$, recognizing that by Eq. (35.15) λ is a constant function of x when evaluated along an optimal curve and agreeing to treat λ as being independent of changes in y for fixed x. Then, Eq. (35.16) can be written as

$$\left(\frac{d}{dx} \frac{\partial}{\partial y'} (F + \lambda G)\right)_{y'} - \frac{\partial}{\partial y} (F + \lambda G) = 0 . \tag{35.17}$$

In view of Eq. (35.17), those familiar with classical theory can see that we may identify S_z with the Lagrange multiplier introduced to include a constraint such as (35.2) in the conventional derivation. This identification shows that the Lagrange multiplier introduced in the conventional approach has a simple physical interpretation. If, for a given initial point, the constraining value z, of the isoperimetric constraint (35.3) is allowed to change, the value of the multiplier is equal to the negative of the resulting rate of change with respect to z of the optimal value of the functional being minimized subject to the constraint. This interpretation, however, requires one additional proviso. We know that the rate of change of the optimal value function S with respect to a change in constraint level z is dependent upon the initial point (x, y) and, in general, is different for each different initial y-value for fixed initial value of x. Yet in writing result (35.16) in the form (35.17), we have to agree to regard λ as independent of y, or Eq. (35.17) would disagree with the correct result (35.16).

36. The Hamilton-Jacobi Equation

In Chapter II, Section 35, we mentioned the Hamilton-Jacobi theory whereby the classical necessary conditions are shown to lead to a partial differential equation, solution of which embodies stationary solutions to any particular problem. Except for sign differences, the equations developed in Chapter II are the equations (18.2) and (18.3) that we deduced from the stronger equation (18.1), our fundamental equation.

In order to obtain the partial differential equation exactly as stated in Chapter II, we use the forward recurrence relation discussed in Chapter I, Section 6. We define $S(x, y)$ as the optimal attainable value of the integral of the given integrand $F(x, y, y')$ *from* the specified initial point (ξ_0, η_0) *to* the general terminal point $\xi = x$, $\eta = y$. We then obtain the recurrence relation

$$S(x, y) = \min_{y'}[F(x, y, y')\, \Delta\xi + o(\Delta\xi) + S(x - \Delta\xi, y - y'\, \Delta\xi + o(\Delta\xi))] ,$$

(36.1)

which yields, in the limit as $\Delta\xi \to 0$,

$$0 = \min_{y'}[F - S_x - S_y y'] . \tag{36.2}$$

This equation, under suitable differentiability conditions, implies the two equations

$$S_x = F - S_y y' \tag{36.3}$$

and

$$F_{y'} = S_y , \tag{36.4}$$

which are those given in Chapter II.

We might also mention that the optimal value function for the forward method of recursion could be made the basis of our entire conceptual approach. Most of the necessary conditions would remain unchanged. Certain results, such as the Jacobi condition and second-order transversality results, are modified. The Jacobi equation would be integrated forward rather than backward, with boundary conditions determined at the initial point rather than at the terminal point. For certain problems this offers a computational simplification. Since various quantities such as S_y or $\partial y'/\partial y$ have interesting geometric or physical meanings which depend on the direction of the recurrence, the direction of solution should generally be dictated by the characteristics of the particular problem and the intended application of the results.

CHAPTER IV

The Problem of Mayer

1. Introduction

In the previous chapter we introduced the optimal value function, characterized it by means of the principle of optimality, and used the resultant fundamental nonlinear partial differential equation to deduce classical necessary conditions for a variety of problems. We restricted our attention to problems with definite integral criteria. The value at the point (x, y) of the optimal value function S was defined to be the value of the given definite integral functional evaluated in terms of the optimal solution function emanating from the initial point (x, y) and satisfying whatever terminal conditions were specified. The classical necessary conditions did not explicitly involve the optimal value function, so, for comparison purposes, we endeavored to eliminate all appearances of the function from our results. Only in the Hamilton-Jacobi theory did the function that we call the optimal value function make its classical debut.

In this chapter we shall investigate a different formulation of the problem. Our new problem, of a type classically called the *problem of Mayer*, has a terminal criterion rather than an integral criterion. That is, a solution curve (called a *trajectory*) is evaluated in terms of where it ultimately terminates. This evaluation does not depend explicitly on the route by which the trajectory reached its terminal point. We shall let time be the independent monotonic stage-variable, a role played previously by the abscissa x. The state of the system at a particular time will be characterized by an n-dimensional vector which we call x, whereas y played the role of state in Chapter III. A given set of n differential equations determines the evolution of the states. These equations depend on a control or decision vector u which is generally of dimension less than n. Rather than choose the derivative vector $\dot{x}$ directly, which would be analogous to the choice of y' in Chapter III, we are asked to choose the optimal control vector u. Since the n-dimensional vector $\dot{x}$ is determined, given the state vector x, by a lower-dimensional control vector u, not all n-dimensional vectors $\dot{x}$ are attainable at a given point in state space. This property, as well as the terminal type of criterion, distinguishes the problem of Mayer from the simplest problem.

This change in emphasis to the Mayer (or terminal control) problem is justified by the convenience of this format for the study of optimal aircraft or missile trajectory problems, a prime contemporary area of application. The change in notation is designed to conform with the most frequent current usage.

It is interesting and propitious that the dynamic programming results of this chapter which involve, as usual, the optimal value function conform quite closely in form (and completely in content, of course) with the classical results. The Lagrange multiplier functions that appear explicitly in the classical results are recognizable as the first partial derivatives of our optimal value function. Hence, various steps of Chapter III concerned with the elimination of the explicit appearance of the optimal value function are unnecessary in this chapter. As a result, the intuitive interpretation of results is aided.

In the Berkovitz-Dreyfus paper that was discussed in Section 34 of Chapter III, we felt a certain obligation to justify rigorously various properties of the optimal value function. But henceforth we shall proceed formally. We shall assume analogous properties hold for the optimal value functions of this and the previous chapter. Our faith is buttressed by the equivalence of our results with the classical ones. A rigorous argument similar to that of the Berkovitz-Dreyfus paper will probably be constructed for the problem of Mayer in the near future.

2. Statement of the Problem

We presented in Section 36 of Chapter II the form of the problem of Mayer that will concern us in this chapter. We shall study here mainly the problem involving a scalar (one-dimensional) control function, which will simplify the notation and interpretation. The results generalize to the case of a vector control function in an obvious fashion.

To repeat the formulation, we seek a control function that causes the state variables to evolve with time in such a manner that, when the process terminates and a criterion function is evaluated, no other control yields a trajectory with a smaller value of the criterion at its termination. The actual time of termination is usually dependent upon the control chosen, since the termination time is determined by the satisfaction of certain specified conditions involving the state variables.

As we discussed in Section 2 of Chapter III, it is desirable in dynamic programming to state the problem in terms of variables designated by Greek letters, reserving certain Latin letters for the designation of the initial point of the problem under investigation. If this is done, the results, which hold for any initial point, involve Latin letters and match the results of the classical theory as we presented them in Chapter II.

Specifically, a set of n differential equations*

$$\dot{\xi}_i(\tau) = f_i(\xi_1, \ldots, \xi_n, \tau, v), \qquad i = 1, \ldots, n, \tag{2.1}$$

where initial conditions specified at time τ_0

$$\xi_i(\tau_0) = \xi_{i_0}, \qquad i = 1, \ldots, n, \tag{2.2}$$

are given. A dot above a function indicates differentiation with respect to τ or t. For a specified choice of the piecewise continuous control function $v(\tau)$, solution of the differential equations (2.1) with initial conditions (2.2) determines a set of functions

$$\xi_i(\tau), \qquad i = 1, \ldots, n, \tag{2.3}$$

called a trajectory. The function $v(\tau)$ is to be chosen so as to yield a trajectory with the property that at some (not necessarily explicitly specified) future time τ_1 a set of equations,

$$\Psi_j(\xi_1(\tau_1), \ldots, \xi_n(\tau_1), \tau_1) = 0, \qquad j = 1, \ldots, p \leq n, \tag{2.4}$$

holds. Among the control functions $v(\tau)$ with this property, one is sought which yields a trajectory that renders minimum a given criterion function

$$\Phi(\xi_1(\tau), \ldots, \xi_n(\tau), \tau), \tag{2.5}$$

when (2.5) is evaluated in terms of the terminal time and states of the trajectory.

Equations (2.4) are called terminal conditions, the portion of $(\xi_1, \ldots, \xi_n, \tau)$-space satisfying (2.4) is called the terminal manifold, and the function (2.5) is the criterion function. A control function $v(\tau)$ that is piecewise continuous and which yields a trajectory satisfying the terminal conditions (2.4) is called admissible. The admissible control function

---

* The dynamical equations (2.1), which pervade the remaining chapters, are customarily written in terms of functions designated by f. In dynamic programming, the optimal value function is generally called f. It is because of this conflict, as well as because of the connection with Hamilton-Jacobi theory discussed in Chapter III, Section 36, that we chose the name S for the optimal value function in this book.

$v(\tau)$ which minimizes (2.5) is called the optimal control function, and the set of functions (2.3) associated with that control function is designated the optimal trajectory.

3. The Optimal Value and Policy Functions

Let R designate the set of all points $(x_1, \ldots, x_n, t)$ having the property that there exists an admissible trajectory emanating from the initial point in $(\xi_1, \ldots, \xi_n, \tau)$-space given by

$$\tau = t, \qquad \xi_i(\tau) = x_i, \qquad i = 1, \ldots, n. \tag{3.1}$$

Trajectories containing points $(\xi_1, \ldots, \xi_n, \tau)$, other than the terminal point, such that $(x_1, \ldots, x_n, t)$, given by (3.1), lies on the boundary of R are called *abnormal*; we shall not consider such trajectories here. Trajectories containing only points interior to R are called *normal*. There exist no admissible trajectories from points exterior to R. That is, no piecewise continuous control yields a trajectory emanating from a point exterior to R that intersects the terminal manifold.

We introduce the *optimal value function* S defined in the region R by means of the definition

$S(x_1, \ldots, x_n, t) =$ the minimum value of Φ attainable by an admissible trajectory consistent with (2.1) and (2.4) emanating from the initial state $\xi_1 = x_1, \ldots, \xi_n = x_n$ at time $\tau = t$.

Associated with the initial conditions (3.1) there is an optimal value of the control v, which we designate by

$$u(x_1, \ldots, x_n, t). \tag{3.2}$$

The function $u(x_1, \ldots, x_n, t)$, which associates an optimal control with each admissible initial point, will be called the *optimal policy function*.

4. The Fundamental Partial Differential Equation

Let us consider a problem with initial conditions (3.1) where $(x_1, \ldots, x_n, t)$ is interior to R, and let us use the particular control function

$$\bar{v}(\tau), \qquad t \leq \tau \leq t + \Delta\tau, \tag{4.1}$$

over a time interval of length $\Delta\tau$, where $\Delta\tau$ is sufficiently small that the state at time $t + \Delta\tau$ is interior to R.* If the functions f_i in the dynamical equations (2.1) have bounded partial derivatives with respect to their arguments, the state at time $t + \Delta\tau$ is given by

$$\xi_i(t + \Delta\tau) = x_i(t) + f_i(x_i(t), \ldots, x_n(t), t, \bar{u}) \, \Delta\tau + o(\Delta\tau)$$

$$i = 1, \ldots, n, \quad (4.2)$$

where

$$\bar{u} = \bar{v}(t). \quad (4.3)$$

The optimal trajectory from the state given by Eq. (4.2) to the terminal manifold (2.4) has the value

$$S(x_1 + f_1 \, \Delta\tau + o(\Delta\tau), \ldots, x_n + f_n \, \Delta\tau + o(\Delta\tau), t + \Delta\tau) \quad (4.4)$$

by the definition of S.

The terminal value (4.4) is attained for the problem with initial condition $(x_1, \ldots, x_n, t)$ if the particular control (4.1) is used over the interval $t \leq \tau \leq t + \Delta\tau$ and the optimal control is used thereafter. Since the minimum attainable value cannot exceed any particular attainable value, we see that

$$S(x_1, \ldots, x_n, t) \leq S(x_1 + f_1 \, \Delta\tau + o(\Delta\tau), \ldots, t + \Delta\tau). \quad (4.5)$$

Furthermore, the optimal control yields equality in (4.5). Consequently, we have the equation

$$S(x_1, \ldots, x_n, t) = \min_u [S(x_1 + f_1 \, \Delta\tau + o(\Delta\tau), \ldots, t + \Delta\tau)], \quad (4.6)$$

where the f_i on the right-hand side of (4.6) depend on u as indicated in Eq. (4.2).

Assuming that the second partial derivatives of S are bounded,† we can expand the right side of Eq. (4.6) in Taylor series to obtain

$$S(x_1, \ldots, x_n, t) = \min_u [S(x_1, \ldots, x_n, t)$$

$$+ \sum_{i=1}^{n} S_{x_i} f_i \, \Delta\tau + S_t \, \Delta\tau + o(\Delta\tau)]. \quad (4.7)$$

Subtracting $S(x_1, \ldots, x_n, t)$ from both sides of Eq. (4.7) and letting $\Delta\tau \to 0$ yields the fundamental partial differential equation, holding at

---

* We assume that $\bar{v}(\tau)$ is continuous over the interval $[t, t + \Delta\tau]$ with no loss of generality; see Chapter III, Section 3.

† We return to this assumption in Section 13.

points in the interior of R,

$$0 = \min_u \left[\sum_{i=1}^{n} S_{x_i} f_i + S_t\right]. \tag{4.8}$$

Equation (4.8) also holds at boundary points of R if the appropriate partial derivatives are treated as one-sided derivatives. At points on the boundary of R, in general, only the single value of the control u that yields a trajectory remaining on the boundary of R is admissible. (If a control exists at a boundary point of R that produces a trajectory that becomes interior to R, by a displacement argument it can generally be shown that the initial point does not lie on the boundary of R and a contradiction can be established.) Hence, while Eq. (4.8) holds, no important consequences of the minimization operation in (4.8) can be deduced at a boundary point of R (such as the condition that the derivative with respect to u of the bracketed expression in (4.8) equals zero). As a result, many of the arguments of later sections cannot be justified at a point on the boundary of R.

5. A Connection with the Simplest Problem

Note that if there were only one state variable ξ, and if the notation of Chapter III were used so that t were replaced by x, x by y, and u by y', and if Eq. (2.1) took the particularly simple form

$$\dot{\xi}(\tau) = f(\xi, \tau, v) = v, \tag{5.1}$$

then Eq. (4.8) would resemble the fundamental equation for the simplest problem: namely, the equation

$$0 = \min_{y'}[F + S_y y' + S_x]. \tag{5.2}$$

However, in Eq. (4.8) the term F is missing because we now have a terminal rather than integral criterion. Also, the terminal boundary condition on S must be modified for the Mayer problem, as we shall see.

6. Interpretation of the Fundamental Equation

The fundamental partial differential equation (4.8) has a natural geometric interpretation. Let us consider the optimal control function

$$\bar{v}(\tau), \qquad t \le \tau \le \tau_1, \tag{6.1}$$

yielding the trajectory

$$\bar{\xi}_i(\tau), \qquad i = 1, \ldots, n, \quad t \leq \tau \leq \tau_1, \tag{6.2}$$

connecting the initial point

$$\tau = t, \qquad \bar{\xi}_i(\tau) = x_i, \qquad i = 1, \ldots, n, \tag{6.3}$$

with a point $(\bar{\xi}_1(\tau_1), \ldots, \bar{\xi}_n(\tau_1), \tau_1)$ on the terminal manifold

$$\Psi_j(\xi_1(\tau), \ldots, \xi_n(\tau), \tau) = 0, \qquad j = 1, \ldots, p \leq n. \tag{6.4}$$

This trajectory terminates at time τ_1 and the criterion function, evaluated at that time, is the number

$$\Phi(\bar{\xi}_1(\tau_1), \ldots, \bar{\xi}_n(\tau_1), \tau_1). \tag{6.5}$$

Consequently,

$$S(x_1, \ldots, x_n, t) = \Phi(\bar{\xi}_1(\tau_1), \ldots, \bar{\xi}_n(\tau_1), \tau_1). \tag{6.6}$$

Since the trajectory (6.2) is optimal from $(x_1, \ldots, x_n, t)$, it must be optimal from any intermediate point on the trajectory to the terminal manifold; otherwise, a better trajectory from $(x_1, \ldots, x_n, t)$ would exist. It follows that the optimal trajectory from any intermediate point on (6.2) to the terminal manifold also has value

$$\Phi(\bar{\xi}_1(\tau_1), \ldots, \bar{\xi}_n(\tau_1), \tau_1). \tag{6.7}$$

Therefore, the function S is constant when evaluated along an optimal trajectory, or, equivalently, its derivative is zero. Hence, we can write

$$(dS/dt)_u = 0, \tag{6.8}$$

where the symbol on the left-hand side in Eq. (6.8) denotes the time derivative of S where the states are considered dependent upon time through the dynamical differential equations

$$\dot{x}_i = f_i(x_1, \ldots, x_n, t, u), \quad i = 1, \ldots, n, \tag{6.9}$$

and the optimal control policy

$$u(x_1, \ldots, x_n, t). \tag{6.10}$$

Not only must the optimal value function assume the same value when evaluated at any point of a particular optimal trajectory, but any control $\tilde{u}$ other than the optimal one at a given point must lead to a state with larger or equal minimum attainable terminal value of Φ. For this reason, for any control $\tilde{u}$ other than the optimal control, we must have

$$(dS/dt)_{\tilde{u}} \geq 0. \tag{6.11}$$

This result combined with Eq. (6.8) yields

$$0 = \min_u (dS/dt)_u , \tag{6.12}$$

which, when written out explicitly, is the fundamental Eq. (4.8)—namely,

$$0 = \min_u \left[\sum_{i=1}^n S_{x_i} f_i + S_t \right]. \tag{6.13}$$

The above two intuitive properties that lead to the fundamental equation for the terminal control problem were deduced for the discrete version of the problem in Section 13 of Chapter I, and analogous properties for the simplest problem were presented in Section 7 of Chapter III.

7. Boundary Conditions for the Fundamental Equation

The value of the optimal trajectory starting, and simultaneously terminating, at a point $(\xi_1 , \ldots, \xi_n , \tau)$ on the terminal manifold (2.4) is equal to the criterion function

$$\Phi(\xi_1 , \ldots, \xi_n , \tau) \tag{7.1}$$

evaluated at that point. Thus, the optimal value function is identically equal to the function Φ at points on the terminal manifold; i.e.,

$$S(x_1 , \ldots, x_n , t) = \Phi(x_1 , \ldots, x_n , t) \tag{7.2}$$

for all sets $(x_1 , \ldots, x_n , t)$ such that

$$\tau_1 = t, \qquad \xi_i(\tau_1) = x_i , \qquad i = 1, \ldots, n \tag{7.3}$$

satisfies Eq. (2.4).

If only one terminal condition—for example, the terminal time—is specified, then $p = 1$ in Eq. (2.4) and S is defined by (7.2) on an n-dimensional manifold. In this case, there is generally a unique solution of the partial differential equation (6.13) satisfying the boundary condition (7.2).

However, if further terminal conditions are specified (i.e., $p > 1$), the boundary condition (7.2) does not determine a unique solution of Eq. (6.13) since S is defined terminally on a manifold of dimension less than n. To resolve this problem, we note that any solution of (6.13) determines an optimal control policy $u(x_1 , \ldots, x_n , t)$ that minimizes the bracketed expression on the right-hand side of (6.13). That control policy determines the optimal trajectory from any initial point in R. A further condition on the solution of (6.13) is, then, that the optimal trajectory from any admissible initial point, as determined by the control policy associated with the solution of (6.13), must intersect the $(n + 1 - p)$-dimensional terminal manifold. This implicit condition, combined with boundary condition (7.2), determines, in general, a unique solution of the fundamental equation (6.13).

8. Discussion

Our discussion above parallels that of Sections 10 and 11 of Chapter III. The basic difference is that the optimal value function was identically zero along the terminal manifold for the simplest (integral criterion) problem, but equal to the criterion function Φ for the Mayer (terminal control) problem.

Note that for the terminal control problem, the term F in the fundamental equation for the simplest problem is replaced by zero, and the boundary condition, that $S = 0$ on the terminal manifold for the simplest problem, is replaced by the condition that $S = \Phi$.

In the Bolza formulation of the problem, one considers both a definite integral of F and terminal evaluation of the function Φ, the criterion being a weighted combination of the two. Then the fundamental partial differential equation contains F and the boundary condition involves Φ. Consequently, the reasoning we shall introduce in this chapter, together with that of Chapter III, characterizes the solution of the Bolza problem.

9. Two Necessary Conditions

The fundamental partial differential equation (6.13) is equivalent to the two conditions:

(1) the optimal value of u, corresponding to a given state $(x_1, \ldots, x_n)$ at time t, minimizes the expression

$$\sum_{i=1}^{n} S_{x_i} f_i + S_t \; ; \tag{9.1}$$

(2) when f_i is evaluated in terms of the optimal u, we have the equation

$$\sum_{i=1}^{n} S_{x_i} f_i + S_t = 0 \,. \tag{9.2}$$

If the functions f_i are continuously differentiable in u, if the problem statement places no bounds on admissible values of u, and if u^*, the optimal value of u, is finite,† then a condition that is necessary if u^* is to minimize expression (9.1) is that the partial derivative of (9.1) with respect to u, with the state held fixed, equal zero when evaluated at u^*. We conclude, then, that

$$\sum_{i=1}^{n} S_{x_i}(\partial f_i/\partial u)\,|_{u^*} = 0 \qquad (9.3)$$

since the optimal value function S and its partial derivatives depend on the state but not explicitly upon the control, S being defined in terms of the optimal control.

Equation (9.3) can, in principle, be solved for u^* as a function of the state $(x_1, \ldots, x_n)$, the time t, and the partial derivatives of S. This expression for u^* can be substituted for the appearances of u as arguments of the functions f_i in Eq. (9.2). Then Eq. (9.2) is a conventional type of partial differential equation, generally nonlinear, that is satisfied by the optimal value function S.

The condition that, in a region of normality R in which the second derivatives of S are bounded, the optimal value function S satisfies this new partial differential equation with boundary conditions as developed above, is necessary, but not sufficient, for minimality because Eq. (9.3) is necessary, but not sufficient, for minimality.

10. The Multiplier Rule

We have deduced that, if the correct values of the partial derivatives of the optimal value function are known at a particular point, condition (9.1) determines the optimal value of the control function at that point. Furthermore, condition (9.3) is a necessary condition for optimality.

Once we know the optimal value of the control u corresponding to the initial condition $(x_1, \ldots, x_n)$ at time t, the dynamical differential equations

$$\dot{x}_i = f_i(x_1, \ldots, x_n, t, u), \qquad i = 1, \ldots, n, \qquad (10.1)$$

determine the way in which the states (which we view as new initial conditions) change with time along an optimal trajectory. If we knew also how the partial derivatives of the optimal value function varied with time along the optimal trajectory, we could continue the process of de-

---

† We shall assume these to be the cases unless stated otherwise. We also assume that the trajectory is normal, as discussed in Sections 3 and 4.

termining u from the minimum condition (9.1) and thereby develop the entire optimal trajectory emanating from $(x_1, \ldots, x_n, t)$. That is, we would like to be able to compute

$$(dS_{x_j}/dt)_u, \qquad j = 1, \ldots, n,$$

where this symbol denotes the time derivative of the partial derivative of S with respect to x_j, the states x_i evolving with time according to the dynamical equations (10.1) evaluated in terms of the optimal control u determined by condition (9.1).

By the chain rule for differentiation we have

$$(dS_{x_j}/dt)_u = \sum_{i=1}^{n} S_{x_i x_j} \dot{x}_i + S_{x_j t} = \sum_{i=1}^{n} S_{x_i x_j} f_i + S_{x_j t}. \qquad (10.2)$$

Partial differentiation of (9.2) with respect to x_j yields

$$\sum_{i=1}^{n} S_{x_i x_j} f_i + S_{x_j t} + \sum_{i=1}^{n} S_{x_i} \left(\frac{\partial f_i}{\partial x_j} + \frac{\partial f_i}{\partial u} \frac{\partial u}{\partial x_j} \right) = 0. \qquad (10.3)$$

Combining these two results, with the aid of (9.3) which eliminates the $\partial u/\partial x_j$ term,* we obtain a system of ordinary differential equations that is satisfied by the partial derivatives of S along an optimal trajectory—namely,

$$\left(\frac{dS_{x_j}}{dt} \right)_u = - \sum_{i=1}^{n} S_{x_i} \frac{\partial f_i}{\partial x_j}, \qquad j = 1, \ldots, n. \qquad (10.4)$$

Note that *along a particular trajectory*, the functions S_{x_i} are regarded as functions of the one independent variable, time. Also, arguing similarly,

$$\left(\frac{dS_t}{dt} \right)_u = - \sum_{i=1}^{n} S_{x_i} \frac{\partial f_i}{\partial t}. \qquad (10.5)$$

Now that we know how the partial derivatives of the optimal value function S, as well as the state variables, vary as functions of time along an optimal trajectory, the necessary condition (9.3) may be used to determine the control u at each time t.

The result that, associated with a normal optimal trajectory, there exist functions $S_{x_i}(t)$ and $S_t(t)$ satisfying (10.4) and (10.5) and, furthermore, u satisfies Eq. (9.3), is called the *multiplier rule* in the classical theory. The functions $S_{x_i}(t)$ are written as $\lambda_j(t)$ in the classical notation and are Lagrange multiplier functions associated with the constraining

---

* Special care must be taken at a point where the optimal control is discontinuous (see the footnote to Section 9 of Chapter III). Equation (10.4) to follow is valid if optimal trajectories *cross* a manifold of discontinuous control, but not if they are tangent to such a manifold.

differential equations (10.1). For reasons of brevity and conformity, we shall often refer to the functions $S_{x_i}(t)$ and $S_t(t)$ as *multiplier functions*.

Reasoning for the simplest problem, analogous to that preceding, is found in Section 19 of Chapter III.

11. The Clebsch Necessary Condition

A control u determined by solution of Eq. (9.3) may not yield the absolute minimum of expression (9.1), but may be either a maximizing or only relatively minimizing control.

Returning to expression (9.1), we invoke a second-order necessary condition of differential calculus for a relative minimum. The second derivative of a function to be minimized must be nonnegative when evaluated in terms of the minimizing argument. This yields the further necessary condition, eliminating most controls that yield relative maxima of expression (9.1),

$$\sum_{i=1}^{n} S_{x_i}(\partial^2 f_i/\partial u^2) \geq 0 . \tag{11.1}$$

Inequality (11.1) must hold when evaluated in terms of the control, the states, and the multiplier functions associated with a particular trajectory at time t. The above condition, necessary for relative minimality of (9.1), is called the *Clebsch condition* for the Mayer problem and is analogous to the Legendre condition (Chapter II, Section 22) of the simplest problem. An analogous condition from multidimensional differential calculus holds if the control is multidimensional.

12. The Weierstrass Necessary Condition

For expression (9.1) to be absolutely minimized by the control u at a point $(x_1, \ldots, x_n, t)$ of a trajectory with associated values of S_{x_i} and S_t given by the multiplier rule (10.4), it is necessary that the inequality

$$\sum_{i=1}^{n} S_{x_i} f_i(x_1, \ldots, x_n, t, u) + S_t \leq \sum_{i=1}^{n} S_{x_i} f_i(x_1, \ldots, x_n, t, U) + S_t$$

$$\tag{12.1}$$

hold for every element $(x_1, \ldots, x_n, t, u, S_{x_1}, \ldots, S_{x_n}, S_t)$ of the trajectory, where U is any admissible control such that $U \neq u$. Subtracting

S_t from both sides of inequality (12.1), we have the Weierstrass condition for the problem of Mayer.

The over-all situation for the Mayer problem parallels that discussed in Section 21 of Chapter III on the simplest problem. Relative minimality of expression (9.1) at each point of a particular trajectory is necessary for weak relative minimality of the trajectory while absolute minimality of (9.1) is needed for strong relative minimality of the trajectory. Only the satisfaction of the fundamental partial differential equation (6.13) at each point of the region R can guarantee absolute minimality of the associated trajectories.

13. A Fourth Condition

In order to deduce the fundamental equation we assumed that the second partial derivatives of S were bounded. If one assumes that these derivatives are bounded (and consequently that the fundamental equation is valid) in some neighborhood N of the terminal point, the results of the above sections can be used to develop a matrix Riccati differential equation, the solution of which is the matrix $(S_{x_i x_j})$ of second partial derivatives of S. Points, if any, at which the solution is unbounded cannot lie within the region N. Such points are called *conjugate* or *focal* points for the Mayer problem and trajectories containing such points are not optimal.

In the following sections we shall study the second partial derivatives of S and produce results that are analogous to the Jacobi condition for the simplest problem. Our path will be eased somewhat by the fact that we are no longer trying to eliminate all explicit appearances of S from the results, as we were in Chapter III. Just as in the earlier case, our analysis will also yield a scheme for adjusting the optimal control if the states at some point of an optimal trajectory are perturbed slightly. We call this consideration *guidance*. Most practical rocket trajectory problems are not really solved by the determination of the optimal trajectory, but require also a guidance scheme to correct the inevitable deviations from optimal.

14. The Second Partial Derivatives of the Optimal Value Function

In Section 9 we deduced the two fundamental necessary conditions

$$(dS/dt)_u = 0 \tag{14.1}$$

and

$$(\partial/\partial u)\,(dS/dt)_u = 0. \tag{14.2}$$

Equation (14.1) states that the optimal value function is constant along an optimal trajectory and (14.2) asserts that the derivative of the optimal value function in the optimal direction is stationary with respect to the control. In expanded form these equations are

$$\sum_{k=1}^{n} S_{x_k} f_k + S_t = 0 \tag{14.3}$$

and

$$\sum_{k=1}^{n} S_{x_k}\,(\partial f_k/\partial u) = 0 \tag{14.4}$$

respectively.

We now seek to compute the time derivative of each of the second partial derivatives of S. The desired derivatives can be written as

$$(dS_{x_i x_j}/dt)_u\,, \qquad i = 1,\ldots,n\,, \quad j = 1,\ldots,n\,. \tag{14.5}$$

By the chain rule for differentiation, we have

$$\left(\frac{dS_{x_i x_j}}{dt}\right)_u = \sum_{k=1}^{n} S_{x_i x_j x_k} f_k + S_{x_i x_j t}\,. \tag{14.6}$$

Partial differentiation of (14.3) with respect to x_i yields

$$\sum_{k=1}^{n} S_{x_k x_i} f_k + \sum_{k=1}^{n} S_{x_k}\left(\frac{\partial f_k}{\partial x_i} + \frac{\partial f_k}{\partial u}\frac{\partial u}{\partial x_i}\right) + S_{t x_i} = 0\,. \tag{14.7}$$

Using identity (14.4) to eliminate one term of (14.7), and then differentiating (14.7) with respect to x_j produces

$$\sum_{k=1}^{n} S_{x_i x_j x_k} f_k + \sum_{k=1}^{n} S_{x_i x_k}\left(\frac{\partial f_k}{\partial x_j} + \frac{\partial f_k}{\partial u}\frac{\partial u}{\partial x_j}\right) + \sum_{k=1}^{n} S_{x_k x_j}\frac{\partial f_k}{\partial x_i}$$

$$+ \sum_{k=1}^{n} S_{x_k}\left(\frac{\partial^2 f_k}{\partial x_i\,\partial x_j} + \frac{\partial^2 f_k}{\partial x_i\,\partial u}\frac{\partial u}{\partial x_j}\right) + S_{x_i x_j t} = 0\,. \tag{14.8}$$

Combining this result with (14.6) gives

$$\left(\frac{dS_{x_i x_j}}{dt}\right)_u = -\sum_{k=1}^{n} S_{x_i x_k}\left(\frac{\partial f_k}{\partial x_j} + \frac{\partial f_k}{\partial u}\frac{\partial u}{\partial x_j}\right) - \sum_{k=1}^{n} S_{x_j x_k}\frac{\partial f_k}{\partial x_i}$$

$$- \sum_{k=1}^{n} S_{x_k}\left(\frac{\partial^2 f_k}{\partial x_i\,\partial x_j} + \frac{\partial^2 f_k}{\partial x_i\,\partial u}\frac{\partial u}{\partial x_j}\right). \tag{14.9}$$

This is a differential equation for the functions $S_{x_i x_i}(t)$ along an optimal trajectory, but it contains terms in $\partial u / \partial x_j$. The value of $(\partial u / \partial x_j)(t)$ is, at the moment, unknown to us. To remedy this situation, we take the partial derivative of (14.4) with respect to x_j, obtaining

$$\sum_{k=1}^{n} S_{x_j x_k} \frac{\partial f_k}{\partial u} + \sum_{k=1}^{n} S_{x_k} \left(\frac{\partial^2 f_k}{\partial x_j \, \partial u} + \frac{\partial^2 f_k}{\partial u^2} \frac{\partial u}{\partial x_j} \right) = 0 . \tag{14.10}$$

If

$$\sum_{k=1}^{n} S_{x_k} \frac{\partial^2 f_k}{\partial u^2} \neq 0 , \tag{14.11}$$

we can solve (14.10) for $\partial u / \partial x_j$ and substitute the result in (14.9). Then we have a set of differential equations for the functions $S_{x_i x_i}(t)$, $i = 1, \ldots, n$; $j = 1, \ldots, n$, which, if we know $S_{x_i}(t)$, $i = 1, \ldots, n$, and have values for $S_{x_i x_i}$, $i = 1, \ldots, n$; $j = 1, \ldots, n$, at one point of an optimal trajectory, allows the determination of the set of functions $S_{x_i x_i}$ at each point of the trajectory.

15. A Matrix Differential Equation of Riccati Type

Let the control u be an r-dimensional vector and define the following matrices whose dimensions are shown in parentheses:

$$S = (S_{x_i x_j}) \qquad\qquad (n \times n)$$

$$A = (\partial f_i / \partial x_j) \qquad\qquad (n \times n)$$

$$B = (\partial f_i / \partial u_j) \qquad\qquad (n \times r)$$

$$C = \left(\sum_{k=1}^{n} S_{x_k} \frac{\partial^2 f_k}{\partial x_i \, \partial x_j} \right) \qquad (n \times n)$$

$$D = \left(\sum_{k=1}^{n} S_{x_k} \frac{\partial^2 f_k}{\partial u_i \, \partial x_j} \right) \qquad (r \times n)$$

$$E = \left(\sum_{k=1}^{n} S_{x_k} \frac{\partial^2 f_k}{\partial u_i \, \partial u_j} \right) \qquad (r \times r)$$

$$F = (\partial u_i / \partial x_j) \qquad\qquad (r \times n).$$

Then we can put the results of Section 14 into compact matrix notation.

The solution of Eq. (14.10) for F, assuming that E^{-1} exists, yields

$$F = -E^{-1}B^{T}S - E^{-1}D. \tag{15.1}$$

Substitution of this result in the matrix form of Eq. (14.9) produces the Riccati matrix differential equation

$$-\dot{S} = SA - SBE^{-1}B^{T}S - SBE^{-1}D + A^{T}S + C - D^{T}E^{-1}B^{T}S$$
$$D^{T}E^{-1}D. \tag{15.2}$$

The solution of this equation with suitable boundary conditions is the matrix, $(S_{x_i x_j})$, of second partial derivatives of S.

16. Terminal Values of the Second Partial Derivatives of the Optimal Value Function

Returning to the terminal control problem that was stated in Section 2, suppose that only one terminal relation (2.4), e.g.,

$$\Psi_1 = \tau - T = 0, \tag{16.1}$$

is specified, the state variables being free at the terminal time T. Let the criterion function be

$$\Phi(\xi_1(T), \ldots, \xi_n(T)). \tag{16.2}$$

Then, at the terminal point of a trajectory, we have the result

$$S_{x_i x_i}|_T = \partial^2\Phi/\partial\xi_i\,\partial\xi_j|_T, \qquad i = 1, \ldots, n \quad j = 1, \ldots, n. \tag{16.3}$$

The case where the terminal manifold is of lower dimension than n (i.e., where more than one terminal relation is specified) is much more complicated. As we saw in Chapter III, while the first partial derivatives of the optimal value function, S_{x_i}, may be undefined at such a terminal point, their limiting values along a given optimal trajectory do exist. In Section 18 we shall see that these values for the terminal control problem can be expressed in terms of multipliers ν_i that depend on the particular trajectory. However, the second partial derivatives of S may become unbounded as the terminal point of a particular optimal trajectory is approached along the trajectory, just as did $\partial y'/\partial y$ and S_{yy} in Section 22 of Chapter III. If this is the case, then behavior in the limit can be determined much as it was in Chapter III, although the algebra is very involved and we shall not go into the details here.

Suppose that the terminal values of $S_{x_i x_j}$ have been determined. Then by integration one can find the particular solution of the differential equation (15.2) that yields the second partial derivatives of S at each point of a given trajectory satisfying the multiplier rule. If $S_{x_i x_j}(t)$ remains bounded at all points of interest, other than perhaps the terminal point of the trajectory, the passage to a limit in the derivation of the fundamental partial differential equation is valid. If $S_{x_i x_j}$ becomes unbounded at some point other than the terminal one, the passage is not necessarily valid. Consequently, we require that $S_{x_i x_j}(t)$ remain bounded. As we indicated in Chapter III, a satisfactory argument establishing the necessity (rather than sufficiency) of this condition is currently lacking.

17. The Guidance Problem

Consider a specific problem of the form given in Section 2. Let τ_0 represent the initial time and let the initial values of the state variables at time τ_0 be given by

$$\xi_i(\tau_0) = \xi_{i0}, \qquad i = 1, \ldots, n. \tag{17.1}$$

Let $\bar{v}(\tau)$ be the optimal control function for this specific problem and let $\bar{\xi}_i(\tau)$ denote the value of the ith state at time τ along this trajectory, which we shall call the *nominal optimal trajectory*. This optimal trajectory terminates at time τ_1.

Now suppose that this trajectory is to be followed by a mechanical system (which we take to be a rocket) and that at some time $\tau = t$ it is observed that the states are not $\bar{\xi}_i(t)$, as desired, but $\bar{\xi}_i(t) + \delta\xi_i(t)$. The $\delta\xi_i(t)$, which we assume to be small, may have been caused by mechanical malfunctions resulting in a control that was $\bar{v}(\tau) + \delta v(\tau)$ for $\tau_0 \leq \tau \leq t$; or, perhaps the assumed dynamical differential equations describing the evolution of state were in error due to some unexpected influences, such as wind or fluctuations in atmospheric density. Control corrections designed to return the vehicle to the original optimal trajectory $\bar{\xi}_i(\tau)$ could be attempted, or a terminal guidance scheme could be developed which attempts to match the terminal conditions $\bar{\xi}_i(\tau_1)$ of the nominal optimal trajectory. However, if it is still desired to minimize the original criterion Φ subject to the terminal conditions $\Psi_j = 0$, neither of the above schemes is optimal. In reality, once a deviation such as described above has been observed, we have a new variational problem, with initial time t and initial states $\bar{\xi}_i(t) + \delta\xi_i(t)$. We desire the optimal trajectory for this new problem. Consequently, we need to know how the optimal control for the above problem would change if the states at some intermediate point of the nominal optimal trajectory were varied.

In the preceding sections we have designated the optimal control, when it is viewed as a function of the initial state, by $u(x_1, \ldots, x_n, t)$, where $\tau = t$, $\xi_i(t) = x_i$ is the initial state. In this notation, if we knew $\partial u/\partial x_j$, the rate of change of optimal control with state, evaluated at points on the nominal optimal trajectory determined by

$$\tilde{v}(\tau),$$

then the linear rule

$$\delta v(t) = \sum_{j=1}^{n} (\partial u/\partial x_j)|_t \, \delta \xi_j(t) , \qquad (17.2)$$

would give, to first order, the change in optimal control associated with the change in state of $\delta \xi_j$ at time t.

But we saw in Section 15 that the matrix of $(\partial u_i/\partial x_j)(t)$, where u was an r-dimensional control vector, is given by Eq. (15.1) in terms of the matrix of second partial derivatives of S and other quantities that are known along an optimal trajectory. These second derivatives of S are given, in turn, along the nominal optimal trajectory by solution of the set of differential equations (15.2), with the appropriate terminal boundary values for the problem.

The solution of the guidance problem is achieved, then, by the following computations. First, the optimal trajectory for the given problem is determined. This calculation yields the states, controls, and first partial derivatives of S as functions of time. Then the matrices A, B, C, D, and E defined in Section 15 can be determined as functions of time along the trajectory. Also, once the terminal point and time are known, the matrix of second partial derivatives of S can, in theory, be evaluated there. (Since, for many problems, these second derivatives are unbounded at the terminal time, they should be evaluated at a time shortly before termination, at which time they are finite.) Then the Riccati differential equation (15.2) can be numerically integrated to determine the $n(n + 1)/2$ functions* $S_{x_i x_j}(t)$, and this computation in turn will yield the set of n functions $F(t)$ by (15.1). All of these computations are performed when the optimal trajectory is being determined and *before* the actual trajectory is flown. The vector function $F(t)$ is stored in the guidance computer of the vehicle, as well as the functions $\bar{\xi}_i(t)$ and $\tilde{v}(t)$ describing the optimal trajectory. During flight, the actual states are monitored and the devia-

---

* There are $n(n + 1)/2$ functions $S_{x_i x_j}(t)$ rather than n^2 because of symmetry, $S_{x_i x_j}(t)$ equaling $S_{x_j x_i}(t)$.

tions $\delta\xi_j(t)$ from the nominal optimal trajectory are determined. Then Eq. (17.2), which in matrix notation for an r-dimensional control and n-dimensional state looks like

$$\delta v(t) = F(t)\, \delta\xi(t), \tag{17.3}$$

yields the control adjustment $\delta v(t)$ that compensates for deviations $\delta\xi_j(t)$ in state at time t from the nominal trajectory. The correction determined by (17.3) should be computed and applied continuously along the trajectory. (A slight modification in the derivation yields the control corrections if the state deviations are sampled only at discrete times.) Note that only the simple linear operation (17.3) need be performed during the actual flight, when time is at a premium.

18. Terminal Transversality Conditions

As in the case of the simplest problem, we can use obvious properties of the optimal value function, such as those developed in Section 7, to deduce results pertinent to the multiplier rule of Section 10. We have, at some loss of generality (see Section 28), converted the optimization problem from one involving the partial differential equation (6.13) to one concerning the ordinary differential equations (10.1), (10.4), (10.5), and minimum condition (9.1). We now obtain sufficient boundary conditions to make the solution of the system of ordinary differential equations a well-posed problem.

Proceeding from the particular to the general, let us suppose initially that the terminal time τ_1 for the problem is specified and that no other conditions at termination are prescribed *a priori*. Then,

$$S(x_1,\ \ldots,\ x_n,\ \tau_1) = \Phi(x_1,\ \ldots,\ x_n,\ \tau_1) \tag{18.1}$$

for all terminal points $(x_1,\ \ldots,\ x_n)$. By partial differentiation of (18.1), we see that the equations

$$S_{x_i}\big|_{\tau_1} = \partial\Phi/\partial x_i\big|_{\tau_1}, \qquad i = 1,\ \ldots,\ n, \tag{18.2}$$

are n terminal conditions that the multiplier functions—i.e., the partial derivatives of S—must satisfy. If the initial time and states are specified, the differential equation problem is then well posed.

Of course, if Φ fails to depend explicitly on some x_k, then

$$S_{x_k}\big|_{\tau_1} = 0 \tag{18.3}$$

is the appropriate boundary condition on the kth multiplier function.

We consider next the case where a single, but more general, terminal condition

$$\Psi(\xi_1, \ldots, \xi_n, \tau) = 0 \tag{18.4}$$

is specified. Consider a point $(x_1, \ldots, x_n, t_1)$ such that the point $\tau = t_1$, $\xi_i(\tau) = x_i$ lies on the terminal manifold (18.4). We denote independent variations in a component of the state x_j by δx_j. Changes in any quantity θ depending on x_j that result from these independent changes are denoted by $d\theta$. Then, varying x_j at the terminal time t_1 and considering the effect of this variation on the dependent values of Φ and Ψ when they are evaluated at the (perhaps perturbed) terminal time and also the effect upon the terminal time t_1 itself, we have the equations

$$d\Phi = (\partial\Phi/\partial x_j)\,|_{t_1}\,\delta x_j + \dot{\Phi}\,|_{t_1}\,dt_1 \tag{18.5}$$

and

$$d\Psi = (\partial\Psi/\partial x_j)\,|_{t_1}\,\delta x_j + \dot{\Psi}\,|_{t_1}\,dt_1, \tag{18.6}$$

where dt_1 is the change in the terminal time. Using the fact that $d\Psi$ must equal zero if $\Psi = 0$ is to be the stopping condition both before and after the variation, we may solve for the first-order change in terminal time dt_1 resulting from a perturbation in x_j of δx_j

$$dt_1 = -\dot{\Psi}^{-1}\,|_{t_1}(\partial\Psi/\partial x_j)\,|_{t_1}\,\delta x_j. \tag{18.7}$$

Therefore,

$$d\Phi = \left[\frac{\partial\Phi}{\partial x_j}\bigg|_{t_1} - \frac{\dot{\Phi}}{\dot{\Psi}}\bigg|_{t_1}\frac{\partial\Psi}{\partial x_j}\bigg|_{t_1}\right]\delta x_j. \tag{18.8}$$

Since $d\Phi/\delta x_j$ is the ratio, evaluated at time t_1, of the change in the value of the terminal criterion Φ (due to a change of δx_j in state x_j) to the change δx_j, we have the result

$$S_{x_j}\big|_{t_1} = \frac{\partial\Phi}{\partial x_j}\bigg|_{t_1} - \frac{\dot{\Phi}}{\dot{\Psi}}\bigg|_{t_1}\frac{\partial\Psi}{\partial x_j}\bigg|_{t_1}. \tag{18.9}$$

Let us now consider the general problem with p terminal constraints

$$\Psi_j(\xi_1, \ldots, \xi_n, \tau) = 0, \qquad j = 1, \ldots, p \le n \tag{18.10}$$

(see Eq. (2.4)).

Let a trajectory start at time $\tau = t_1$, in state $\xi_i(t_1) = x_i$, $i = 1, \ldots, n$, and let these values satisfy Eqs. (18.10) so that the initial point is also the terminal point. Then

$$S(x_1, \ldots, x_n, t_1) = \Phi(x_1, \ldots, x_n, t_1). \tag{18.11}$$

If the values of $x_1, \ldots, x_n$ and t_1 are varied by amounts $\delta x_1, \ldots, \delta x_n$, and δt_1 *in such a way that Eqs. (18.10) remain satisfied*, the change in the optimal value function S—since the new point $(x_1 + \delta x_1, \ldots, x_n + \delta x_n, t_1 + \delta t_1)$ is still a terminal point—is merely the change in Φ. Hence,

$$dS = \sum_{i=1}^{n} S_{x_i} |_{t_1} \, \delta x_i + S_{t_1} \, \delta t_1$$

$$= \sum_{i=1}^{n} \frac{\partial \Phi}{\partial x_i}\bigg|_{t_1} \delta x_i + \frac{\partial \Phi}{\partial t_1} \delta t_1, \qquad (18.12)$$

where, since (18.10) must remain satisfied, we have the p equations relating the variations δx_j and δt_1 (letting $\xi_i = x_i$ and $\tau = t_1$ in (18.10))

$$\sum_{i=1}^{n} \frac{\partial \Psi_j}{\partial x_i}\bigg|_{t_1} \delta x_i + \frac{\partial \Psi_j}{\partial t_1} \delta t_1 = 0, \qquad j = 1, \ldots, p. \qquad (18.13)$$

The satisfaction of (18.12) subject to constraints (18.13) is equivalent to

$$\sum_{i=1}^{n} S_{x_i} |_{t_1} \, \delta x_i + S_{t_1} \, \delta t_1 = \sum_{i=1}^{n} \frac{\partial \Phi}{\partial x_i}\bigg|_{t_1} \delta x_i + \frac{\partial \Phi}{\partial t_1} \delta t_1$$

$$- \sum_{j=1}^{p} \nu_j \left(\sum_{i=1}^{n} \frac{\partial \Psi_j}{\partial x_i}\bigg|_{t_1} \delta x_i + \frac{\partial \Psi_j}{\partial t_1} \delta t_1 \right), \quad (18.14)$$

where the δx_i and δt_1 can now be varied independently and the ν_i are constant Lagrange multipliers which are unique if the rank of the $p \times (n + 1)$ matrix

$$\left\| \frac{\partial \Psi_i}{\partial x_j}\bigg|_{t_1} \frac{\partial \Psi_i}{\partial t_1} \right\|$$

is p.* Equation (18.14) can be written

$$\sum_{i=1}^{n} S_{x_i} |_{t_1} \, \delta x_i + S_{t_1} \, \delta t_1 = \sum_{i=1}^{n} \left[\frac{\partial \Phi}{\partial x_i}\bigg|_{t_1} - \sum_{j=1}^{p} \nu_j \frac{\partial \Psi_j}{\partial x_i}\bigg|_{t_1} \right] \delta x_i$$

$$+ \left(\frac{\partial \Phi}{\partial t_1} - \sum_{j=1}^{p} \nu_j \frac{\partial \Psi_j}{\partial t_1} \right) \delta t_1, \qquad (18.15)$$

and, since the δx_i and δt_1 are to be treated as independent, this implies the

---

* We consider here only the normal case where the rank is indeed p.

$n + 1$ equations

$$S_{x_i}\big|_{t_1} = \frac{\partial \Phi}{\partial x_i}\bigg|_{t_1} - \sum_{j=1}^{p} \nu_j \frac{\partial \Psi_j}{\partial x_i}\bigg|_{t_1}, \qquad i = 1, \ldots, n, \qquad (18.16)$$

and

$$S_{t_1} = \frac{\partial \Phi}{\partial t_1} - \sum_{j=1}^{p} \nu_j \frac{\partial \Psi_j}{\partial t_1}. \qquad (18.17)$$

Identifying S_{x_i} with λ_i, and using Eq. (9.2) to replace S_{t_1}, we see that conditions (18.16) and (18.17) are identical with the classical result stated in Section 41 of Chapter II, Eqs. (41.8) and (41.9).

We discussed in Chapter II how, if the initial values of the state variables are specified, the above equations represent the appropriate number of boundary conditions and the problem is well posed.

Note from Eqs. (18.16) and (18.17) that if x_i appears in neither the criterion function nor the constraint equations, $S_{x_i} = 0$ at the terminal point. This corresponds to the fact that changing such a state variable at the end point affects neither the criterion function nor the terminal time and, hence, does not affect the optimal value function S.

19. Initial Transversality Conditions

Equations (18.16) and (18.17) are $(n + 1)$ terminal conditions on the differential equations that are satisfied by the multiplier functions. The remaining $(n + 1)$ conditions on the $(2n + 2)$ differential equations for states and multipliers are the initial values of the state variables, if these are given. At initial time $\tau = t_0$, the equation

$$S_{x_i}\big|_{t_0} = 0 \qquad (19.1)$$

holds if the initial value of the state variable $\xi_i(t_0)$ is not specified. This equation follows from the definition of S, and the fact that an unspecified initial state x_i should be chosen so as to minimize S, just as it was in Section 29 of Chapter III.

If the initial point is to be chosen optimally from among the points on a specified manifold, the problem is one of minimizing the function S subject to constraints. First-order stationarity conditions similar to Eqs. (18.16) and (18.17) are obtained. A second-order condition, to be developed in Section 25, also applies.

20. Homogeneity

One special aspect of these results deserves mention. Multiplying the criterion function Φ for a given problem by a positive constant k, does not affect the optimal trajectory for the problem. The trajectory that minimizes time to a given terminal manifold, for example, also minimizes ten times the terminal time. Such a change of scale does, however, affect S_{x_i} and S_t for the problem. Recalling the definition of S, it is clear that changing the scale of the criterion simply changes the scale of S and its partial derivatives, multiplying them by k. (The reader can verify that the optimal control, as given by the multiplier rule, is unaffected if S_{x_i} is replaced by kS_{x_i} and S_t by kS_t.) Thus, should a trajectory be found that (1) emanates from a given initial point, (2) has associated with it multiplier functions $S_{x_i}(t)$ and $S_t(t)$ and control $u(t)$ which satisfy the multiplier rule, (3) intersects the specified terminal manifold

$$\Psi_j = 0, \qquad j = 1, \ldots, p, \tag{20.1}$$

and (4) such that there exist ν_j, $j = 1, \ldots, p$, *and a number k such that*

$$S_{x_i}\big|_{t_1} = k\left.\frac{\partial \Phi}{\partial x_i}\right|_{t_1} - k\sum_{j=1}^{p} \nu_j \left.\frac{\partial \Psi_j}{\partial x_i}\right|_{t_1}, \quad i = 1, \ldots, n, \tag{20.2}$$

$$S_t\big|_{t_1} = k\left.\frac{\partial \Phi}{\partial t}\right|_{t_1} - k\sum_{j=1}^{p} \nu_j \left.\frac{\partial \Psi_j}{\partial t}\right|_{t_1} \tag{20.3}$$

(rather than Eqs. (18.16) and (18.17)); this trajectory is extremal and the true $S_{x_i}(t)$ and $S_t(t)$ (in the sense that S represents the optimal value of Φ) are $1/k$ times the ones found above.

Because of this homogeneity property of the multiplier functions, it is often convenient to arbitrarily set one multiplier function equal to 1 at either the initial or terminal point and thereby reduce the problem by one dimension. This procedure is mathematically proper but it must then be realized that the multipliers so determined cannot be interpreted as partial derivatives of the optimal value function.

21. A First Integral of the Solution

If the dynamical equations

$$\dot{\xi}_i = f_i(\xi_1, \ldots, \xi_n, \tau, v), \qquad i = 1, \ldots, n, \tag{21.1}$$

are not explicitly time-dependent, we see by Eq. (10.5) that S_t is constant along an optimal trajectory. Then, by Eq. (9.2),

$$\sum_{i=1}^{n} S_{x_i} f_i = -S_t = \text{constant}. \tag{21.2}$$

This result constitutes a *first integral* of the solution, with the value of the constant depending upon the problem statement.

Note that if neither the criterion Φ, nor the equations of the terminal manifold

$$\Psi_j(\xi_1, \ldots, \xi_n, \tau) = 0, \qquad j = 1, \ldots, p, \tag{21.3}$$

explicitly depend upon time τ, then, evaluated at the terminal time t_1,

$$S_t \big|_{t_1} = 0, \tag{21.4}$$

so the constant in the first integral equals zero.

Also, if the terminal time is to be minimized—i.e.,

$$\Phi(\xi_1, \ldots, \xi_n, \tau) = \tau \tag{21.5}$$

and (21.3) is independent of any explicit appearance of τ—then

$$S_t \big|_{t_1} = 1, \tag{21.6}$$

so the constant in Eq. (21.2) equals 1.

22. The Variational Hamiltonian

In the conventional notation of modern control theory, the expression

$$\sum_{i=1}^{n} S_{x_i} f_i \tag{22.1}$$

is denoted by the symbol H and called the *variational Hamiltonian*. We have already seen that the quantity S_{x_i} is often written as λ_i, so, in the classical notation,

$$H = \sum_{i=1}^{n} \lambda_i f_i. \tag{22.2}$$

Many of the above results are conveniently written in terms of the Hamiltonian. If the λ_i are viewed as functions of time (which they are when evaluated along any particular trajectory) rather than functions of state (which they are in the more general sense of dynamic programming), the multiplier rule (10.4) can be written

$$\dot{\lambda}_j = -H_{x_j}, \qquad j = 1, \ldots, n, \qquad (22.3)$$

and the dynamical equations become

$$\dot{x}_j = H_{\lambda_j}, \qquad j = 1, \ldots, n. \qquad (22.4)$$

In this notation, the Weierstrass condition requires that H be minimized over the set of all admissible controls u.

While all this symmetry and simplicity is admirable, we reject it because H lacks the geometrical meaning that the derivative of the optimal value function given by

$$(dS/dt)_u = \sum_{i=1}^{n} S_{x_i} f_i + S_t \qquad (22.5)$$

possesses. From Eqs. (22.1) and (22.5), we see that

$$H = (dS/dt)_u - S_t, \qquad (22.6)$$

and, unless the identity

$$S_t \equiv 0 \qquad (22.7)$$

holds for all t (as it does in one of the special cases discussed in Section 21), the Hamiltonian function H of optimal control theory has little geometrical or physical meaning.

23. Corner Conditions

It was shown in Section 9 that two fundamental conditions hold at each point of an optimal trajectory: The derivative of the optimal value function is zero; and, the value of the derivative for any control other than the optimal one is nonnegative. Furthermore, it can be shown that the partial derivatives of the optimal value function are continuous along an optimal trajectory—even across a corner, a point of discontinuous control.*

The fact that the time derivative of the optimal value function is zero, both before and after a corner, and the continuity of $S_{x_i}(t)$ and $S_t(t)$

---

* Using dynamic programming, this result has been established rigorously for the simplest problem under certain assumptions (see Berkovitz and Dreyfus (1964)). While a similar argument should hold for the problem of Mayer, the details have yet to be rigorously worked out.

imply the corner condition

$$\sum_{i=1}^{n} S_{x_i} f_i(x_1, \ldots, x_n, t, u^-) = \sum_{i=1}^{n} S_{x_i} f_i(x_1, \ldots, x_n, t, u^+), \quad (23.1)$$

where u^- indicates the control just before the discontinuity and u^+ is the control just afterward.

The stationarity condition (9.3) that the control satisfies on both sides of the discontinuity implies that

$$\sum_{i=1}^{n} S_{x_i} \frac{\partial f_i}{\partial u} \bigg|_{u-} = \sum_{i=1}^{n} S_{x_i} \frac{\partial f_i}{\partial u} \bigg|_{u+}. \quad (23.2)$$

A discontinuity in control u along an optimal trajectory can occur only if the corner conditions (23.1) and (23.2) are both satisfied.

24. An Example

To illustrate some of the above results, let us consider the problem of steering a particle, moving with constant velocity in (ξ_1, ξ_2)-space, from the initial point (x_1, x_2), specified at time t, to the terminal point (x_{11}, x_{21}), in such a way that the time of termination of the process is minimum. The dynamical equations are assumed to be

$$\dot{\xi}_1 = v \cos v \quad (24.1)$$

and

$$\dot{\xi}_2 = v \sin v, \quad (24.2)$$

where $v(\tau)$ is the control function and the velocity v is a specified constant. The criterion function for this minimum-time-of-termination problem is

$$\Phi(\xi_1, \xi_2, \tau) = \tau, \quad (24.3)$$

and the terminal conditions are

$$\Psi_1(\xi_1, \xi_2, \tau) = \xi_1 - x_{11} = 0 \quad (24.4)$$

and

$$\Psi_2(\xi_1, \xi_2, \tau) = \xi_2 - x_{21} = 0. \quad (24.5)$$

This is, of course, merely the minimum-distance problem disguised as a terminal control problem.

The fundamental partial differential equation for this problem is

$$0 = \min_u [S_{x_1} v \cos u + S_{x_2} v \sin u + S_t], \quad (24.6)$$

and the boundary conditions are the implicit condition that optimal trajectories from any initial point (x_1, x_2) should reach the terminal point (x_{11}, x_{21}), as well as the condition that

$$S(x_{11}, x_{21}, t) = t. \tag{24.7}$$

The reader can verify that the function

$$S(x_1, x_2, t) = t + (1/v)((x_{11} - x_1)^2 + (x_{21} - x_2)^2)^{1/2}, \tag{24.8}$$

with u given by

$$u(x_1, x_2, t) = \tan^{-1}(x_{21} - x_2)/(x_{11} - x_1), \tag{24.9}$$

satisfies both Eqs. (24.6) and (24.7), and that trajectories emanating from (x_1, x_2) reach (x_{11}, x_{21}). We actually obtained (24.8) and (24.9) by recognizing that the particle should follow a straight-line path toward (x_{11}, x_{21}) and that the time of arrival equals the initial time plus the time of transit.

Since we cannot, generally, solve the fundamental partial differential equation as we did in this special case, let us turn to the ordinary differential equation analysis associated with the multiplier rule. This leads to the results:

$$\left(\frac{dS_{x_1}}{dt}\right)_u = \left(\frac{dS_{x_2}}{dt}\right)_u = \left(\frac{dS_t}{dt}\right)_u = 0 ; \tag{24.10}$$

at the terminal time τ_1

$$S_t |_{\tau_1} = 1 ,$$
$$S_{x_1} |_{\tau_1} = -\nu_1 , \tag{24.11}$$

and

$$S_{x_2} |_{\tau_1} = -\nu_2 ;$$

the optimal control u is given by the equation

$$\tan u = S_{x_2}/S_{x_1} = \nu_2/\nu_1 = \text{constant} ; \tag{24.12}$$

and

$$0 = 1 - \nu_1 v \cos u - \nu_2 v \sin u . \tag{24.13}$$

The requirement that optimal trajectories must reach (x_{11}, x_{21}) dictates that

$$\nu_1 = k(x_{11} - x_1) , \qquad \nu_2 = k(x_{21} - x_2) , \tag{24.14}$$

where k is some constant, and (24.13) leads to the result

$$k = \frac{1}{v((x_{11} - x_1)^2 + (x_{21} - x_2)^2)^{1/2}} . \tag{24.15}$$

Therefore,

$$S_{x_1} = -\frac{x_{11} - x_1}{v((x_{11} - x_1)^2 + (x_{21} - x_2)^2)^{1/2}} \qquad (24.16)$$

and

$$S_{x_2} = -\frac{x_{21} - x_2}{v((x_{11} - x_1)^2 + (x_{21} - x_2)^2)^{1/2}},$$

a result that may be checked by partial differentiation of Eq. (24.8).

25. Second-Order Transversality Conditions

Having developed, discussed, and illustrated various first-order conditions that are satisfied by optimal (and all stationary) trajectories, let us turn next to more complicated conditions.

Once an equation is established for the second partial derivatives of the optimal value function, as it was in Sections 14–16, second-order transversality conditions are easily produced. If an initial manifold is specified but the precise initial point is free on that manifold, the optimal initial point must be the point of the initial manifold at which the optimal value function assumes its minimum value. No local condition, however, can characterize such a point. As noted in Section 19, a first-order condition necessary for this occurrence is the stationarity condition that, when evaluated at the initial point, the differential of S, dS, which is given by the equation

$$dS = \sum_{i=1}^{n} S_{x_i} \, \delta x_i + S_t \, \delta t, \qquad (25.1)$$

equals zero for all perturbations δx_i and δt such that the perturbed initial point still lies on the given initial manifold.

A second-order necessary condition is that the second differential d^2S, when evaluated at the initial point, be nonnegative. This yields the condition

$$\sum_{i=1}^{n} \sum_{j=1}^{n} S_{x_i x_j} \, \delta x_i \, \delta x_j + 2 \sum_{i=1}^{n} S_{x_i t} \, \delta x_i \, \delta t + S_{tt} \, \delta t^2$$

$$+ \sum_{i=1}^{n} S_{x_i} \, \delta^2 x_i + S_t \, \delta^2 t \geq 0 \quad (25.2)$$

for all admissible perturbations δx_i, δt, $\delta^2 x_i$, and $\delta^2 t$.

The above situation parallels that discussed in Section 30 of Chapter III and an illustrative example of the use of a result like (25.2) is found in Section 31 of Chapter III.

26. Problem Discontinuities

We turn now to a brief treatment of certain modifications of the original problem statement of Section 2. We have assumed so far that the right-hand sides of the dynamical equations

$$\dot{\xi}_i = f_i(\xi_1, \ldots, \xi_n, \tau, v) \qquad i = 1, \ldots, n \qquad (26.1)$$

are continuous functions of their arguments and that the state variables are continuous functions of time. Let us examine the situation if, when a certain equation

$$\theta(\xi_1, \ldots, \xi_n, \tau) = 0 \qquad (26.2)$$

is satisfied, either the form of the f_i changes or a state jumps discontinuously to a different value. We call this a *problem discontinuity*.

For example, the latter of the above two phenomena occurs in missile trajectory applications if, when a certain condition is satisfied (usually that the mass decreases to a certain value), a stage is dropped and mass decreases instantaneously by a given finite amount.

We now show that the situation described above results in a *finite discontinuity* in those multiplier functions $S_{x_i}(t)$ for which x_i explicitly appears in the equation

$$\theta(x_1, \ldots, x_n, t) = 0 \qquad (26.3)$$

which determines the time of the problem discontinuity. Consider what the expression S_{x_i} means when evaluated at a time just after the time of the problem discontinuity (we denote this quantity by $S_{x_i}{}^+$), and what $S_{x_i}{}^-$, the value of S_{x_i} just before the discontinuity, signifies. A change in the state x_i just after the discontinuity implies a change in optimal trajectory and a change in the value of the terminal criterion Φ, and $S_{x_i}{}^+$ equals the rate at which the optimal terminal value of Φ changes as x_i changes. This is its usual meaning, since the problem, starting after the point of discontinuity, is a perfectly conventional problem. Now examine $S_{x_i}{}^-$. A change in a state x_i appearing in Eq. (26.3) now has two effects. Not only does it change the remaining optimal trajectory, as above, but it changes the time when the problem discontinuity occurs. Unless the terminal value of the criterion Φ is insensitive to first-order to the actual time of the discontinuity (this situation occurs in practice when the time of the problem discontinuity is chosen optimally rather than determined by a given relation such as (26.3)), this second effect of a change in x_i must be added to the usual one when $S_{x_i}^-$ is computed. The vanishing of this extra term at the time of the problem discontinuity results in a discontinuous $S_{x_i}(t)$.

If we denote by t_D the time of the problem discontinuity associated with a particular optimal trajectory (i.e., the time when Eq. (26.3) is satisfied), and if we let $\partial S/\partial t_D$ represent the rate at which the terminal value of Φ changes if the time of the problem discontinuity is varied but the initial state is unchanged, our verbal discussion above takes the mathematical form

$$
\begin{aligned}
S_{x_i}^-(t_D) &= S_{x_i}^+(t_D) + \frac{\partial S}{\partial t_D}\bigg|_{t_D}\frac{\partial t_D}{\partial x_i} \\[2mm]
&= S_{x_i}^+(t_D) + \left(\frac{\partial S}{\partial t_D}\frac{dt_D}{d\theta}\frac{\partial\theta}{\partial x_i}\right)\bigg|_{t_D} \\[2mm]
&= S_{x_i}^+(t_D) + \left(\frac{\partial S}{\partial t_D}\frac{1}{\dot\theta}\frac{\partial\theta}{\partial x_i}\right)\bigg|_{t_D} \\[2mm]
&= S_{x_i}^+(t_D) + k\frac{\partial\theta}{\partial x_i}\bigg|_{t_D}, \qquad i = 1, \ldots, n,
\end{aligned}
\tag{26.4}
$$

and

$$
S_t^-(t_D) = S_t^+(t_D) + k\frac{\partial\theta}{\partial t}\bigg|_{t_D}.
\tag{26.5}
$$

We see that the discontinuity in the vector multiplier function $S_{x_i}(t)$ is proportional to the vector of partial derivatives with respect to x of the relation determining the time of the problem discontinuity.

To determine the constant of proportionality k, we observe that the time derivative of the optimal value function must equal zero, both before and after the problem discontinuity, and u must minimize this derivative, both before and after the discontinuity. Consequently,

$$
\sum_{i=1}^{n} S_{x_i}^+ f_i^+ + S_t^+ = \sum_{i=1}^{n} S_{x_i}^- f_i^- + S_t^-, \qquad i = 1, \ldots, n,
\tag{26.6}
$$

and

$$
\sum_{i=1}^{n} S_{x_i}^+ \frac{\partial f_i^+}{\partial u} = \sum_{i=1}^{n} S_{x_i}^- \frac{\partial f_i^-}{\partial u}, \qquad i = 1, \ldots, n,
\tag{26.7}
$$

where the functions f_i, or the value of a state variable, or both, will be different on the two sides of the problem discontinuity (the difference being specified explicitly as part of the problem statement). Furthermore, the optimal control u will generally be discontinuous at the time of the problem discontinuity. If the $S_{x_i}{}^-$ are assumed known at time $t_D{}^-$ just before the problem discontinuity, the $S_{x_i}{}^+$ in Eqs. (26.6) and (26.7) can be expressed, by means of Eqs. (26.4) and (26.5), in terms of the known $S_{x_i}{}^-$,

$$\partial\theta/\partial x_i \big|_{t_D},$$

and the unknown constant k. Then, viewing Eqs. (26.6) and (26.7) as two equations in two unknowns (these being the constant of proportionality k and the jump in the optimal control u), one can solve for these numbers just after the problem discontinuity, and with the $S_{x_i}{}^+(t)$ and $S_t{}^+(t)$ given by (26.4) and (26.5), one can then continue the solution via the multiplier rule.

If the time of the problem discontinuity were specified by an equation independent of the states, such as

$$\theta = t - t_D = 0, \tag{26.8}$$

only S_t would experience a discontinuity.

If the time of the problem discontinuity is not specified by an equation of the form (26.3), but can be chosen optimally, then the discontinuity should occur when k, as determined by the simultaneous equations (26.6) and (26.7), equals zero. Only then is the result stationary as a function of the time of the problem discontinuity, since k is proportional to $\partial S/\partial t_D$. Higher-order necessary conditions to separate the worst time of the problem discontinuity from the best are easily devised.

27. Optimization of Parameters

Suppose that the dynamical differential equations contain certain design parameters as well as, or instead of, the control function. Part of the problem is then to choose these parameters, as well as the control, optimally. Let the dynamical equations be

$$\dot{\xi}_i = f_i(\xi_1, \ldots, \xi_n, \alpha_1, \ldots, \alpha_m, \tau, v), \qquad i = 1, \ldots, n, \tag{27.1}$$

where the α_j are parameters (aspects of the system configuration) that must remain constant during the problem, the actual constant value to be chosen optimally.

We define the optimal value function by

$S(x_1, \ldots, x_n, a_1, \ldots, a_m, t)$ = the minimum value of Φ attainable by a trajectory consistent with (27.1) and the terminal conditions (2.4) starting from the initial point $\xi_1 = x_1$, $\xi_2 = x_2$, ..., $\xi_n = x_n$ at time $\tau = t$ with the constant parameter values fixed at $\alpha_1 = a_1$, ..., $\alpha_m = a_m$.

The function S satisfies the relationship

$$S(x_1, \ldots, x_n, a_1, \ldots, a_m, t) = \min_u [S(x_1 + f_1 \Delta\tau + o(\Delta\tau), \ldots, x_n$$

$$+ f_n \Delta\tau + o(\Delta\tau), a_1, \ldots, a_m, t + \Delta\tau)], \quad (27.2)$$

or, in the limit,

$$0 = \min_u [\sum_{i=1}^{n} S_{x_i} f_i + S_t]. \quad (27.3)$$

This equation, in turn, implies the equations

$$0 = \sum_{i=1}^{n} S_{x_i} f_i + S_t \quad (27.4)$$

and

$$0 = \sum_{i=1}^{n} S_{x_i} \frac{\partial f_i}{\partial u}. \quad (27.5)$$

We have seen that the functions S_{x_j} satisfy the differential equations

$$\left(\frac{dS_{x_j}}{dt}\right)_u = -\sum_{i=1}^{n} S_{x_i} \frac{\partial f_i}{\partial x_j}, \quad j = 1, \ldots, n, \quad (27.6)$$

along an optimal trajectory. Let us compute

$$(dS_{a_j}/dt)_u, \quad (27.7)$$

since we shall require the values of S_{a_j} at the initial point for later analysis. We have, by the rules of differentiation,

$$(dS_{a_j}/dt)_u = \sum_{i=1}^{n} S_{a_j x_i} f_i + S_{a_j t}. \quad (27.8)$$

No $S_{a_i a_j}$ terms appear in Eq. (27.8) because the $\dot{a}_i$ which multiply these terms are zero, the parameters a_j being constant. Partial differentiation of the identity (27.4) with respect to a_j yields the equation

$$0 = \sum_{i=1}^{n} S_{a_j x_i} f_i + S_{a_j t} + \sum_{i=1}^{n} S_{x_i}\left(\frac{\partial f_i}{\partial a_j} + \frac{\partial f_i}{\partial u}\frac{\partial u}{\partial a_j}\right). \qquad (27.9)$$

Combining Eqs. (27.8) and (27.9), and using (27.5) to eliminate the $\partial u/\partial a_j$ term, gives

$$(dS_{a_j}/dt)_u = -\sum_{i=1}^{n} S_{x_i}(\partial f_i/\partial a_j), \qquad j = 1, \ldots, m. \qquad (27.10)$$

The function $S_{a_j}(t)$ describes how a change at time t in one of the constant parameters α_j with the new value of the parameter used throughout the remaining process, affects the terminal value of Φ. At points on the terminal manifold (2.4), changing a parameter does not affect the terminal value of Φ. Consequently,

$$S_{a_j}|_{\tau_1} = 0, \qquad j = 1, \ldots, m. \qquad (27.11)$$

The differential equation (27.10) with terminal boundary conditions (27.11) determines S_{a_j} at each point of an optimal trajectory. If the α_j are to be chosen optimally, for a problem starting at time t in state $(x_1, \ldots, x_n)$, then it is necessary that S be stationary with respect to the α_j when evaluated at the initial point; i.e.,

$$S_{a_j}|_t = 0, \qquad j = 1, \ldots, m. \qquad (27.12)$$

Second-order conditions, and conditions that must hold if the α_j must satisfy some specified relationships

$$g_k(\alpha_x, \ldots, \alpha_m) = 0, \qquad k = 1, \ldots, q, \qquad (27.13)$$

are easily determined by the methods of Sections 19 and 25.

In short, the parameters α_j can be treated as additional states, satisfying the dynamical differential equations

$$\dot{\alpha}_j = 0, \qquad (27.14)$$

that are free to be chosen optimally at the initial point.

28. A Caution

Our derivational route for both the simplest problem and the terminal control problem has been to proceed from a fundamental partial differential equation to ordinary differential equations and conditions concerning the solution of the ordinary differential equations. It is obvious what we have gained by this conversion. Ordinary differential equations, even large sets of them, are much easier to solve numerically on a digital computer than is a partial differential equation. It is perhaps not quite so obvious what we have lost.

First of all, consider a region R of $(x_1, \ldots, x_n, t)$-space, from each interior point of which there exists an optimal trajectory remaining in R and reaching the terminal manifold, and in which the optimal value function has bounded second partial derivatives. Let a function S satisfy, at interior points of R, the fundamental partial differential equation with appropriate boundary conditions as developed in earlier sections. Then, the trajectories generated by the optimal control function associated with the optimal value function are absolutely minimizing trajectories with respect to all trajectories remaining entirely within R. Such is the power of the fundamental partial differential equations.

Now, let us suppose that we are given a control function $v(\tau)$ and resultant trajectory $\xi_i(\tau)$ satisfying the specified initial and terminal conditions and the given dynamical equations. Then, if associated multiplier functions (i.e., partial derivatives of S) and multiplier numbers ν_j can be found satisfying the multiplier rule with the appropriate boundary conditions (18.16) and (18.17) and with $v(\tau)$ satisfying (9.3), and if the trajectory contains no conjugate points, the trajectory furnishes a weak stationary value of the criterion Φ. That is, admissible small perturbations of the control $v(\tau)$ do not affect, to first order, the value of Φ.

If the Clebsch condition with strict inequality is also satisfied along the trajectory, the solution furnishes a weak relative minimum of Φ. Admissible small perturbations of $v(\tau)$ result in an increase in the terminal value of Φ.

If the Weierstrass condition is also satisfied at each point of the trajectory, the trajectory furnishes a strong relative minimum of Φ. To understand this statement, recall that the control $v(\tau)$ determines the $\dot{\xi}_i$, the time derivatives of the states. A discontinuity in $v(\tau)$ (i.e., a large change) results in a discontinuity in $\dot{\xi}(\tau)$ but not in $\xi(\tau)$. A strong relative minimum means that all admissible small changes in the actual trajectory $\xi(\tau)$, even those caused by discontinuities in the control function $v(\tau)$, yield larger values of Φ.

Yet all these conditions do not guarantee absolute minimality. Suppose that given initial and terminal manifolds can be connected by two different trajectories, each yielding a strong relative minimum of Φ in its own neighborhood. Then, each trajectory will have associated with it different multiplier functions, etc., satisfying all the above necessary conditions. This can happen because there is no uniqueness-of-solution theorem for nonlinear differential equations with two-point boundary conditions.

For this reason, finding one such set allows, in general, no stronger conclusion than strong relative minimality. Only if sufficient convexity is present to guarantee *a priori* that only one strong relative minimum can exist is it possible to use the ordinary differential equation analysis to prove absolute minimality.

29. Summary

The techniques and results of this chapter on the problem of Mayer, or the terminal control problem, do not differ significantly from those of Chapter III. The principal novelty of this form of the problem is that the classical results involve a set of associated multiplier functions. Since these functions are recognizable as the partial derivatives of the optimal value function, quantities entering naturally and necessarily in the dynamic programming analysis, the problem of establishing equivalence with classical results is greatly simplified.

We have investigated optimal trajectories for problems whose solutions exhibited no peculiar behavior requiring special treatment. We treated, as a result, the most general and, at the same time, the simplest situation. (Certain special cases requiring a modification in methodology will be investigated in Chapters V and VI.) We invoked the principle of optimality and used standard dynamic programming concepts to produce a fundamental partial differential equation. This equation was compared and contrasted with the principal result of Chapter III. Then it was shown how the fundamental equation implied the multiplier rule (a stationarity condition analogous to the Euler-Lagrange equation of the simplest problem), the Clebsch condition (a second-order necessary condition analogous to the Legendre condition), and the Weierstrass necessary condition for strong relative minimality. A relationship between the Jacobi condition and the second partial derivatives of the optimal value function was developed and the connection of this analysis with the guidance problem was discussed. Following the pattern of Chapter III, we then presented first- and second-order transversality conditions and corner conditions. Finally, just as at the end of Chapter III, we treated certain generalizations of the basic problem that did not lead to analyses sufficiently new to justify treatment in a separate chapter.

We turn now to certain problem generalizations that, by their importance, merit and, by their nature, require special treatment.

CHAPTER V

Inequality Constraints

1. Introduction

In Chapter IV we deduced the fundamental partial differential equation for a problem of the Mayer type. We then studied various conditions, usually concerning the solution of an associated set of ordinary differential equations, that the fundamental equation implied. Such conditions, in a region in which the assumptions leading to the fundamental equation are valid, are necessary conditions for absolute minimality. Toward the end of Chapter IV we considered certain modifications of the problem statement and their effect upon the results.

In this chapter we consider one more modification; one which occurs so often in applications and which so drastically affects certain results, that we devote a separate chapter to the subject. We shall treat problems for which either admissible control functions or admissible trajectories are restricted, by inequality constraints included in the statement of the problem, to lie within a specified region. Of course, should the optimal solution of the problem, ignoring the inequality constraints, happen to satisfy the constraints, then the solution is also optimal for the constrained problem. Consequently, in order that our results differ from those of the previous chapter, we shall be concerned with situations where the constraint is meaningful and a portion of the optimal trajectory lies on the boundary of the constrained region. We shall seek conditions that the optimal trajectories for such problems must satisfy.

2. Control-Variable Inequality Constraints

The first type of inequality constraint that we shall consider is of the form

$$g(v) \leq 0. \tag{2.1}$$

This constraint, involving only the control (or controls if $v(\tau)$ is a vector function), is to hold at all times. We designate by U the admissible region of control space.

If the control function must be nonnegative, then (2.1) takes the form

$$-v \leq 0. \tag{2.2}$$

Or, if v is bounded between K_1 and K_2, we can write the single inequality

$$(v - K_1)(v - K_2) \leq 0. \tag{2.3}$$

Such inequalities occur quite naturally in missile trajectory problems, where only nonnegative thrusts, bounded above by some physical limit, are permitted. Or, the radius of curvature of a maneuvering vehicle may be limited by how great a deflection of thrust is mechanically possible.

3. The Appropriate Multiplier Rule

We deduced in Chapter IV that the optimal value function S satisfied two properties. First, it took on the same value when evaluated at any point on the particular optimal trajectory connecting a specified initial point with the terminal manifold. This led to the conclusion that

$$(dS/dt)_u = 0, \tag{3.1}$$

where u is the optimal control. If the partial derivatives of S exist, Eq. (3.1) can be written as

$$\sum_{i=1}^{n} S_{x_i} f_i + S_t = 0. \tag{3.2}$$

Second, we showed that the optimal value of the control associated with any particular initial point $(x_1, \ldots, x_n, t)$, a value denoted by $u(x_1, \ldots, x_n, t)$, should be chosen so as to render the derivative on the left in Eq. (3.1), considered as a function of u, absolutely minimum.

We then used the condition necessary for a finite minimizing control, if u is not bounded by an inequality constraint and the functions f_i are continuously differentiable in u, that

$$\sum_{i=1}^{n} S_{x_i} \frac{\partial f_i}{\partial u} = 0 \tag{3.3}$$

in order to derive the differential equations

$$\left(\frac{dS_{x_j}}{dt}\right)_u = -\sum_{i=1}^{n} S_{x_i} \frac{\partial f_i}{\partial x_j}, \qquad j = 1, \ldots, n \tag{3.4}$$

and

$$\left(\frac{dS_i}{dt}\right)_u = -\sum_{i=1}^{n} S_{x_i} \frac{\partial f_i}{\partial t} \tag{3.5}$$

for the time derivatives of the partial derivatives of S along an optimal trajectory.

We now pursue the same course, as far as allowable, for the case where the optimal control u is bounded at each point of state space by the inequality constraint

$$g(u) \leq 0. \tag{3.6}$$

We write, as before, the desired time derivative of the partial derivative of S as

$$\left(\frac{dS_{x_j}}{dt}\right)_u = \sum_{i=1}^{n} S_{x_j x_i} f_i + S_{x_j t}, \qquad j = 1, \ldots, n, \tag{3.7}$$

by the chain rule for the derivative of a function whose arguments are functions of the independent variable. Then, as previously, we take the partial derivative of (3.2) with respect to x_j, recognizing that u depends on x_j, to obtain

$$\sum_{i=1}^{n} S_{x_i x_j} f_i + S_{x_j t} + \sum_{i=1}^{n} S_{x_i}\left(\frac{\partial f_i}{\partial x_j} + \frac{\partial f_i}{\partial u}\frac{\partial u}{\partial x_j}\right) = 0,$$

$$j = 1, \ldots, n. \tag{3.8}$$

From (3.7) and (3.8) we see that

$$\left(\frac{dS_{x_j}}{dt}\right)_u = -\sum_{i=1}^{n} S_{x_i} \frac{\partial f_i}{\partial x_j} - \left(\sum_{i=1}^{n} S_{x_i} \frac{\partial f_i}{\partial u}\right)\frac{\partial u}{\partial x_j}, \qquad j = 1, \ldots, n. \tag{3.9}$$

Then, in our previous derivation, we used (3.3) to eliminate the second term on the right-hand side of (3.9), thereby obtaining the multiplier rule (3.4). A similar process produced Eq. (3.5).

Case 1. For the constrained problem, if the absolutely minimizing value of u at a particular time is finite and lies in the interior of the admissible region of control space U, defined by (3.6), Eq. (3.3) is indeed a necessary condition for minimality, and the rule (3.4) is seen to hold.

Case 2. If, on the other hand, the minimizing *admissible* u lies on the boundary of U, then the expression

$$\sum_{i=1}^{n} S_{x_i} \frac{\partial f_i}{\partial u} \tag{3.10}$$

will not in general equal zero when evaluated in terms of the optimal u.

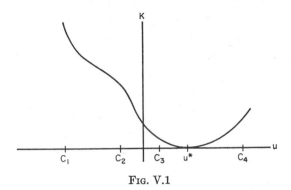

Fɪɢ. V.1

Let us examine a particular optimal trajectory and let us regard the states x_i and partial derivatives S_{x_i} as functions of time along that trajectory. At a given time t, the quantities $x_i(t)$, $S_{x_i}(t)$, and $S_t(t)$ have specific numerical values. The time derivative of the optimal value function, taken with the x_i dependent upon the time through the control u, which need not be the optimal control, is given by

$$K(t, u) = \sum_{i=1}^{n} S_{x_i} f_i + S_t . \tag{3.11}$$

At time t we are to minimize $K(t, u)$ with respect to u in order to determine the optimal value of u. For fixed t, let us plot $K(t, u)$ as a function of u. Case 1, when graphed, may look like Fig. V.1, where, perhaps, values of u between c_1 and c_2, and those between c_3 and c_4, satisfy the inequality (3.6) and are therefore admissible. Then, u^* in the figure is the minimizing value of u and

$$dK/du \mid_{u^*} = 0 , \tag{3.12}$$

so that both Eqs. (3.2) and (3.3) hold there.

In Case 2, however, the regions of admissible u might be the same as above but $K(t, u)$ for fixed t might look like the function shown in Fig. V.2. Then, c_3 is the minimizing admissible value of u, and both Eq. (3.2) and, since c_3 lies on the boundary of the region defined by (3.6), the relation

$$g(c_3) = 0 \tag{3.13}$$

holds. However, Eq. (3.3) is violated since

$$dK/du \mid_{c_3} \cong 1 \tag{3.14}$$

for the situation shown in Fig. V.2.

If a component of state x_j is varied by an infinitesimal amount at a

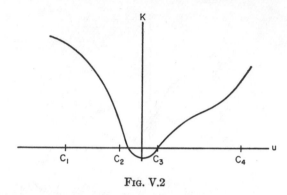

FIG. V.2

fixed time t, the quantities S_{x_i}, S_t, and f_i are perturbed infinitesimally,[*] and therefore, the function $K(t, u)$ is infinitesimally perturbed. In Case 1, the optimal value of u is also perturbed infinitesimally, and the ratio of the change in u to the change in x_j is the finite quantity $\partial u / \partial x_j$. In Case 2, if the minimizing control c_3 is unique at the fixed time that we are considering (there could be a tie such as shown in Fig. V.3), then c_3 remains the optimal control after an infinitesimal perturbation in x_j, and therefore,

$$\partial u / \partial x_j = 0. \tag{3.15}$$

Since either Eq. (3.12) or (3.15) holds if the optimal control is unique at a point in time, the last term on the right-hand side of Eq. (3.9) is zero, even if the optimal control lies on the boundary of U. Hence, we have the usual multiplier differential equations

$$\left(\frac{dS_{x_j}}{dt}\right)_u = -\sum_{i=1}^{n} S_{x_i} \frac{\partial f_i}{\partial x_j}, \qquad j = 1, \ldots, n. \tag{3.16}$$

Consequently, while the derivation is a bit more involved, no modification of the multiplier differential equations is required for problems with control-variable constraints as long as the optimal control function is unique at each point in time.

In case of nonuniqueness of the optimal control at a particular instant of time, such as in the case in Fig. V.3, or the even more extreme case of Fig. V. 4, it is not clear in Eq. (3.9) that the last term on the right-hand side is zero *at that instant*. A *finite* change in the time derivative of S_{x_i} at an instant would have no effect on the function $S_{x_i}(t)$ itself for a continuous process. One is concerned only if the second term on the right-

---

* We assume the continuity of the partial derivatives of S. This assumption is valid except when optimal trajectories are tangent to a manifold of discontinuity in control.

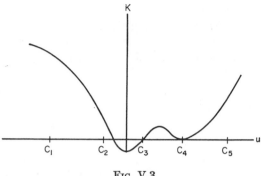

FIG. V.3

hand side in (3.9) is infinite, so that there is a discontinuity in S_{x_i}. But an argument of the type mentioned in Section 34 of Chapter III shows that the partial derivatives of S are continuous across such a corner if a nontangency condition holds, and the multiplier equation (3.16) remains valid.

4. A Second Derivation of the Result of Section 3

The derivational technique used in the latter part of Section 9 of Chapter III can also be used here to yield the conclusion that the multiplier differential equations are not modified along a boundary segment of an optimal trajectory. The fundamental equation

$$0 = \min_{u \in U} \left[\sum_{i=1}^{n} S_{x_i} f_i + S_t \right] \tag{4.1}$$

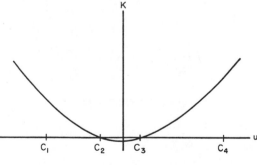

FIG. V.4

holds for all x at which S is defined. We assume that S is twice continuously differentiable. Let $(\bar{x}, \bar{t})$ denote a point on an optimal trajectory for which the optimal control $\bar{u}$ lies on the boundary of U. From the identity (4.1) we see that, if we set u equal to $\bar{u}$ and consider the function of x and t

$$\sum_{i=1}^{n} S_{x_i} f_i(x, t, \bar{u}) + S_t,\tag{4.2}$$

this expression assumes the value 0 at $(x, t) = (\bar{x}, \bar{t})$ and cannot assume a smaller value for any other (x, t). Since expression (4.2) assumes its minimum over all (x, t) at $(\bar{x}, \bar{t})$, the partial derivative of expression (4.2) taken with respect to any component of state, with u held fixed at $\bar{u}$ rather than considered a function of the state, equals zero at $(\bar{x}, \bar{t})$, and we have the result

$$\sum_{i=1}^{n} S_{x_i x_j} f_i + S_{x_j t} + \sum_{i=1}^{n} S_{x_i} \frac{\partial f_i}{\partial x_j} = 0, \qquad j = 1, \ldots, n,\tag{4.3}$$

which, in conjunction with Eq. (3.7), yields Eq. (3.16) of the previous section.

We shall use the above type of reasoning at two other points later in this chapter. While it represents an auxiliary method of derivation here and also at its next appearance, in Section 15 it appears to be the only way of using dynamic programming to obtain the desired result.

Let us summarize the basic result, which we deduced for normal problems whose optimal trajectories exhibit certain regularity properties, for a problem with control constrained to lie within a specified set U: Associated with an optimal trajectory, there exist multiplier functions $S_{x_i}(t)$ satisfying the differential equations

$$\left(\frac{dS_{x_i}}{dt}\right)_u = -\sum_{j=1}^{n} S_{x_j} \frac{\partial f_j}{\partial x_i}, \qquad i = 1, \ldots, n\tag{4.4}$$

and

$$\left(\frac{dS_t}{dt}\right)_u = -\sum_{j=1}^{n} S_{x_j} \frac{\partial f_j}{\partial t},\tag{4.5}$$

such that the optimal control u renders the expression

$$\sum_{i=1}^{n} S_{x_i} f_i + S_t\tag{4.6}$$

minimal over all u in U and the minimum value of (4.6) equals zero.

This coincides with the result deduced in Chapter IV, except we have now shown it to hold when the control is restricted to the elements of a set U. In Chapter IV the admissible choices of control at any given time were unconstrained.

The above result was derived by Valentine in the 1930's by modifying classical arguments (see Valentine (1937)), and recently was rederived by the eminent Russian mathematician L. S. Pontryagin (Pontryagin (1962)), who termed it "the maximum principle." These derivations require less restrictive assumptions than those used in this book.*

5. Discussion

The result that $S_{x_i}(t)$ and $S_t(t)$ are computed along an optimal trajectory by the same differential equations,† whether the optimal control lies on the boundary of the admissible control region or not, can be justified and clarified heuristically.

First, consider an optimal trajectory for an unconstrained problem. The optimal control function $v(\tau)$ has the property that the value of the criterion is unaffected to first order by first-order perturbations of the control function; otherwise, a better control function would exist. This property is called stationarity and is assured by the satisfaction of the Euler-Lagrange equation (for the Lagrange problem) or the multiplier rule (for the Mayer problem). To determine, for a stationary trajectory, the first-order effect of a change in *initial state* on the terminal criterion (a nonzero effect, in general), one can, for the above reasons, assume that the control function is unaffected by the small change in initial state. By determining how the initial-value perturbation propagates to the terminal point given a fixed control (by using the multiplier, or adjoint, equations) one can determine the functions $S_{x_i}(t)$ and $S_t(t)$ along the trajectory.

An inequality-constrained trajectory is not stationary in the above sense. When the control is at its bound, it is generally true that a first-order change in control that violates the boundary will improve the value

---

* For more information about the relationships between various classical arguments and those leading to the maximum principle, see Hestenes (1964).

† Consider two problems that differ only in that one contains a constraint on admissible control and one does not. Since the constraint affects admissible trajectories, the statement in the text that the same multiplier differential equations apply along optimal trajectories for the two problems does not imply that the optimal value functions for the two problems are identical, nor that, at a given point in (x, t)-space, the two optimal value functions have the same partial derivatives.

of the criterion function to first order, but such a change is prohibited. For portions of such a trajectory for which the optimal control is not at its bound, first-order control changes do not affect the criterion to first order.

Let us examine a particular optimal trajectory and let us regard the states and S_{x_i} as functions of time. We designate the derivative of the optimal value function, regarded as a function of the control u at time t, by $K(t, u)$, just as in Section 3, so that

$$K(t, u) = \sum_{i=1}^{n} S_{x_i}(t) f_i(t, u) + S_t(t) \tag{5.1}$$

and

$$K(t, u^*) = 0 , \tag{5.2}$$

if u^* is the optimal control at time t. Then, the function $D(t)$, given by

$$D(t) = \left. \frac{\partial K(t, u)}{\partial u} \right|_{u*} = \left. \sum_{i=1}^{n} S_{x_i} \frac{\partial f_i}{\partial u} \right|_{u*} \tag{5.3}$$

(which is zero along an unconstrained optimal trajectory), is a measure of how the terminal criterion is affected by a change in u. We shall call the function $D(t)$ the *control impulse response function*. The total first-order change in the terminal criterion Φ resulting from a first-order change $\delta u(t)$ in the control function is given by the formula

$$\Delta\Phi = \int_{t_0}^{t_1} D(t) \, \delta u(t) \, dt . \tag{5.4}$$

Since the value of a definite integral is not affected by a finite change of the integrand at an *isolated* value of the independent variable, it follows that no finite change in control δu at *an instant of time* affects this value. However, $D(t)$ can be interpreted as the effect on $\Delta\Phi$ of an impulsive change in u at time t (a change at the instant of time t so great that its time integral over that instant of time equals 1); or, alternatively, the quantity

$$D(t) \, \Delta t \tag{5.5}$$

can be viewed as the change in the terminal criterion resulting from a unit change in u lasting over a time interval of length Δt.

If the optimal control function for a constrained problem, with initial time t_0 and terminal time t_1, is at its bound during the time interval $[t_2, t_3]$ and at an interior point of the control space U during $[t_0, t_2]$ and $[t_3, t_1]$, where $t_0 < t_2 < t_3 < t_1$, the control impulse response function

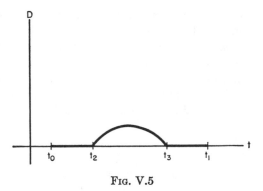

FIG. V.5

(5.3) will generally appear as shown in Fig. V.5, although $D(t)$ can be discontinuous at t_2 or t_3 if the optimal control is discontinuous there. (The appropriate sign of $D(t)$ when it is nonzero will be the subject of the next section.)

With the help of the above observations, we now can investigate the differential equations for the functions $S_{x_i}(t)$ along an optimal trajectory, during part of which the control lies at its bound. As with the unbounded control case, the multiplier equations compute the effect of initial-condition changes on the terminal criterion, the control held fixed. In the unbounded case, we observed that this was proper because along an optimal trajectory the criterion is, to first order, necessarily insensitive to first-order control changes. Along a trajectory, during part of which the control is at a bound, this insensitivity property does not apply when the control is at the bound (which is when $D(t) \neq 0$ in Fig. V.5). A small change in the initial state at time t, $t_0 \leq t \leq t_2$, does not affect the optimal control when it is at its bound (since it stays at its bound) except that it changes, to first order, the time t_2 when the constraint takes effect, and t_3 when it ceases to restrain. However, this time change is first order and the control change during this interval (if u is continuous) is first order so the contributions to the integral (5.4), namely,

$$\int_{t_2}^{t_2+\Delta t} D(t) \, \delta u \, dt \tag{5.6}$$

and

$$\int_{t_3}^{t_3+\Delta t} D(t) \, \delta u \, dt , \tag{5.7}$$

are second order and, therefore, negligible. Consequently, for the case of a control constraint which is independent of both time and the state variables, if the optimal control function is a continuous function of time, then the method of computing the $S_{x_i}(t)$ is unaffected by the constraint.

This conclusion also holds for an optimal control function that jumps discontinuously to or from the boundary since a first-order change in the time of the jump cannot affect the result to first order, or the time of the jump would not be optimal. This is really the meaning of the Weierstrass-Erdmann corner conditions that must hold at the time of such a jump.

We shall presently see that if the constraint involves both the control and the state variables, the method of computing the function $S_{x_i}(t)$ is indeed modified. Then we shall show why the above heuristic reasoning fails to apply in that case and why this modification was to be expected.

6. The Sign of the Control Impulse Response Function

The quantity

$$D(t) = \sum_{i=1}^{n} S_{x_i} \frac{\partial f_i}{\partial u}\bigg|_{u*}, \tag{6.1}$$

can be interpreted as a measure of the influence of control changes on the terminal value of the criterion, as we saw in the previous section. It is zero along an unconstrained optimal trajectory and along portions of a constrained optimal trajectory for which the optimal control lies at an interior point of U. When the optimal control takes on a value at its bound, this quantity is generally nonzero. We plotted a typical function $D(t)$ in Fig. V.5 of the previous section.

An interesting conclusion can be drawn about the sign of the control impulse response function $D(t)$, which equals the rate of change of the derivative of the optimal value function with respect to the control variable. If the problem is a minimization problem and the optimal u is bounded *below* and is at its boundary, then it must be that the derivative of S would *decrease* if u could *decrease* (more precisely, it *cannot* decrease as u *increases*), so

$$D(t) \geq 0. \tag{6.2}$$

The function $D(t)$ will also be nonnegative along the constraint for a maximization problem with u bounded above. For a minimization problem with u bounded above, or a maximization problem with u bounded below, one can see that

$$D(t) \leq 0 \tag{6.3}$$

when the optimal value of u lies on the constraint.

Consequently, one can deduce *a priori* the sign of the quantity $D(t)$ when the optimal control is at its bound. If it should assume the wrong sign, the trajectory under study cannot be optimal, and a perturbation in the control away from the bound toward the interior of u will lead to an improved value of the terminal criterion Φ.

7. Mixed Control-State Inequality Constraints

We now consider a minimization problem with the admissible control, at time $\tau = t$ in state $(\xi_1(\tau), \ldots, \xi_n(\tau)) = (x_1, \ldots, x_n)$, restricted to those values of u satisfying an inequality constraint

$$g(x_1, \ldots, x_n, t, u) \leq 0. \tag{7.1}$$

For an airplane trajectory problem, the altitude h and velocity v are typical state variables. One control variable is generally the angle of attack α—the angle between the axis of the plane and the velocity vector. Too great an angle of attack can cause a stall, with the upper bound of permissible angles of attack usually depending upon altitude and velocity. This leads to a natural constraint of the type (7.1). Also, the heating rate and the forces of acceleration depend on the angle of attack, the altitude, and the velocity. As a result, inequality constraints such as (7.1) often must be imposed due to structural limitations.

8. The Appropriate Modification of the Multiplier Rule

Our analysis proceeds just as in both the unconstrained and control-constrained problems, until Eq. (3.9),

$$\left(\frac{dS_{x_j}}{dt}\right)_u = -\sum_{i=1}^{n} S_{x_i} \frac{\partial f_i}{\partial x_j} - \left(\sum_{i=1}^{n} S_{x_i} \frac{\partial f_i}{\partial u}\right) \frac{\partial u}{\partial x_j}, \qquad j = 1, \ldots, n, \tag{8.1}$$

is obtained.

Suppose now that, for a particular trajectory, the optimal control is unique and is at its bound at a given instant of time, so that equality holds in (7.1)—namely,

$$g(x_1, \ldots, x_n, t, u) = 0. \tag{8.2}$$

Let us assume that $g_u \neq 0$. The quantity $\partial u/\partial x_j$ needed in Eq. (8.1) can be obtained by partial differentiation of the identity (8.2) with respect to x_j, the control u being dependent upon x_j. This yields

$$\frac{\partial g}{\partial x_j} + \frac{\partial g}{\partial u}\frac{\partial u}{\partial x_j} = 0, \qquad j = 1, \ldots, n. \tag{8.3}$$

Solving for $\partial u/\partial x_j$ and substituting in (8.1), we obtain

$$\left(\frac{dS_{x_j}}{dt}\right)_u = -\sum_{i=1}^{n} S_{x_i}\frac{\partial f_i}{\partial x_j} + \left[\left(\sum_{i=1}^{n} S_{x_i}\frac{\partial f_i}{\partial u}\right)\frac{\partial g}{\partial x_j} \Big/ \frac{\partial g}{\partial u}\right], \qquad j = 1, \ldots, n. \tag{8.4}$$

All the terms on the right-hand side in (8.4) are computable during that portion of an optimal trajectory when u is given by (8.2), so (8.4) represents a differential equation for the partial derivatives of S along the boundary portion of an optimal trajectory. During that portion of a trajectory when the optimal u is an interior point of the admissible region defined by (7.1), the expression

$$\sum_{i=1}^{n} S_{x_i}\frac{\partial f_i}{\partial u} \tag{8.5}$$

equals zero, so the last term on the right-hand side in (8.4) is omitted.

A similar result for the variable t, namely,

$$\left(\frac{dS_t}{dt}\right)_u = -\sum_{i=1}^{n} S_{x_i}\frac{\partial f_i}{\partial t} + \left[\left(\sum_{i=1}^{n} S_{x_i}\frac{\partial f_i}{\partial u}\right)\frac{\partial g}{\partial t} \Big/ \frac{\partial g}{\partial u}\right], \tag{8.6}$$

is easily derived. (In reality t is just the $(n + 1)$st component of the state, but we have chosen to write it separately.)

Note that if the constraint depends only upon u and not the state, as it did in Section 2, then $\partial g/\partial x_j$ and $\partial g/\partial t$ equal zero and Eqs. (8.4) and (8.6) duplicate the result for that problem, which in turn duplicated the result for the unconstrained problem.

9. The Conventional Notation

In the conventional notation, the result (8.4) appears as

$$\lambda_j = -\sum_{i=1}^{n} \lambda_i\frac{\partial f_i}{\partial x_j} + \mu\frac{\partial g}{\partial x_j}, \qquad j = 1, \ldots, n, \tag{9.1}$$

where λ_j and μ are time-dependent Lagrange multiplier functions. Our derivation confirms this result and tells us that we can give the multipliers a physical interpretation by means of the relationships

$$\lambda_j = S_{x_j} \qquad j = 1, \ldots, n , \tag{9.2}$$

$$\mu = \left(\sum_{i=1}^{n} S_{x_i} \frac{\partial f_i}{\partial u} \Big/ \frac{\partial g}{\partial u} \right) = \left(\sum_{i=1}^{n} \lambda_i \frac{\partial f_i}{\partial u} \Big/ \frac{\partial g}{\partial u} \right), \tag{9.3}$$

or

$$\dot{\lambda}_j = -\sum_{i=1}^{n} \lambda_i \left[\frac{\partial f_i}{\partial x_j} - \frac{\partial g}{\partial x_j} \frac{\partial f_i}{\partial u} \frac{1}{\partial g / \partial u} \right], \tag{9.4}$$

along the boundary

$$g = 0 . \tag{9.5}$$

10. A Second Derivation of the Result of Section 9

We can reason somewhat as in Section 4 to obtain the result (9.1). If we denote by the symbol $U(x, t)$ the set of admissible controls given the state x at time t, the fundamental equation holding in a region of (x, t)-space is

$$0 = \min_{u \in U(x,t)} \left[\sum_{i=1}^{n} S_{x_i} f_i + S_t \right]. \tag{10.1}$$

Consider a point $x = \bar{x}, t = \bar{t}$ at which the optimal u, $\bar{u}$, lies on the boundary of $U(\bar{x}, \bar{t})$. Then, the expression $(dS/dt)_{\bar{u}}$ given by

$$\left(\frac{dS}{dt} \right)_{\bar{u}} = \sum_{i=1}^{n} S_{x_i} f_i(x, t, \bar{u}) + S_t \tag{10.2}$$

is nonnegative at all points (x, t) such that

$$\bar{u} \in U(x, t) , \tag{10.3}$$

and is zero at $x = \bar{x}, t = \bar{t}$. Hence, for all $(n + 1)$-dimensional vectors v such that

$$\nabla g(\bar{x}, \bar{t}) \cdot v \leq 0 , \tag{10.4}$$

where

$$\nabla g(\bar{x}, \bar{t}) = (g_{x_1}(x, t, \bar{u}), \ldots, g_{x_n}(x, t, \bar{u}), g_t(x, t, \bar{u})) \big|_{\bar{x}, \bar{t}}, \tag{10.5}$$

and where we assume $\nabla g \neq 0$, we must have

$$\nabla (dS(\bar{x}, \bar{t})/dt)_{\bar{u}} \cdot v \geq 0 . \tag{10.6}$$

Equation (10.6) asserts that $(dS/dt)_{\bar{u}}$, with $\bar{u}$ fixed, must be nondecreasing as the point $(\bar{x}, \bar{t})$ is perturbed in any direction in (x, t)-space having the property, assured by (10.4), that $g(x, t, \bar{u})$ is a nonincreasing function of (x, t), and, hence, that $\bar{u}$ remains an admissible control at the perturbed point. If $(\bar{x}, \bar{t})$ is perturbed in a direction such that the value of $g(x, t, \bar{u})$ remains zero, then $(\bar{x}, \bar{t})$ can also be perturbed in the opposite direction, and $\bar{u}$ remains admissible at points (x, t) in both directions. That is, if v is such that

$$\nabla g(\bar{x}, \bar{t}) \cdot v = 0, \tag{10.7}$$

then both v and $-v$ satisfy (10.4), and we must have

$$\nabla (dS/dt)_{\bar{u}} \cdot v = 0 \tag{10.8}$$

for (10.6) to hold. From (10.7) and (10.8), we conclude that there exists a number μ, which may depend upon the point $(\bar{x}, \bar{t})$, such that the vector equation

$$\nabla (dS(\bar{x}, \bar{t})/dt)_{\bar{u}} = \mu \nabla g(\bar{x}, \bar{t}) \tag{10.9}$$

holds, and, hence, that

$$\frac{\partial}{\partial x_j} \left\{ \sum_{i=1}^{n} S_{x_i} f_i(x, t, \bar{u}) + S_t \right\} \Bigg|_{\bar{x}, \bar{t}} = \mu \frac{\partial g(x, t, \bar{u})}{\partial x_j} \Bigg|_{\bar{x}, \bar{t}}, \qquad j = 1, \ldots, n. \tag{10.10}$$

Consequently, for any point (x, t) such that the optimal control lies on the boundary of $U(x, t)$, we have

$$\sum_{i=1}^{n} S_{x_i x_j} f_i + S_{x_j t} + \sum_{i=1}^{n} S_{x_i} \frac{\partial f_i}{\partial x_j} = \mu \frac{\partial g}{\partial x_j}, \qquad j = 1, \ldots, n, \tag{10.11}$$

which, combined with the result

$$(dS_{x_i}/dt)_u = \sum_{i=1}^{n} S_{x_i x_i} f_i + S_{x_i t}, \tag{10.12}$$

yields (9.1).

By substituting Eq. (10.9) into inequality (10.6) and comparing the result with inequality (10.4), we see that

$$\mu \leq 0. \tag{10.13}$$

11. Discussion

We have seen from two different viewpoints that, for a portion of an optimal trajectory during which the control lies at its bound, the differen-

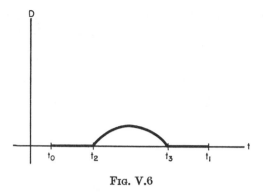

FIG. V.6

tial equations for $S_{x_i}(t)$ and $S_t(t)$ are modified from what they were for unconstrained and control-constrained problems. We shall now explain this difference.

If the optimal control $u^*(t)$ lies at an interior point of the admissible region during time intervals $[t_0, t_2]$ and $[t_3, t_1]$ and at its bound during time $[t_2, t_3]$, where $t_0 < t_2 < t_3 < t_1$, a plot of the control impulse response function

$$D(t) = \sum_{i=1}^{n} S_{x_i} \left. \frac{\partial f_i}{\partial u} \right|_{u*}, \tag{11.1}$$

will typically appear as shown in Fig. V. 6. We have discussed the meaning of this result in Section 5. Recall that $S_{x_i}(t)$, in the unconstrained case, is equal to the ratio of the first-order change in the terminal criterion Φ, resulting from a first-order change in state x_i at time t, to the change in x_i. The control function is held fixed in this process. For a constrained problem of the type that we are now investigating, a first-order change in state at time t, $t_0 \leq t \leq t_2$, results in a first-order change in the time t_2 when the constraint becomes operative and also in the values of states at the time t_2. This change in the state values, unlike the pure control-constraint case of Section 3, results in a first-order change in control *during the time interval* of constraint $[t_2, t_3]$. The total effect is then the direct effect of the change in state at time t, control held fixed, plus

$$\int_{t_2+\Delta t_2}^{t_3+\Delta t_3} D(t) \, \delta u(t) \, dt, \tag{11.2}$$

where δu is dependent upon the change in state and is not generally zero. Since the length of the above interval of integration and the function $D(t)$ are finite and since $\delta u(t)$ is a first-order quantity, the net contribution of (11.2) to $\Delta \Phi$ is a first-order quantity, and, therefore, nonnegligible. It is this additional effect of changes in state at times before the mixed control-state constraint becomes binding—namely, the effect of the resulting control change along the boundary—that leads to the modification in the differential equations for $S_{x_i}(t)$ and $S_t(t)$. Similarly, a first-order change in state at time t, $t_2 \leq t \leq t_3$, when the trajectory lies on the constraint, changes the control used up to time t_3 and this affects the terminal value of Φ to first order.

12. The Sign of the New Multiplier Function

The modified differential equations for $S_{x_i}(t)$ and $S_t(t)$, Eqs. (8.4) and (8.6), when written in the conventional form (9.1), contain a multiplier function $\mu(t)$ given by

$$\mu(t) = \left(\sum_{i=1}^{n} S_{x_i} \frac{\partial f_i}{\partial u} \bigg/ \frac{\partial g}{\partial u} \right). \tag{12.1}$$

We have seen that the numerator of (12.1) equals $D(t)$, the partial derivative with respect to u of the time derivative of the optimal value function.

Since we are minimizing Φ, we are, at each point in time, minimizing over u the derivative $K(t, u)$ of the optimal value function. If the constraint (7.1) prevents our choice of the absolutely minimizing value of u, we have two possible situations: Either

(1) $K(t, u)$ would decrease if u were increased, but the constraint (7.1) prevents us from increasing u to take advantage of this decrease; or

(2) $K(t, u)$ would decrease if u were decreased, but the constraint prevents us from decreasing u.

Recall that $D(t)$ represents $\partial K/\partial u$ evaluated in terms of the optimal admissible u. In Case 1, $D(t) < 0$, but $\partial g/\partial u > 0$, so we cannot increase u without violating (7.1). In Case 2, $D(t) > 0$, but $\partial g/\partial u < 0$. In either case, we conclude that

$$\frac{D(t)}{\partial g/\partial u} < 0 \tag{12.2}$$

and, consequently, that

$$\mu < 0 \tag{12.3}$$

when $u \neq 0$. This result is in agreement with conclusion (10.13) which was deduced somewhat differently.

If we were maximizing, or if the sense of inequality (7.1) were reversed, we would conclude that μ was greater than zero by the same argument.

13. State-Variable Inequality Constraints

In the following sections we shall consider a terminal control problem of the type discussed in Chapter IV, but where, in addition, admissible trajectories must lie in a region of state-variable space such that the inequality

$$h(\xi_1, \ldots, \xi_n, \tau) \leq 0 \tag{13.1}$$

is satisfied.

We have seen how inequality constraints simultaneously and explicitly involving both the control variable and the state variables may be incorporated into the standard format of Chapter IV. The time derivatives of the partial derivatives of S merely satisfy a modified differential equation along a boundary. Otherwise, the results are just as in the unconstrained case.

Since the constraint equation (13.1) does not contain the control variable, the device of Section 8, whereby $\partial u / \partial x_j$ was computed by partial differentiation of the boundary equation

$$g(x_1, \ldots, x_n, t, u) = 0, \tag{13.2}$$

fails.

In a previously published paper (Dreyfus (1962)) we modified the type of argument employed in Section 8 in order to deduce necessary conditions involving a reduced set of partial derivatives on a boundary segment. As a result, the conditions we derived were not really extensions of the results for the unconstrained, control-constrained, and state-control constrained cases, but differed considerably in form. Other authors (Gamkrelidze (1960) Berkovitz (1962) Bryson *et al.* (1963)) have maintained a complete set of multiplier functions and deduced conditions rather similar to those for the earlier problems. These conditions, however, involved discontinuities in the multiplier functions (jump conditions). In Berkovitz and Dreyfus (1965), an equivalence is established between the results involving jump conditions and those of Dreyfus previously cited. In the following sections, we shall use an argument similar to that of Section 10 to obtain results completely analogous in form to those of the earlier problems. Under certain regularity assumptions, we determine, and interpret, a full set of multiplier functions associated with a given optimal trajectory. These functions do not, in general, have jumps. Our results appear to agree in form with those of Chang (1963). They do not, of course, contradict any of the results given in the above references.

14. The Optimal Value Function for a State-Constrained Problem

Consider the set R of initial points $\tau = t$, $\xi_i(\tau) = x_i$, such that an admissible trajectory connects (x, t) with the specified terminal manifold. If the satisfaction of the inequality constraint

$$h(\xi_1, \ldots, \xi_n, \tau) \leq 0 \tag{14.1}$$

is required in the problem statement, then R includes, at most, points (x, t) such that

$$h(x_1, \ldots, x_n, t) \leq 0. \tag{14.2}$$

We define the optimal value function at points of R by the usual definition

$S(x_1, \ldots, x_n, t) = $ the minimum value of the criterion Φ that can be obtained by an admissible trajectory starting at time $\tau = t$ in state $\xi_i(\tau) = x_i$.

If we designate by $U(x, t)$ the set of admissible controls at the point (x, t), we see that S satisfies, at points of R, the fundamental equation

$$0 = \min_{u \in U(x,t)} \left[\sum_{i=1}^{n} S_{x_i} f_i + S_t \right]. \tag{14.3}$$

At points on the boundary of R at which

$$h(x_1, \ldots, x_n, t) = 0, \tag{14.4}$$

the partial derivatives of S are one-sided into the interior of R.

At interior points of R, admissible values of u are not constrained by the inequality constraint (14.1). If we denote by $U_1(x, t)$ the set of admissible controls at a point (x, t) such that $\tau = t$, $\xi_i(\tau) = x_i$ satisfies strict inequality in (14.1), the fundamental equation becomes

$$0 = \min_{u \in U_1(x,t)} \left[\sum_{i=1}^{n} S_{x_i} f_i + S_t \right] \tag{14.5}$$

at such points (x, t). The set U_1 will contain all finite values of the control variable unless constraints other than (14.1) are also present in the problem statement.

We now argue formally that Eq. (14.3) can be replaced by Eq. (14.5), even at boundary points such that Eq. (14.4) is satisfied. At boundary points, $U_1(x, t)$ is defined to be the set of controls that are admissible if the inequality constraint (14.2) is ignored. We assume that at boundary points the one-sided second derivatives of S and the one-sided first derivatives of f with respect to x and t are finite. Suppose that at a boundary point $(\bar{x}, \bar{t})$ a control belonging to U_1, but not to U, rendered the expression

$$\sum_{i=1}^{n} S_{x_i} f_i + S_t \tag{14.6}$$

negative, so that minimizing over elements of U_1 is different from minimizing over elements of the smaller set U. Then, that control would render (14.6) negative for points (x, t) satisfying strict inequality in (14.2) and lying in the neighborhood of $(\bar{x}, \bar{t})$. But this would contradict (14.5). Hence, we have that the equation

$$0 = \min_{u \in U_1(x, t)} \left[\sum_{i=1}^{n} S_{x_i} f_i + S_t \right] \tag{14.7}$$

holds at all points (x, t) of the set R, including boundary points.*

15. Derivation of a Multiplier Rule

We now derive the differential equations that are satisfied by S_{x_i} along an optimal trajectory. We consider a trajectory, a portion of which consists of points $\tau = t$, $\xi_i(\tau) = x_i$ satisfying Eq. (14.4). Let $(\bar{x}, \bar{t})$ denote a point on the boundary segment and let $\bar{u}$ be the optimal control at that point. Assume that no other inequality constraint is simultaneously binding at $(\bar{x}, \bar{t})$. We assume further that there exists a unique hyperplane tangent to R at the point $(\bar{x}, \bar{t})$.

Arguing as in Section 10, we now examine $(dS/dt)_{\bar{u}}$ which is given by

$$(dS/dt)_{\bar{u}} = \sum_{i=1}^{n} S_{x_i} f_i(x, t, \bar{u}) + S_t \tag{15.1}$$

and which we regard as a function of x and t. This function assumes its minimum value at $(\bar{x}, \bar{t})$. Assuming that $\nabla h \neq 0$, for all $(n + 1)$-dimen-

---

* This argument cannot be used in the case of a mixed control-state inequality constraint. If a point (x, t), with the property that the optimal control u at that point is at its bound, is perturbed slightly, the set of admissible controls is only slightly changed. Hence, an inadmissible control at the point (x, t) for which $\check{S}$ is negative will remain inadmissible after the perturbation and no contradiction can be established.

sional vectors v such that

$$\nabla h(\bar{x}, \bar{t}) \cdot v \leq 0, \tag{15.2}$$

where

$$\nabla h(\bar{x}, \bar{t}) = (h_{x_1}(x, t, \bar{u}), \ldots, h_{x_n}(x, t, \bar{u}), h_t(x, t, \bar{u})) \mid_{\bar{x}, \bar{t}}, \tag{15.3}$$

we must have

$$\nabla (dS(\bar{x}, \bar{t})/dt)_{\bar{u}} \cdot v \geq 0. \tag{15.4}$$

The above results imply that

$$\nabla (dS(\bar{x}, \bar{t})/dt)_{\bar{u}} \cdot v = 0 \tag{15.5}$$

for all v such that

$$\nabla h(\bar{x}, \bar{t}) \cdot v = 0. \tag{15.6}$$

Hence, we can conclude that the vector equation

$$\nabla (dS(\bar{x}, \bar{t})/dt)_{\bar{u}} = \mu \nabla h(\bar{x}, \bar{t}) \tag{15.7}$$

holds for some scalar μ, where μ depends on the point $(\bar{x}, \bar{t})$ and can be written as $\mu(t)$ if one considers states $x_i(t)$ along a particular trajectory. Consequently, at any point of an optimal trajectory that lies on the boundary (14.4), we have

$$\sum_{i=1}^{n} S_{x_i x_j} f_i + S_{x_j t} + \sum_{i=1}^{n} S_{x_i} \frac{\partial f_i}{\partial x_j} = \mu(t) \frac{\partial h}{\partial x_j}, \quad j = 1, \ldots, n. \tag{15.8}$$

This allows the conclusion*

$$\left(\frac{dS_{x_j}}{dt} \right)_u = - \sum_{i=1}^{n} S_{x_i} \frac{\partial f_i}{\partial x_j} + \mu(t) \frac{\partial h}{\partial x_j}, \quad j = 1, \ldots, n. \tag{15.9}$$

This result, together with result (14.7), is the multiplier rule that holds during a boundary portion of an optimal trajectory. We can also conclude that

$$\mu(t) \leq 0 \tag{15.10}$$

by the same argument as given in Section 10.

---

* Special care must be taken when dh/dt does not depend on u. For such problems S_{x_i} evaluated at a particular boundary point may differ for different trajectories leading into the same point. As a result, certain $S_{x_i x_j}$ become unbounded in the neighborhood of the boundary point. (A similar phenomenon occurs, at the terminal point of optimal trajectories for problems without inequality constraints such as were studied in Chapter IV, when a terminal manifold of dimension lower than n is specified.) Then the assumptions preceding conclusion (14.7) are violated and, furthermore, μ in Eq. (15.9) may be infinite. I thank J. Speyer for bringing this situation to my attention and suggest the resolution of this matter as a research problem.

We determine $\mu(t)$ as follows: At a point on the boundary (14.4) where the optimal control u is finite and not at a boundary point of $U_1(x, t)$ (i.e., no inequality constraint other than the state-variable constraint is binding), we have, from (14.7), the condition

$$0 = \sum_{j=1}^{n} S_{x_j} \frac{\partial f_j}{\partial u}. \tag{15.11}$$

Differentiation of this equation yields

$$0 = \sum_{j=1}^{n} \left(\frac{dS_{x_j}}{dt} \right)_u \frac{\partial f_j}{\partial u} + \sum_{j=1}^{n} S_{x_j} \frac{d}{dt} \left(\frac{\partial f_j}{\partial u} \right). \tag{15.12}$$

If we multiply the jth equation of the set (15.9) by $\partial f_j / \partial u$ and the sum the resulting n equations, we get

$$\sum_{j=1}^{n} \left(\frac{dS_{x_j}}{dt} \right)_u \frac{\partial f_j}{\partial u} = - \sum_{i=1}^{n} \sum_{j=1}^{n} S_{x_i} \frac{\partial f_i}{\partial x_j} \frac{\partial f_j}{\partial u} + \mu(t) \sum_{j=1}^{n} \frac{\partial f_j}{\partial u} \frac{\partial h}{\partial x_j}. \tag{15.13}$$

If

$$(\partial / \partial u)(\nabla h \cdot f) |_{\bar{x}, \bar{t}, \bar{u}} \neq 0, \tag{15.14}$$

where

$$f = (f_1, \ldots, f_n, 1), \tag{15.15}$$

combining (15.12) and (15.13) yields the equation for $\mu(t)$

$$\mu(t) = \left[\sum_{i=1}^{n} \sum_{j=1}^{n} S_{x_i} \frac{\partial f_i}{\partial x_j} \frac{\partial f_j}{\partial u} - \sum_{j=1}^{n} S_{x_j} \frac{d}{dt} \left(\frac{\partial f_j}{\partial u} \right) \right] / \sum_{j=1}^{n} \frac{\partial f_j}{\partial u} \frac{\partial h}{\partial x_j}. \tag{15.16}$$

If dh/dt does not involve u, so that (15.14) is violated, Eqs. (15.12) and (15.13) yield

$$0 = \sum_{i=1}^{n} \sum_{j=1}^{n} S_{x_i} \frac{\partial f_i}{\partial x_j} \frac{\partial f_j}{\partial u} - \sum_{j=1}^{n} S_{x_j} \frac{d}{dt} \left(\frac{\partial f_j}{\partial u} \right). \tag{15.17}$$

Differentiation of this equation and the use of (15.9) yields an expression for $\mu(t)$ unless $\dot{h}$ is independent of u, in which case further differentiations are necessary.

We conclude then, that along a boundary portion of an optimal trajectory for a state-variable constrained problem, the partial derivatives of the optimal value function satisfy the differential equations (15.9) where, generally, μ is given by (15.16) and satisfies inequality (15.10). Along unconstrained portions of the trajectory, the usual multiplier rule holds.

16. Generalizations

The above results can be extended to include more complicated situations. We shall consider the case here where there are two state-variable inequality constraints

$$h \leq 0 \quad \text{and} \quad g \leq 0, \qquad (16.1)\text{-}(16.2)$$

and two control variables u_1 and u_2. Consider a point $(\bar{x}, \bar{t})$ at which both

$$h = 0 \quad \text{and} \quad g = 0 \qquad (16.3)\text{-}(16.4)$$

hold. We assume that a unique $(n - 1)$-dimensional tangent plane to R exists at $(\bar{x}, \bar{t})$, that

$$\nabla h \neq 0 \quad \text{and} \quad \nabla g \neq 0, \qquad (16.5)\text{-}(16.6)$$

and that both $\dot{h}$ and $\dot{g}$ depend upon u_1 and u_2. We can only assert, in the argument of Section 15, that for all $(n + 1)$-dimensional vectors v such that both

$$\nabla h \cdot v = 0 \quad \text{and} \quad \nabla g \cdot v = 0 \qquad (16.7)\text{-}(16.8)$$

hold, the equation

$$\nabla (dS/dt)_{\tilde{u}} \cdot v = 0 \qquad (16.9)$$

must hold. Equations (16.7), (16.8), and (16.9) imply that there exist scalars μ_1 and μ_2, dependent upon the point (x, t), such that the vector equation

$$\nabla (dS/dt)_{\tilde{u}} = \mu_1 \nabla h + \mu_2 \nabla g \qquad (16.10)$$

holds. Consequently,

$$\left(\frac{dS_{x_j}}{dt}\right)_u = -\sum_{i=1}^{n} S_{x_i} \frac{\partial f_i}{\partial x_j} + \mu_1(t) \frac{\partial h}{\partial x_j} + \mu_2(t) \frac{\partial g}{\partial x_j}, \quad j = 1, \ldots, n \quad (16.11)$$

is the appropriate multiplier rule.

The multiplier functions $\mu_1(t)$ and $\mu_2(t)$ are determined by differentiation of the equations

$$\sum_j S_{x_j}(\partial f_j/\partial u_1) = 0 \qquad (16.12)$$

and

$$\sum_j S_{x_j}(\partial f_j/\partial u_2) = 0, \qquad (16.13)$$

much as in the previous section.

17. A Connection with Other Forms of the Results

In the papers of Berkovitz (1962) and others, multiplier functions $\lambda_i(t)$ appear that may be discontinuous at junction points and which satisfy a different differential equation from ours during portions of an optimal trajectory lying on a boundary. Specifically, along a boundary it is asserted that, under certain regularity conditions including condition (15.14),

$$\dot{\lambda}_j = -\sum_{i=1}^{n} \lambda_i \frac{\partial f_i}{\partial x_j} - \nu(t) \frac{\partial (dh/dt)}{\partial x_j} \qquad j = 1, \ldots, n, \qquad (17.1)$$

where $\nu(t)$ satisfies the equation

$$\sum_{i=1}^{n} \lambda_i \frac{\partial f_i}{\partial u} + \nu(t) \frac{\partial}{\partial u} \left(\frac{dh}{dt} \right) = 0 . \qquad (17.2)$$

At a junction point it is asserted that, in general, the $\lambda_j(t)$ are discontinuous and that the discontinuity in the vector λ is proportional to the vector ∇h.

It can be verified that the identification

$$\lambda_i = S_{x_i} - \left[\int_{t_0}^{t} \mu(\tau) \, d\tau \right] h_{x_i} , \qquad i = 1, \ldots, n , \qquad (17.3)$$

$$dv/dt = \mu(t) , \qquad (17.4)$$

where t_0 is the time at which the trajectory intersects the boundary, renders the results above consistent with those of Section 15. If we take

$$\lambda_i = S_{x_i} , \qquad i = 1, \ldots, n \qquad (17.5)$$

at points not on a constraint boundary, we see that λ_i jumps at the exiting junction, which occurs at time t_1, by the amount

$$\left[\int_{t_0}^{t_1} \mu(\tau) \, d\tau \right] h_{x_i} . \qquad (17.6)$$

Should (15.14) be violated, but

$$\partial \ddot{h}/\partial u \neq 0 , \qquad (17.7)$$

then the classical results read

$$\dot{\lambda}_j = -\sum_{i=1}^{n} \lambda_i \frac{\partial f_i}{\partial x_j} - \nu(t) \frac{\partial \ddot{h}}{\partial x_j}, \qquad j = 1, \ldots, n \qquad (17.8)$$

and

$$\sum_{i=1}^{n} \lambda_i \frac{\partial f_i}{\partial u} + \nu(t) \frac{\partial \ddot{h}}{\partial u} = 0 . \qquad (17.9)$$

Then λ_i and S_{x_i} can be identified off the boundary, while on the boundary the identification

$$\lambda_i = S_{x_i} - \left[\int_{t_0}^{t} \mu(\tau) \, d\tau \right] h_{x_i} - \left[\int_{t_0}^{t} \int_{t_0}^{\tau_2} \mu(\tau_1) \, d\tau_1 \, d\tau_2 \right] \frac{\partial \dot{h}}{\partial x_i}, \quad (17.10)$$

$$\ddot{\nu} = \mu, \quad (17.11)$$

holds. As stated earlier, the situation in this case is rather pathological and this identification should be regarded merely as suggestive.

18. Summary

We saw in Chapter IV that, associated with the optimal trajectory for an unconstrained problem, there exist multiplier functions $S_{x_i}(t)$, $i = 1, \ldots, n$, and $S_t(t)$, satisfying certain differential equations. These functions also satisfy certain initial and treminal relations, depending on the specifications of the problem. The optimal control function minimizes, at each point, the derivative of the optimal value function—this derivative can be expressed in terms of the multiplier functions—and can be determined by setting the partial derivative with respect to the control of the derivative of the optimal value function equal to zero.

In this chapter we have seen that if the control function is explicitly restricted by an inequality constraint, the optimal trajectory still has multiplier functions associated with it satisfying the same differential equations and the same boundary conditions as in the unconstrained case. The optimal control still minimizes, over all admissible controls, the derivative of the optimal value function. When the optimal control lies at its bound, however, the minimization does not imply that the control impulse response function $D(t)$ (i.e., the partial derivative with respect to the control of the derivative of the optimal value function) equals zero.

When a constraint involving both control and state is imposed, the differential equations for the multiplier functions $S_{x_i}(t)$ and $S_t(t)$ must be modified. Again, the optimal control minimizes the derivative of the optimal value function over all admissible controls, with the minimization implying that the control impulse response function equals zero when the optimal control lies at an interior point of the admissible control space, but not necessarily that it equals zero when the control is at its bound.

Finally, we have considered constraints involving only state variables. We obtained a modification of the multiplier rule that applies during that portion of an optimal trajectory that lies on the boundary of the admissible region of state space. This rule resembles the modified rule for problems with mixed control-state constraints. The only difference is that the function $\mu(t)$ appearing in the result for state-constrained problems is determined, when the optimal trajectory lies along the boundary, from the condition that the control impulse response function is zero—a condition that is not generally valid for problems with control, or mixed control-state, inequality constraints.

CHAPTER VI

Problems with Special
Linear Structures

1. Introduction

In this brief chapter we shall investigate certain problems for which the optimal trajectories do not exhibit the regularity properties assumed in earlier chapters. It appears that, on an individual basis, these problems can still be handled successfully by dynamic programming techniques. At present, the catalog of special problems that have been so treated is incomplete, and what we present here concerning certain situations is far from rigorous.

The troublesome types of problems that we shall investigate have what seem to be particularly simple forms and appear frequently in the literature. While it is certainly advisable to study simplified problems before attacking the complicated situations found in nature, the properties of the simplified problems that are treated in this chapter turn out to be *atypical* of the properties of most practical problems. For this reason, we feel that these special types of problems have been receiving undue emphasis and that a short chapter near the end of this book is their appropriate habitat. There will be no loss of continuity for the reader who is little interested in pathological problems and who proceeds directly to Chapter VII.

2. Switching Manifolds

A point on an optimal curve or trajectory at which the derivative or control is discontinuous is called a *corner*. Consider the region R of admissible initial points for a given variational problem. Let the optimal curve from some particular initial point A have a corner at B and suppose

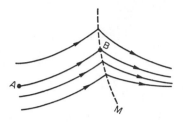

FIG. VI.1

that the optimal curves from neighboring initial points have corners that lie on a manifold containing B; see Fig. VI.1. Then the set of corner points constitutes a *switching manifold M* in state space.

The study of problems with special structures almost always involves the investigation of switching manifolds. In the situation shown in Fig. VI.1, optimal curves are said to be nontangent to the switching manifold and, by the argument outlined in Section 34 of Chapter III, the general theory is shown to be applicable with no modification. However, should portions of optimal curves be tangent to, or coincident with, a switching manifold—such as in the case shown in Fig. VI.2.—some of the arguments of earlier chapters are invalid. These are the special cases that will concern us in this chapter.

3. A Problem That Is Linear in the Derivative

The problem to be investigated first has a definite integral criterion. We wish to choose an admissible function

$$\eta(\xi) , \tag{3.1}$$

with

$$\eta(\xi_0) = \eta_0 , \qquad \eta(\xi_1) = \eta_1 , \tag{3.2}$$

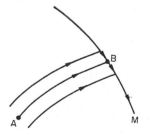

FIG. VI.2

subject to the constraint

$$-1 \leq \eta'(\xi) \leq 1, \tag{3.3}$$

such that $J[\eta]$, given by

$$J[\eta] = \int_{\xi_0}^{\xi_1} [A(\xi, \eta) + B(\xi, \eta)\eta'] \, d\xi, \tag{3.4}$$

is minimized. The functions A and B are nonlinear functions of the independent variable ξ and of the value η of the solution function at the point ξ. The integrand of (3.4) is linear in the derivative η' of the solution function.

4. Analysis of the Problem of Section 3

Consider the (x, y)-space of possible initial points

$$\xi = x, \qquad \eta(\xi) = y \tag{4.1}$$

for the variational problem of Section 3. We designate as Region I that portion of (x, y)-space for which the optimal value of η' is $+1$, the upper bound of admissible values allowed by the inequality constraint (3.3). The portion of (x, y)-space for which -1 is the optimal choice of η' is designated as Region II.

A region, containing interior points, in which the optimal η' assumes values between -1 and $+1$ cannot exist. This assertion is proven as follows: In such a region, the fundamental equation

$$0 = \min_{|y'| \leq 1} [A + By' + S_x + S_y y'] \tag{4.2}$$

would be valid, as well as the condition

$$B + S_y = 0 \tag{4.3}$$

that is necessary unless an extremal admissible value of y' is optimal. For Eq. (4.3) to hold identically in the region, the equation

$$\left(\frac{d}{dx} (B + S_y) \right)_{y'} = 0 \tag{4.4}$$

must hold in the interior of the region for all y' (the notation used in Eq. (4.4) was defined and explained in Section 6 of Chapter III). Also, since the multiplier rule given by Eq. (9.8) of Chapter III is valid in such a region, we have

$$(dS_y/dx)_{y'} = -A_y - B_y y', \tag{4.5}$$

where y' is the optimal value of the derivative η'. From Eqs. (4.4) and (4.5), we conclude that the equation

$$B_x - A_y = 0 \qquad (4.6)$$

must hold at all points of the region. But, Eq. (4.6) represents a curve in (x, y)-space, not a region with an interior, and a contradiction to the assumption of the existence of such a region has been established. A curve rather than a region, therefore, separates Regions I and II.

While we have established Eq. (4.6) if there were a region in which the optimal value of y' were neither $+1$ nor -1, we have not yet established that the curve separating Regions I and II is described by Eq. (4.6). This is because we have yet to establish the validity of the multiplier rule (4.5) at a point on the curve separating Regions I and II, since the regularity assumptions that were used to derive (4.5) are not valid at such a point.

Suppose that, on the boundary curve—designated $y = g(x)$—separating Regions I and II, the optimal value of η' equals neither $+1$ nor -1, but assumes a value g' somewhere between these bounds. Then the optimal curve, emanating from a point on $y = g(x)$, coincides with the curve $y = g(x)$, and the nontangency assumption concerning a switching manifold is violated. We wish to characterize the curve $y = g(x)$ in this case. Geometrically, we are investigating a situation such as is shown in Fig. VI.3, where the segments with arrows are portions of optimal curves to a specified terminal point.

At every point of (x, y)-space, the equation

$$0 = \min_{|y'|\leq 1} [A + By' + (dS/dx)_{y'}] \qquad (4.7)$$

holds. At points in the interior of Region I, Eq. (4.7) implies the results

$$0 = A + B + S_x^{(\mathrm{I})} + S_y^{(\mathrm{I})}, \qquad (4.8)$$

$$B + S_y^{(\mathrm{I})} < 0, \qquad (4.9)$$

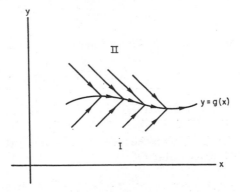

FIG. VI.3

since the y' value of $+1$ is optimal. We use the superscript notation to indicate the region since we have not shown, at this point, that the partial derivatives of S are continuous across the boundary curve $y = g(x)$. In Region II, we have

$$0 = A - B + S_x^{(II)} - S_y^{(II)} , \tag{4.10}$$

$$B + S_y^{(II)} > 0 . \tag{4.11}$$

At points in the interior of Regions I and II, the optimal policy function exhibits sufficient regularity (in fact, constancy) to allow the derivation of the results

$$(dS_x/dx)_{y'} = -A_x - B_x y' \tag{4.12}$$

and

$$(dS_y/dx)_{y'} = -A_y - B_y y' \tag{4.13}$$

by the method of Section 9 of Chapter III. Here, y' is the optimal slope. Since, by assumption, optimal curves follow (rather than cross) the switching curve $y = g(x)$, we cannot yet assert that the two different one-sided partial derivatives $S_x^{(I)}$ and $S_x^{(II)}$, evaluated at a point on $y = g(x)$, are equal, nor that $S_y^{(I)}$ equals $S_y^{(II)}$.

Each point of $y = g(x)$ is a corner point for both curves coming down from above and up from below. Consequently, at points on the curve $y = g(x)$ the equations

$$0 = B + S_y^{(I)} \tag{4.14}$$

and

$$0 = B + S_y^{(II)} \tag{4.15}$$

hold. Hence, assuming that B is a continuous function of its arguments, we conclude that

$$S_y^{(I)} = S_y^{(II)} , \tag{4.16}$$

and, since S is continuous across $y = g(x)$, we also have that

$$S_x^{(I)} = S_x^{(II)} . \tag{4.17}$$

We see, then, that the optimal value function has continuous partial derivatives across the switching curve $y = g(x)$.

In the interior of both Regions I and II, the result

$$\left(\frac{d}{dx} (B + S_y) \right)_{y'} = B_x - A_y \tag{4.18}$$

follows from Eq. (4.13). Since in the interior of Region I the control $y' = +1$ is assumed optimal, the expression

$$B + S_y \tag{4.19}$$

must be less than zero (see Eq. (4.9)). Furthermore, expression (4.19) must equal zero along $y = g(x)$, each point of which is a switching point. Consequently, the derivative of $B + S_y$ taken along an optimal curve must be nonnegative in the interior of Region I at points in the neighborhood of $y = g(x)$. Therefore,

$$B_x - A_y \geq 0 \tag{4.20}$$

in Region I in the neighborhood of the curve $y = g(x)$. But, expression (4.19) must be positive in Region II and zero along $y = g(x)$. Hence,

$$\left(\frac{d}{dx}(B + S_y)\right)_{y'} \leq 0 \tag{4.21}$$

in Region II at points in the neighborhood of $y = g(x)$, and, consequently,

$$B_x - A_y \leq 0 \tag{4.22}$$

in that neighborhood. Results (4.20) and (4.22) in combination—assuming A and B have continuous partial derivatives in their arguments—imply that the equation of the curve $y = g(x)$ must be

$$B_x - A_y = 0 . \tag{4.23}$$

The curve given by Eq. (4.23) is called a *singular arc* by some authors. Both classical analysis (Leitmann (1963)) and a special argument built upon Green's theorem (Miele (1962)) confirm that a problem of the sort we are treating can have singular arcs—arcs along which y' does not take on either of its extreme allowable values–as long as the singular arc satisfies Eq. (4.23).

We see (from the fact that the derivative of $B + S_y$ equals zero along a singular arc given by Eq. (4.23)) that along a singular arc the result

$$(dS_y/dx)_{y'} = -(dB/dx)_{y'} = -B_x - B_y y' = -A_y - B_y y' \tag{4.24}$$

holds. Consequently, the multiplier equation (4.13)—which is easily seen to hold under regularity assumptions—also holds without modification along a singular arc in the above special case in spite of the nonvalidity of the nontangency assumption required in previous derivations.

5. Discussion

The above problem, which is linear in the control but not in the state, becomes quite complicated when generalized to more than two dimensions. However, the heuristic reasoning presented above would still seem to permit analysis. The solution of higher-dimensional problems that are linear in the derivatives appears to involve singular surfaces, and thus, the synthesis of the optimal curve can be very involved.

6. A Problem with Linear Dynamics and Criterion

We have studied a problem with a criterion that was linear in the decision variable but nonlinear in the stage and state variables. We concluded that the optimal curve for such a problem could contain a segment along which the derivative was not at its bound, and we found the equation for such a segment. We also concluded that the partial derivatives of the optimal value function were continuous across such a segment, and that they satisfied the usual multiplier rule along such a segment.

We turn now to a different problem. It is even simpler in formulation than the problem of Section 3 in that it contains no nonlinear aspects at all. Just as the study of the problem of Section 3 turned out to be more complicated than the investigation of the general problems of earlier chapters, the solution of our new problem involves even more special arguments than the solution of the problem of Section 3. It will be found, for the problem of this section, that there exist switching surfaces across which the partial derivatives of S are discontinuous, and furthermore, that the differential equations that are satisfied by the partial derivatives of S must be modified for segments of optimal curves that are coincident with the switching surfaces.

Let us consider a time-optimal control problem. A control function

$$v(\tau), \qquad t_0 \leq \tau \leq t_1, \tag{6.1}$$

is to be chosen, subject to the control inequality constraint

$$-1 \leq v(\tau) \leq 1, \qquad t_0 \leq \tau \leq t_1. \tag{6.2}$$

The control yields a trajectory

$$\xi_i(\tau), \qquad i = 1, 2, \tag{6.3}$$

in accordance with the linear differential equations

$$\dot{\xi}_1(\tau) = \xi_2, \qquad \dot{\xi}_2(\tau) = v, \tag{6.4}$$

with initial conditions at the specified time t_0,

$$\xi_i(t_0) = \xi_{i_0}, \qquad i = 1, 2. \tag{6.5}$$

The time t_1 at which the terminal conditions

$$\xi_i(t_1) = 0, \quad i = 1, 2 \tag{6.6}$$

are satisfied is to be made minimum by the choice of the control function.

The inequality constraint (6.2) is essential to the problem. Without it, the difference between the terminal time t_1 and the initial time t_0 can be made arbitrarily small by the use of an impulsive (unbounded) control. This is because the special problem we are considering has linear dynamics and the criterion does not explicitly involve the control variable.

Equations (6.4) result when the one-dimensional second-order dynamical equation

$$\ddot{\xi}(\tau) = v \tag{6.7}$$

is written as a first-order-system. In terms of the one-dimensional model, we seek to drive the controlled object to rest (i.e., zero velocity) at the origin in the least possible time.

7. Investigation of the Problem of Section 6

Let us consider the general initial point

$$\tau = t, \qquad \xi_1(\tau) = x_1, \qquad \xi_2(\tau) = x_2, \tag{7.1}$$

and define the optimal value function $S(x_1, x_2, t)$ by

$S(x_1, x_2, t)$ = the time of arrival at the terminal point (6.6) of a particle moving according to the dynamical law (6.4) where its initial position, at time t, is (x_1, x_2) and the control $v(\tau)$ that minimizes the time of arrival is used.

Let us call *regular* any region of (x_1, x_2, t)-space where the optimal control policy $u(x_1, x_2, t)$ is a continuous function of its arguments or where there is a manifold of discontinuous control (as long as trajectories are not tangent to the manifold). The optimal value function satisfies the fundamental partial differential equation

$$0 = \min_{|u| \leq 1} [S_{x_1} x_2 + S_{x_2} u + S_t] \tag{7.2}$$

in a region of regularity. In such a region, S_t is constant along an optimal trajectory and we can deduce, from the boundary condition

$$S(0, 0, t) = t, \tag{7.3}$$

that

$$S_t \mid _{t_1} = 1 \,. \tag{7.4}$$

At any point of regular behavior of optimal trajectories, the two multiplier equations

$$(dS_{x_1}/dt)_u = 0 \quad \text{and} \quad (dS_{x_2}/dt)_u = -S_{x_1} \tag{7.5}$$

hold when u is the optimal control since, as we saw in Chapter V, the multiplier equations are unaffected by the introduction of inequality constraints on control alone.

Since the expression in (7.2) that is to be minimized is linear in u, at a point of regular behavior of optimal trajectories either

$$u = +1 \tag{7.6}$$

$$u = -1 \,, \tag{7.7}$$

or

$$S_{x_2} = 0 \tag{7.8}$$

holds. The left-hand side of Eq. (7.8) is the coefficient of u in (7.2). If Eq. (7.8) were to hold along an optimal trajectory over an interval of time, then u could conceivably assume an intermediate value between $+1$ and -1 during that interval. But for (7.8) to hold during an interval, all the time derivatives of the left-hand side of Eq. (7.8) must equal zero. But by (7.5) this would mean that S_{x_1} must equal zero, which would contradict Eq. (7.2). Consequently, it is impossible at regular points for u to assume an intermediate value between -1 and $+1$ during a finite interval of time.

But if u assumes only the values $+1$ or -1, no more than two different optimal trajectories lead into the origin. Optimal trajectories from initial points not on one of these two trajectories must ultimately intersect one of these two trajectories and then switch controls and enter along it. This means that optimal trajectories do not always *cross* these manifolds of discontinuous control leading into the origin, but sooner or later *follow* them. This violates the nontangency condition that was assumed at regular points, which in turn means we must expect to encounter irregular conditions and must distrust, when a trajectory coincides with a switching manifold, our previous derivation of the fundamental equation (7.2) and conclusions extracted from it

8. Further Analysis of the Problem of Section 6

Consider the situation where optimal trajectories all intersect a switching manifold M from the same side, and then switch control and follow the

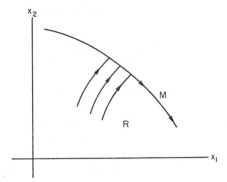

x_2

M

R

x_1

FIG. VI.4

manifold. An example of such a case is shown in Fig. VI.4. Trajectories and the manifold M actually exist in the three-dimensional (x_1, x_2, t)-space, but the projection of M onto the (x_1, x_2)-plane defines a curve. This is because a change in the t coordinate of a given initial point (x_1, x_2, t), with x_1 and x_2 held fixed, does not affect the x_1 and x_2 coordinates of the switching point on the associated optimal trajectory, but only the value of S, the time of termination. Initial points (x_1, x_2, t) that we shall study, have coordinates (x_1, x_2) lying in the region R and may have any values of the t coordinate. Since we have seen that the control can assume only its extreme values, the control variable equals either $+1$ or -1 in the interior of R and takes on the other value on the switching manifold M.

We saw in Section 7 that our prior results about S and its partial derivatives hold in the interior of R. Consider a particular optimal trajectory with a segment that is coincident with the switching manifold M. The same terminal time is associated with each point (x_1, x_2, t) on the trajectory, and consequently, the time derivative of the optimal value function is zero. We have, therefore, the equation

$$0 = S_{x_1}x_2 + S_{x_2}u^{(M)} + S_t, \qquad (8.1)$$

where $u^{(M)}$ indicates the control that yields motion along M, and the partial derivatives are one-sided into R. As before, S_t obviously equals 1 since time is being minimized and the dynamics are not time-dependent.

Since Eq. (8.1) holds identically along a particular trajectory lying on M, we can differentiate the equation to obtain the result

$$0 = (dS_{x_1}/dt)_{u^{(M)}}x_2 + (dS_{x_2}/dt)_{u^{(M)}}u^{(M)} + S_{x_1}u^{(M)}. \qquad (8.2)$$

Furthermore, since M is a manifold of discontinuous control, the coefficient S_{x_2} of the control variable in Eq. (7.2) must equal zero at all points on M. Therefore,

$$S_{x_2} = 0 \qquad (8.3)$$

holds identically on M and, differentiating Eq. (8.3) with respect to time, we obtain

$$(dS_{x_2}/dt)_{u^{(M)}} = 0 . \tag{8.4}$$

Substitution of this result into Eq. (8.2) yields

$$(dS_{x_1}/dt)_{u^{(M)}} = -(S_{x_1}u^{(M)}/x_2) . \tag{8.5}$$

These equations give the rate of change of S_{x_1} and S_{x_2} along a trajectory lying on the switching manifold M. These results differ from those of Eqs. (7.5) which held at points lying in the interior of R. Our new result is not contradictory, since the assumptions used to derive Eqs. (7.5)* are not valid along M, where an infinitesimal change in state to an interior point of R results in a finite change in control.

The trajectories through (x_1, x_2, t)-space that lead into admissible terminal points $(0, 0, t_1)$ are independent of the absolute time t and lie either in the surface

$$x_2 \le 0, \qquad \tfrac{1}{2}x_2{}^2 - x_1 = 0 \tag{8.6}$$

which results when $u^{(M)} = 1$, or the surface

$$x_2 \ge 0, \qquad \tfrac{1}{2}x_2{}^2 + x_1 = 0 \tag{8.7}$$

which occurs when $u^{(M)} = -1$; the projections of these trajectories onto the (x_1, x_2)-plane are shown in Fig. VI.5, where the arrows indicate the direction of the projected paths through (x_1, x_2)-space corresponding to increasing time. Note that S_{x_2} is a linear function of time (see Eqs. (7.5)) at points not on the manifold M, and equals zero at points on M. Consequently, there can be at most one discontinuity in control along any optimal trajectory, since a linear nonconstant† function has only one zero. As a result, any optimal trajectory starting from a point in Region I in Fig. VI.6 must use control

$$u = -1 , \tag{8.8}$$

until the curve

$$\tfrac{1}{2}x_2{}^2 - x_1 = 0 \tag{8.9}$$

is reached; then, control

$$u = +1 \tag{8.10}$$

brings the trajectory to the origin. Similarly, any trajectory at a point in

---

* See Chapter IV. Eq. (10.3), where we used the fact that the partial derivative with respect to u of the expression being minimized equals zero, and the assumption that $\partial u/\partial x_j$ is finite in order to deduce the multiplier rule.

† We have seen that $S_{x_1} \ne 0$ at a point on M. Since S_{x_1} is continuous and is constant along trajectories in R which intersect M, it cannot be zero at any point in R.

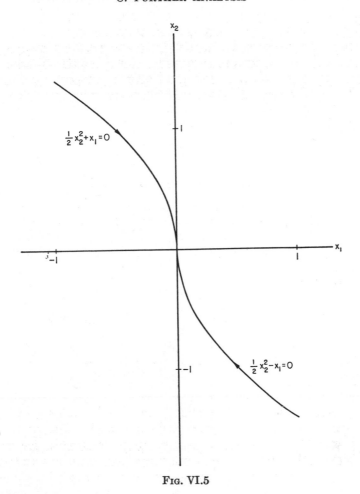

$$\frac{1}{2}x_2^2 + x_1 = 0$$

$$\frac{1}{2}x_2^2 - x_1 = 0$$

Fig. VI.5

Region II uses control

$$u = +1 , \tag{8.11}$$

and then reaches the origin along the curve

$$\tfrac{1}{2}x_2{}^2 + x_1 = 0 , \tag{8.12}$$

with

$$u = -1 . \tag{8.13}$$

We can now use this information about optimal trajectories to compute the optimal value function explicitly and thus verify results (7.2), (8.1), and (8.5). It turns out that

$$S(x_1, x_2, t) = t + x_2 + (2(x_2{}^2 + 2x_1))^{1/2} \tag{8.14}$$

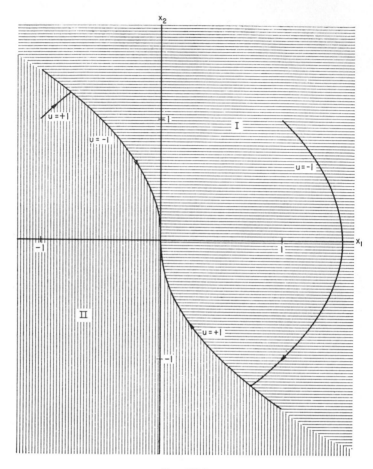

Fig. VI.6

in Region I, and

$$S(x_1, x_2, t) = t - x_2 + (2(x_2{}^2 - 2x_1))^{1/2} \tag{8.15}$$

in Region II. The square-root term is always taken to be nonnegative. The function S is continuous across the switching manifolds.

In Region I, including the switching manifold (8.6), partial differentiation of Eq. (8.14) yields the results

$$S_{x_1} = 2/(2(x_2{}^2 + 2x_1))^{1/2} \tag{8.16}$$

and

$$S_{x_2} = 1 + [2x_2/(2(x_2{}^2 + 2x_1))^{1/2}]. \tag{8.17}$$

This is consistent with Eqs. (7.2) and (8.1).* In Region II and on its switching manifold (8.7), we have

$$S_{x_1} = -2/(2(x_2{}^2 - 2x_1))^{1/2} \tag{8.18}$$

and

$$S_{x_2} = [2x_2/(2(x_2{}^2 - 2x_1))^{1/2}] - 1 , \tag{8.19}$$

which again checks with prior conclusions. Furthermore, from (8.16) we see that, along the switching manifold (8.6), we have

$$S_{x_1} = -1/x_2 . \tag{8.20}$$

(We use the minus sign because S_{x_1} is nonnegative by Eq. (8.16) and x_2 is negative along (8.6).) Consequently,

$$\left(\frac{dS_{x_1}}{dt}\right)_{u(M)} = \frac{\dot{x}_2}{x_2{}^2} = -\frac{S_{x_1}u^{(M)}}{x_2} \tag{8.21}$$

as asserted in Eq. (8.5).

9. Discussion

Note that the functions $S_{x_1}(x_1, x_2, t)$ and $S_{x_2}(x_1, x_2, t)$ are not continuous functions of the arguments x_1 and x_2 across the manifold separating Region I from Region II. In fact, they jump from a finite to an infinite value. This fact would cause us some dismay in our developments were it not for one important fact: *Trajectories do not cross the manifold of discontinuous S_{x_1} and S_{x_2}.* If they did, an argument of the type given in the Berkovitz-Dreyfus paper could be developed to show that the partial derivatives *were* continuous. We see then that linear problems with bounded control have solution trajectories using only extremal values of the control variable (called bang-bang control). For such problems, the state space may be separable into regions, each of which has the property that all trajectories originating in the region stay in the region. Then, in each individual region, the fundamental equation is valid, as are deductions from it as long as special care is taken when studying points on the boundary of the region. The fact that the partial derivatives of the optimal value function are discontinuous across manifolds separating such regions is of no great concern.

It is interesting to note that the formulas for the time derivatives of the partial derivatives of S differ, along the switching boundaries, from their

---

* Note that for points on the switching curve $\frac{1}{2}x_2{}^2 - x_1 = 0$, the numerator of the quotient in (8.17) is negative and the denominator is positive, so the ratio is -1.

usual form. In the classical literature, where multiplier functions appear in place of the partial derivatives of S, *no such modification* in the formulas for derivatives of multipliers takes place. The conclusions about the optimal control based upon the classical form of the results turn out to be identical with ours, but we have the interesting phenomenon, in this linear case, that the classical multiplier functions differ numerically from our one-sided partial derivatives, and, therefore, the classical multipliers *cannot be interpreted as partial derivatives of the optimal value function*. In fact, the classical multipliers apparently have no physical or geometrical interpretation.

10. Summary

We have presented and discussed two examples of problems with special structures. These problems have solution curves that violate our earlier hypotheses concerning regularity. We have seen that such problems can be handled on an individual basis by dynamic programming techniques. Doing so has both advantages and disadvantages. On the credit side of the ledger, the expressions appearing in our analysis possess useful physical and geometrical interpretations. This property is not shared by the classical results. On the debit side, special arguments are necessary for each problem, with the form of the results differing for different problem statements. Another debit, but one that we feel is transient, is the current lack of completeness or rigor in the specialized arguments that have been developed.

CHAPTER VII

Stochastic and Adaptive
Optimization Problems

1. Introduction

In earlier chapters we dealt with deterministic problems. In the simplest problem of Chapter III, for a specified initial point, the choice of a policy $y'(x, y)$ uniquely determined a curve $y = y(x)$ and also the value of the criterion functional $J[y(x)]$. In the subsequent chapters on the problem of Mayer, the specification of a control policy $u(x, t)$, for given initial values of the state variables x and time t and for given dynamical equations, completely determined a trajectory and a value of the terminal criterion. We turn now to a class of problems, not considered in the classical variational literature, where the specification of a control does not uniquely determine a trajectory. The dynamical equations for a typical problem in this chapter will contain random variables as well as the usual state-dependent and control-dependent terms. These random variables may depend upon the time, the state, or the control, or they may be independent of all three. As a result of this randomness in the evolution of a process, the selection of a particular control function (if the control is viewed as a function of time) or a control policy (if the control depends on both the time and the state) determines a probability measure defined over the space of all possible trajectories, but does not determine which trajectory actually occurs. We postulate, as before, a criterion functional that associates a value with each trajectory. The *expected value* of the criterion functional associated with a particular control is then to be calculated by weighting the criterion value of each possible trajectory by the probability (density) of its occurrence and summing (integrating) over all possibilities. This yields a scalar expected value associated with each control function or policy. We shall seek a way of determining, for problems of the foregoing type, the control policy which has associated with it the minimum expected value of the criterion.

An elaborate theory justifies the use of an expected value criterion in a stochastic environment where the process is to evolve only once. This theory is based on the determination of a "utility," which is a function associating real numbers with consequences by means of a person's personal evaluation of preferences among gambles (Von Neumann and Morgenstern, 1947; Savage, 1954). The expected value of the utility is then optimized. In this context, our criterion function should be interpreted as a utility function.

We shall be concerned initially with processes which evolve by discrete steps, since the concept of a sequence of random variables is intuitively easier to grasp than the concept of a continuous stochastic process. For such problems, we shall obtain by the principle of optimality a recurrence relation characterizing the optimal expected value function. In those cases where we consider the continuous problem, we shall find that a fundamental partial differential equation is obtained as the limiting form of the recurrence relation, just as it was for deterministic problems. One of the most interesting and important properties of dynamic programming is that neither the techniques nor the results need be significantly modified to include problems with stochastic aspects.

Actually, most practical and realistic control problems are neither deterministic nor stochastic as we have defined them. Both of these models lack an important aspect of almost all behavior, and certainly of optimal behavior: the learning element. When learning is present, we speak of *adaptive* control processes. While the dynamics of a *stochastic* control process involves incomplete knowledge, the nature of the uncertainty (i.e., the density functions of the random variables involved) is known initially and no new information about the underlying dynamics becomes available as the process evolves. In an adaptive process, information about the underlying dynamics (perhaps about the initial conditions of the problem, perhaps about the means or variances or other parameters of the density functions for the random variables in the dynamical differential equations, or perhaps about the form of the equations themselves) becomes available as the process evolves. The optimal control policy then reflects (1) the initial uncertainty about the problem dynamics and the desire to reduce this uncertainty, and (2) the ultimate and basic desire to minimize the objective criterion.

This chapter is only an introduction to the vast domain of stochastic and adaptive optimization problems, and we shall be more concerned with concepts than with results.

While the application of what we have called "dynamic programming ideas" to deterministic variational problems is fairly new, these ideas and the additional ones developed in this chapter are not entirely novel to the treatment of stochastic and adaptive problems. A considerable literature in statistical decision theory, some of it preceding the coining of the term "dynamic programming," develops and uses the ideas presented in this chapter. Therefore, the reader should not embark upon research in this area without consulting this literature.* With particular regard to the stochastic and adaptive generalizations of variational problems that we shall treat, current research is directed toward adapting this body of statistical knowledge to multistage and, ultimately, continuous decision problems.

2. A Deterministic Problem

Let us begin by considering a simple three-stage discrete deterministic control problem of the type investigated in Chapter I. Given the directed network shown in Fig. VII.1, we wish to determine that path from vertex A to line B which has the property that the sum of the numbers written along the three arcs of the path is minimum.

Let us denote by U the decision to choose the diagonally-upward arc from a vertex, and by D the choice of the diagonally-downward arc. Suppose that we consider that we are at the vertex A at time 0, at either the vertex diagonally up from A or the one diagonally down from A (depending upon the decision at A) at time 1, and at one of the three vertices one step from B at time 2. We can then determine a path by specifying a decision (either U or D) at time 0, a decision at time 1, and a decision at time 2. By examining all eight possible sequences of three decisions, we discover that the path produced by the sequence of decisions D-U-D (diagonally downward, then upward, then downward) has sum-of-arc-numbers zero and is the unique optimal solution. We shall call a designation of the optimal sequence of control decisions to be followed from a given initial vertex to the termination, the optimal *open-loop* control function.

The continuous analog of this problem is the search for the derivative function $\eta'(\xi)$ (or the control function $v(\tau)$) that yields a curve connecting specified initial and terminal manifolds while minimizing a given criterion. We obtained an open-loop characterization of the solution function in earlier chapters by converting the fundamental partial differential equation to a system of ordinary differential equations.

---

* Some important contributions are: Raiffa and Schlaifer (1961), and Wald (1950).

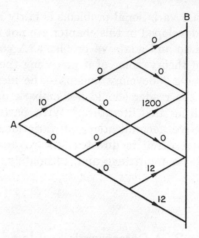

FIG. VII.1

A second way of presenting the solution to the above problem is to associate with each vertex of Fig. VII.1 a decision, either U or D, that is the initial decision of the optimal sequence of decisions yielding a path from that vertex to the terminal line. This set of decisions associated with vertices is efficiently determined by proceeding recursively backward from the terminal line. We initially record the optimal decision and minimum sum to termination (encircled) at each vertex along the line C, in Fig. VII.2, and then use the circled numbers to determine the optimal decision and minimum sum associated with each vertex on the line D, and, finally, with the vertex A; this yields Fig. VII.3. We shall call a designation of the solution that associates an optimal decision with each

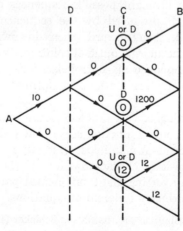

FIG. VII.2

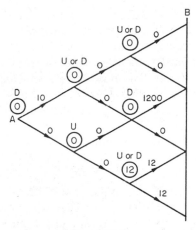

FIG. VII.3

possible initial stage and state of the system (i.e., with each vertex) the optimal *feedback* control policy.*

This is, of course, the dynamic programming view that led in earlier chapters to the fundamental partial differential equation that is satisfied by the optimal value function and the associated optimal policy function.

The interpretation of Fig. VII.3 is that the optimal path from vertex A has the value zero and its initial arc slopes diagonally downward. The vertex at the right-hand end of this downward arc has a U written by it, indicating that the optimal decision associated with the vertex is the diagonally-upward arc. This choice, in turn, leads to a vertex with a downward decision. Hence, D-U-D is the optimal sequence of decisions leading from the vertex A. Note that the feedback representation of the solution also yields the best path starting from other vertices not along the D-U-D path. The open-loop solution does not yield such information.

The important observation here is that for a specified initial vertex such as A, the open-loop and feedback representation of the solution are equivalent for this and, more generally, for any deterministic process.

3. A Stochastic Problem

Let us now modify the above problem by introducing a stochastic aspect. We shall assume that the decision designated by U results in a

---

* A policy is a function of both the stage and the state variables. We use the term "control function" here in a special sense to indicate a control that is a function of one variable, the stage.

probability of $\frac{3}{4}$ of a diagonally-upward transition from a given vertex, and in a probability of $\frac{1}{4}$ of a diagonally-downward move. The alternative decision D has a $\frac{3}{4}$ chance of producing a diagonally-downward move and a $\frac{1}{4}$ chance of an upward transition. Once a transition occurs, it can be observed by the controller. We now have a stochastic control problem. We can still exert a controlling influence, but the randomness that we have introduced determines the actual transformations of state at any vertex.

Associated with each transition between vertices is a value given by the arc number of the arc connecting the vertices. A path between the vertex A and the line B is determined by three successive transitions, and its value is given by the sum of the values of the three arcs. A control function or policy does not determine the path that will result, but it does determine the probability of each path occurring. Consequently, each control scheme has an expected value determined by summing the products of the probability of each path and the value of the corresponding path. We seek that control function or policy with minimum expected value.

To determine the best *open-loop* control function, we consider all eight possible sequences of three decisions each, and choose the one with minimum expected value. For example, the decision sequence D-U-D that optimized the deterministic version of this problem has a probability of 27/64 of actually yielding the path associated with a downward, then an upward, and finally a downward transition; this path has value 0. There is a probability of 9/64 of an upward-upward-downward path of value 10. Unfortunately, there is also a probability of 9/64 of a downward-upward-upward path of value 1200. Multiplying the eight appropriate values by their probabilities and adding, we obtain an expected value E_{DUD} given by

$$E_{\text{DUD}} = \frac{27}{64} \cdot 0 + \frac{9}{64} (10 + 12 + 1200)$$

$$+ \frac{3}{64} (12 + 10 + 10) + \frac{1}{64} \cdot 1210 \cong 190 .$$

It turns out that the decision sequence U-U-D has the minimum expected value—approximately 120.

The optimal *feedback* control policy may be computed recursively just as in the deterministic example. Suppose that, for a given vertex, the minimum expected value associated with starting at each of the two adjacent vertices to which a transition might possibly occur has been determined. Then the expected value of the transitions from the given vertex to the termination if decision U is chosen initially is obtained as follows: The upward arc number and the expected value associated with the vertex at the right-hand end of the upward arc are added and the result is multiplied by $\frac{3}{4}$; then, the downward arc number is added to the expected value associated with the vertex at its right-hand end and the sum is multiplied by $\frac{1}{4}$; finally, the two resulting numbers are added. Decision D is similarly evaluated with the probabilities—$\frac{3}{4}$ and $\frac{1}{4}$—reversed. Then the minimum of these two results is the optimal expected value of the remaining transitions. The minimizing decision and expected value of the remaining transitions (encircled) are recorded at the vertex; this computation leads to Fig. VII.4. The expected value using the optimal feedback control policy is $84\frac{1}{4}$ and the optimal policy function is the set of letters associated with the vertices in Fig. VII.4.

At this point, we would like to introduce a third control scheme. Let us use the optimal open-loop solution to yield our initial decision for the three-stage problem. Then, after a transition has occurred, let us observe the result and determine the best open-loop solution for the new two-stage problem. After implementing the initial control decision of this optimal open-loop solution, a transition occurs and we again observe the state and use the optimal control decision for the remaining one-stage problem. This scheme uses the optimal open-loop initial decision at each stage, but incorporates feedback in the observation of the actual state attained. We call this scheme *open-loop-optimal feedback* control.

For the example problem of this section, this control scheme differs from both of the previous schemes. It turns out that the open-loop-optimal feedback decision coincides with the optimal feedback decision at each vertex of this example, except for vertex A. There, as has been shown, the optimal open-loop control sequence dictates an upward decision, whereas

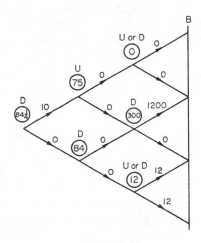

FIG. VII.4

the optimal feedback decision is D. Therefore, the expected value E of the open-loop-optimal feedback control scheme is computed as in Fig. VII.4, except that U rather than D is chosen at vertex A. Consequently, at vertex A, we have the result

$$E = \tfrac{1}{4}(0 + 84) + \tfrac{3}{4}(10 + 75) = 84\tfrac{3}{4}.$$

We assert on the basis of this example that

(1)   The optimal *open-loop* scheme incorporating no use of subsequent information about actual transitions yields a large expected value;

(2)   The optimal *feedback* scheme where the state is assumed known when the decision is made yields the smallest possible expected value for this type of stochastic problem;

(3)   The hybrid *open-loop-optimal feedback* scheme yields an intermediate expected value. Although feedback is used, the fact that feedback is to be used is withheld from the computation determining the control decisions, and this results in a control scheme that is inferior to true optimal feedback control.

4. Discussion

We have distinguished two types of optimal control of a stochastic system: open-loop and feedback. Each is optimal with respect to the information it utilizes in its realization. The optimal feedback scheme performs at least as well as the optimal open-loop scheme *on the average*.* There is no assurance, however, that it will be superior for each particular realization of the stochastic process. The third scheme that we distinguished, open-loop-optimal feedback control, is not truly optimal for the information it uses (namely, the observation of the state after each transition occurs and before the next decision is rendered). We mentioned it only because there is a tendency to confuse it with optimal feedback control.

In the next 14 sections, we shall seek to characterize the optimal feedback control policies for various stochastic problems. We shall investigate problems for which the criterion is additive and in which the random elements depend upon the current state but do not, explicitly, depend upon the past. It will be seen that dynamic programming is ideally suited

---

* This is because the set of all open-loop control schemes can be considered as a subset of the set of all possible feedback control schemes. The same decision, for an open-loop scheme, must be associated with all states at a given stage.

to the task we face. Should the optimal open-loop control function, rather than the optimal feedback control policy, be required or desired, the dynamic programming approach does not appear to be applicable. For a treatment of a specific open-loop stochastic control problem by a non-dynamic programming method, the reader is referred to the work of Mishchenko (Pontryagin *et al.* (1962), Chapter VII).

5. Another Discrete Stochastic Problem

We now consider a problem midway between the relatively unstructured numerical example of Section 3 and the continuous stochastic problem we shall introduce in Section 9.

Suppose that a system may be found in any one of m states s_i, $i = 1$. ..., m, at each of the n discrete times t_j, $j = 1, ..., n$. A set of q control decisions d_k, $k = 1, ..., q$, is available in each state at each time. If the kth control decision d_k is chosen when the system is in state s_i at time t_j, there is a known probability $p(s_i, t_j, d_k, s_l)$ that the system will be transformed into state s_l, $l = 1, ..., m$, at time t_{j+1}. Associated with the transition from state s_i at time t_j to state s_l at time t_{j+1} due to a choice of control d_k, is a value $F(s_i, t_j, d_k, s_l)$ determined by a given function F of the four variables. Also, at the time t_n when the process terminates, if the state is s_r, $r = 1, ..., m$, a value $\Phi(s_r)$ is obtained. The process starts in state s_1 at time t_1. We seek a control policy

$$u(s_i, t_j), \quad i = 1, ..., m, \quad j = 1, ..., n-1 \qquad (5.1)$$

(a function of two variables associating a control decision with each state s_i at each time t_j) that will minimize the expected value of J, where J equals the sum of the transitional values and the terminal value, and is given by the equation

$$J = \sum_{j=1}^{n-1} F(s_i, t_j, d_k, s_l) + \Phi(s_r) . \qquad (5.2)$$

6. The Optimal Expected Value Function

We take a cue from our study of deterministic processes and consider a family of problems, each starting at different times in different states. The criterion for the process starting in state s_i at time t_j is the sum of the transition values F for the remainder of the process plus the terminal value Φ.

We define the auxiliary function $S(s_i, t_j)$ by

$S(s_i, t_j)$ = the expected value of the process described above where the process starts in state s_i at time t_j and where an optimal control policy is used.

The function $S(s_i, t_j)$ is called the *optimal expected value function*.

7. The Fundamental Recurrence Relation

Suppose that a process starts in state s_i at time t_j, that control decision d_k is chosen at time t_j, and that an optimal control policy is used thereafter. With probability $p(s_i, t_j, d_k, s_{\bar{l}})$, the system transforms into state $s_{\bar{l}}$ at time t_{j+1}. Given that a transition to state $s_{\bar{l}}$ occurs, the expected value of the entire process equals

$$F(s_i, t_j, d_k, s_{\bar{l}}) + S(s_{\bar{l}}, t_{j+1}),\tag{7.1}$$

where the first term is the value of the initial transition and the second term equals the expected value of the remaining process. Since the transition to state $s_{\bar{l}}$ occurs with probability $p(s_i, t_j, d_k, s_{\bar{l}})$, the process, if it starts at time t_j in state s_i and control d_k is chosen, has the expected value (7.1) with probability $p(s_i, t_j, d_k, s_{\bar{l}})$. Multiplying the expected value of the entire remaining process associated with each initial transition by the probability of the initial transition if decision d_k is chosen, and summing the products over all possible initial transitions, we obtain the formula

$$V(s_i, t_j, d_k) = \sum_{l=1}^{m} p(s_i, t_j, d_k, s_l)[F(s_i, t_j, d_k, s_l) + S(s_l, t_{j+1})],$$

$$\tag{7.2}$$

where $V(s_i, t_j, d_k)$ is the expected value of using control d_k in state s_i at time t_j, and the optimal control policy thereafter. Clearly,

$$S(s_i, t_j) = \min_{d_k} V(s_i, t_j, d_k).\tag{7.3}$$

Therefore, we obtain the recurrence relation

$$S(s_i, t_j) = \min_{d_k}\{\sum_{l=1}^{m} p(s_i, t_j, d_k, s_l)[F(s_i, t_j, d_k, s_l)$$
$$+ S(s_l, t_{j+1})]\}, \quad i = 1, \ldots, m; \quad j = 1, \ldots, n-1 \tag{7.4}$$

relating S evaluated at a particular state s_i at time t_j and S evaluated at all possible states s_l at time t_{j+1}.

Since a process starting at time t_n in state s_r also terminates there, with no control or transition, we have the boundary condition

$$S(s_r, t_n) = \Phi(s_r), \qquad r = 1, \ldots, m. \tag{7.5}$$

The solution of recurrence relation (7.4) with boundary condition (7.5) involves the determination of a minimizing control decision d_k for each initial condition (s_i, t_j). We designate by $u(s_i, t_j)$ the optimal policy function associating the minimizing d_k with each (s_i, t_j).

The numerical solution of this type of problem is discussed in the literature (Bellman and Dreyfus (1962), Chapter XI; Howard (1960)).

8. Discussion

Note that $S(s_i, t_j)$, for fixed i and j, depends upon the values of $S(s_l, t_{j+1})$ for all l, even when the optimal decision $u(s_i, t_j)$ is known. This is quite different from the deterministic case where, along an optimal trajectory, S evaluated at a particular state at time t could be related to S evaluated at a particular nearby state at time $t + \Delta\tau$. This "fanning-out" property of stochastic problems appears to make it difficult to reduce the fundamental recurrence relation or, in the continuous case, the partial differential equation to related ordinary difference or differential equations. Recent research has, however, shown that the solution of a stochastic problem can be characterized in terms of *stochastic* ordinary differential equations (Kushner (1963)). From a computational viewpoint, unfortunately, the "reduced" problem seems to be as difficult to solve as a partial differential equation.

We have shown how a discrete stochastic decision process problem can be solved by the determination of the solution of a recurrence relation with terminal boundary conditions. We now treat two types of continuous stochastic control problems and show how their formulations lead to partial differential equations.

9. A Continuous Stochastic Control Problem

To construct our next stochastic control process we adopt the differential equation model that was the subject of Chapter IV and attach a stochastic process to the dynamical equations defining the evolution of the states. The process is easier to visualize, perhaps, if we begin by treating a discrete problem with time increments of $\Delta\tau$, and then let $\Delta\tau$ approach zero. We commence by writing the discrete dynamical equations for the evolution of the states ξ_i as

$$\xi_i(\tau + \Delta\tau) = \xi_i(\tau) + f_i(\xi_1, \ldots, \xi_n, \tau, u)\, \Delta\tau + g_i,$$

$$i = 1, \ldots, n, \quad (9.1)$$

where

$$u = u(\xi_1, \ldots, \xi_n, \tau) \quad (9.2)$$

is the control policy* and where the g_i, $i = 1, \ldots, n$, are n random variables whose joint density function $p(g_1, \ldots, g_n; \xi_1, \ldots, \xi_n, \tau, u, \Delta\tau)$ depends upon the state, time, control, and time increment. We denote the expected value, or mean, of g_i, given the state, time, control, and time increment, by $E[g_i]$, which is defined by the equation

$$E[g_i] = \int_{-\infty}^{\infty}\!\!\cdots\!\int g_i p(g_1, \ldots, g_n; \xi_1, \ldots, \xi_n, \tau, u, \Delta\tau)\, dg_1 \ldots dg_n. \quad (9.3)$$

The covariance, or joint moment about the mean of the product of two random variables, of g_i and g_j is denoted by σ_{ij} and defined by

$$\sigma_{ij} = \int_{-\infty}^{\infty}\!\!\cdots\!\int (g_i - E[g_i])(g_j - E[g_j])p(g_1, \ldots, g_n;$$

$$\xi_1, \ldots, \xi_n, \tau, u, \Delta\tau)\, dg_1 \ldots dg_n. \quad (9.4)$$

The covariance σ_{ii} of a random variable with itself is called the variance of the random variable. The joint moments about the mean of the product of three or more of the random variables g_i, $i = 1, \ldots, n$, are defined analogously with Eq. (9.4) and are called higher-order moments.

We assume that, at the individual times $t, t + \Delta\tau, \ldots, t + k\,\Delta\tau, \ldots,$ the random variables g_i have the properties

(1) $E[g_i] = 0$ for all i;
(2) $\sigma_{ij} = h_{ij}(\xi_1, \ldots, \xi_n, \tau, u)\,\Delta\tau$;
(3) the moments higher than the second are $o(\Delta\tau)$ (i.e., of order smaller than $\Delta\tau$); and
(4) g_i at time $t + k\,\Delta\tau$ is independent of all g_j at all times $t + m\,\Delta\tau$ different from $t + k\,\Delta\tau$.

---

* In earlier chapters we used the notation $v(\tau)$ to denote the optimal control *function* for a particular problem, in order to distinguish it from $u(x_1, \ldots, x_n, t)$, the optimal control policy for the more general problem in which we imbedded the particular problem. No such distinction is necessary here since we seek the optimal policy, even for a particular problem with specified initial condition.

In the terminology of some probability texts, g_i at time t is written as the increment $\Delta z_t = z(t + \Delta \tau) - z(t)$ where $z(t)$ is called a *Brownian motion process* with independent increments.

Note that in assumption 2 above, the second moment is taken to be proportional to the time increment. This is done in order that, when $\Delta \tau$ approaches zero, the randomness neither "washes out" nor does it "smother" the process.

We now consider the limit of the process (9.1) as $\Delta \tau$ approaches zero to be the dynamical stochastic control process that we wish to optimize. For generality, we shall allow a criterion that involves a combination of a definite integral and a function evaluated at the terminal time (this would be called a problem of the Bolza type if it were deterministic). We seek that control policy $u(\xi_1, \ldots, \xi_n, \tau)$ that minimizes the functional $J[u]$ given by

$$J[u] = E\left[\int_{t_0}^{T} F(\xi_1, \ldots, \xi_n, \tau, u) \, d\tau + \Phi(\xi_1(T), \ldots, \xi_n(T)) \right], \quad (9.5)$$

where the initial time t_0 and terminal time T are specified, as are the initial conditions

$$\xi_i(t_0) = \xi_{i_0}, \quad i = 1, \ldots, n. \quad (9.6)$$

Note that since the process evolution is stochastic, we do not specify a set of simultaneous terminal conditions but rather define termination in terms of one or more deterministic quantities. In this example we chose time, which evolves with certainty. The problem of driving the stochastic state ξ into some region R in an optimal fashion is more complicated.

10. The Optimal Expected Value Function

A number S can be associated with the initial condition

$$\tau = t,$$
$$\xi_i(\tau) = x_i, \quad i = 1, \ldots, n, \quad (10.1)$$

by means of the definition

$S(x_i, \ldots, x_n, t) = $ the value of the criterion (9.5) with t_0 replaced by t where the process starts in state $(x_i, \ldots, x_n)$ at time t and an optimal control policy is used.

This function, which assigns an expected value to each initial condition, is called the *optimal expected value function*.

11. The Fundamental Partial Differential Equation

Let us consider the discrete process with time increments $\Delta\tau$. If the process starts in state $(x_1, \ldots, x_n)$ at time t, and control u is used during the initial interval of time, by an argument completely analogous to that of Section 7 we obtain the recurrence relation

$$S(x_1, \ldots, x_n, t) = \min_{u} \; E_g[F(x_1, \ldots, x_n, t, u)\,\Delta\tau + o(\Delta\tau)$$

$$+ \; S(x_1 + f_1\,\Delta\tau + g_1 + o(\Delta\tau), \ldots, t + \Delta\tau)].$$

$$(11.1)$$

Assuming that the third partial derivatives of S are bounded, Taylor series expansion of the right-hand side of Eq. (11.1) about $(x_1, \ldots, x_n, t)$, and cancellation of $S(x_1, \ldots, x_n, t)$ yields

$$0 = \min_{u} \; E_g \Bigg[F\,\Delta\tau + \sum_{i=1}^{n} S_{x_i}(f_i\,\Delta\tau + g_i) + S_t\,\Delta\tau$$

$$+ \frac{1}{2} \sum_{i=1}^{n} \sum_{j=1}^{n} S_{x_i x_j}(f_i\,\Delta\tau + g_i)(f_j\,\Delta\tau + g_j) + o(\Delta\tau) \Bigg]. \qquad (11.2)$$

Using Assumptions 1–4 of Section 9 to take the expectations, we obtain

$$0 = \min_{u} \Bigg[F\,\Delta\tau + \sum_{i=1}^{n} S_{x_i} f_i\,\Delta\tau + S_t\,\Delta\tau + \frac{1}{2} \sum_{i=1}^{n} \sum_{j=1}^{n} S_{x_i x_j} h_{ij}\,\Delta\tau + o(\Delta\tau) \Bigg].$$

$$(11.3)$$

Dividing by $\Delta\tau$ and letting $\Delta\tau$ approach zero produces the fundamental partial differential equation for a Brownian motion control process,

$$0 = \min_{u} \Bigg[F + \sum_{i=1}^{n} S_{x_i} f_i + S_t + \frac{1}{2} \sum_{i=1}^{n} \sum_{j=1}^{n} S_{x_i x_j} h_{ij} \Bigg].$$

$$(11.4)$$

The control u enters through the term F and also by way of the f_i and the h_{ij} terms.

Note that this equation differs from the fundamental equation for the deterministic case by the appearance of terms involving the second partial derivatives of the optimal expected value function S.

Since the process terminates at time T, at which time the terminal contribution to the criterion is assessed, the boundary condition is

$$S(x_1, \ldots, x_n, T) = \Phi(x_1, \ldots, x_n).$$ (11.5)

12. Discussion

At this point, the reader should note two important facts concerning the above characterization of the solution of a stochastic optimal control problem. First, Eq. (11.4) is a *deterministic* partial differential equation. The optimal policy function $u(x_1, \ldots, x_n, t)$ associated with the solution of (11.4) is a conventional function of $n + 1$ variables. Thus, although the controlled process itself evolves stochastically, both the mathematical problem to which the optimal control problem has been reduced and its solution are deterministic and involve no such concepts as the mixed or random optimal strategies of the theory of games.

A second point of interest, which we mentioned in Section 8 with respect to a discrete stochastic problem, is that the deterministic fundamental partial differential equation (11.4) cannot be reduced to deterministic ordinary differential equations. In Section 8 we saw how the mixing at each transition prevented this reduction. In mathematical terms, we find that an equation of the form (11.4) does not possess associated characteristic curves having the property that knowledge of the solution at one point of the curve determines the value of the solution at other points of the curve.

Fortunately, techniques exist for the analytic solution of certain simple problems of the above type. This affords some insight into the structure of solutions and behavior of optimally controlled systems. These techniques also might prove useful in developing methods for the successive approximation to the solution of more complex problems. We shall solve the fundamental partial differential equations of two simple problems in subsequent sections. The solution technique employed can be used also to solve, in complete generality, certain simple deterministic problems. In that case, of course, other more conventional techniques based on the Euler-Lagrange equations can be used to solve the same problems.

The particular stochastic models and techniques of Sections 9–18 are due to Fleming (1963), Florentin (1961), and Kushner (1962). The general applicability of dynamic programming to the problem of the optimal feedback control of a stochastic system is discussed by Bellman (1957). For more explicit details of the solutions of the examples of these sections, see Dreyfus (1964).

13. The Analytic Solution of an Example

In the Brownian motion model of Section 9, let us specialize by letting $n = 1$ and taking

$$f_1 = a\xi + bu, \tag{13.1}$$

$$h_{11} = \sigma^2, \tag{13.2}$$

$$F = u^2, \tag{13.3}$$

and

$$\Phi = \xi^2(T), \tag{13.4}$$

where a, b, and σ^2 are constants. The dynamical equation (13.1) is linear in state and control, and the components, (13.3) and (13.4), of the criterion are quadratic. The problem calls for driving the state ξ toward the value zero at time T, subject to a cost-of-control reflected by the integrand F.

For this problem, the fundamental equation (11.4) takes the form

$$0 = \min_u [u^2 + S_x(ax + bu) + S_t + \tfrac{1}{2}S_{xx}\sigma^2], \tag{13.5}$$

and the boundary condition (11.5) is

$$S(x, T) = x^2. \tag{13.6}$$

To find the value of u that minimizes (13.5), we set the derivative of the bracketed expression equal to zero, obtaining

$$0 = 2u + S_x b, \tag{13.7}$$

and, solving for u,

$$u = -bS_x/2. \tag{13.8}$$

Substituting this result into (13.5), we find we must now solve the nonlinear partial differential equation

$$0 = -(b^2/4)\, S_x^2 + axS_x + \tfrac{1}{2}\sigma^2 S_{xx} + S_t, \tag{13.9}$$

with boundary condition (13.6).

Solution is accomplished as follows. Assume a solution of the form

$$S(x, t) = h(t)x^2 + k(t). \tag{13.10}$$

If

$$h(T) = 1 \tag{13.11}$$

and

$$k(T) = 0, \tag{13.12}$$

the assumed solution will satisfy at least the terminal boundary condition. Substitution of form (13.10) into Eq. (13.9) yields the equation

$$0 = -b^2h^2(t)x^2 + 2ah(t)x^2 + h(t)\sigma^2$$
$$+ h'(t)x^2 + k'(t). \tag{13.13}$$

Let $h(t)$ be chosen such that it satisfies the Riccati ordinary differential equation

$$-b^2h^2(t) + 2ah(t) + h'(t) = 0 \tag{13.14}$$

with terminal boundary condition (13.11), and let $k(t)$, once $h(t)$ is determined, be chosen such that

$$h(t)\sigma^2 + k'(t) = 0 \tag{13.15}$$

with terminal boundary condition (13.12). Then, Eq. (13.13)—and therefore Eq. (13.9)—will be satisfied.

Solution of Eq. (13.14) for $h(t)$ yields

$$h(t) = \frac{\exp\left[2a(T-t)\right]}{1 - (b^2/2a) + (b^2/2a)\exp[2a(T-t)]}, \tag{13.16}$$

where $\exp[c] = e^c$.

Then, from Eq. (13.8), the optimal control policy $u(x, t)$ is given by

$$u(x, t) = -\frac{bx\exp\left[2a(T-t)\right]}{1 - (b^2/2a) + (b^2/2a)\exp\left[2a(T-t)\right]}. \tag{13.17}$$

Note that it was not necessary to solve Eq. (13.15) for $k(t)$ in order to find the optimal policy function. Determination of $k(t)$ would be necessary, however, in order to find the optimal expected value function using Eq. (13.10).

14. Discussion

The solution of this particularly simple problem has several interesting features. Suppose that, in the dynamical equations (9.1) of the problem, the random variables g_i are replaced by their expected values, zero. We can then solve the resulting deterministic problem, specialized as in Section 13, by either conventional or dynamic programming methods. If we express the optimal control as a function of state, it turns out that we obtain exactly the same result as rule (13.17). This rather amazing coincidence, which only seems to occur for a linear dynamics-quadratic criterion model such as that of Section 13, is an example of what is called *certainty equivalence* due to the fact that the random variables in the problem can be replaced by their expected values and the optimal current action is unaffected. This result was first derived for problems with discrete stages by Simon (1956) and Theil (1957).

Another surprising property of this particular problem concerns the optimal open-loop control (the best control function of the form $u(t)$ without feedback on the state) for the stochastic problem. If the optimal open-loop control decision for a problem with general initial state is expressed in terms of the state and implemented (this is what we called the open-loop-optimal feedback control philosophy in Section 3), the resulting control scheme again duplicates the above two.

We see then that three control philosophies which we might expect to be distinct (particularly in view of the example of Section 3), are equivalent for the problem of Section 13. We now treat briefly a slight modification of the problem of Section 13 that still admits an analytic solution but for which the above three control schemes differ.

15. A Modification of an Earlier Problem

In the one-dimensional example of Section 13 we assumed that the expected value of g^2, the variance of the random variable g, equaled $\sigma^2 \Delta\tau$, where σ^2 was a constant. In the general model of earlier sections, however, we assumed that the variances and covariances could be functions of state, time, and control, as well as of the time increment.

Let us now assume that the variance of g depends upon the control decision and that no control implies no randomness. The assumption that the application of control produces the uncertainty in the dynamics reflects reality in many applications. If there is to be no randomness in the evolution of the state variable when no control is exerted, the variance of g must be zero when u equals zero. To attain this end, we let h_{11} of Section 13 equal $u^2\sigma^2$, where σ^2 is a constant. To simplify matters further, we neglect the cost of control integral in the criterion, letting F equal zero identically. The cost of control is now reflected in the uncertainty attendant upon the use of control. Hence, the problem is still meaningful. Our criterion function $J[u]$ is now given by

$$J[u] = E[\xi^2(T)]. \tag{15.1}$$

For simplicity, we let $a = 0$ in the equation of evolution, and use the continuous limit of the recurrence relation

$$\xi(\tau + \Delta\tau) = \xi(\tau) + bu(\tau)\,\Delta\tau + g \qquad (15.2)$$

as the stochastic dynamical equation of our system.

Development of the optimal feedback scheme begins with the definition of $S(x, t)$ as the value of the criterion if the process starts in state x at time t, $t_0 \leq t \leq T$, and an optimal feedback control policy is used. Applying the principle of optimality, we have the relation

$$S(x, t) = \min_u \; E[S(x + bu\,\Delta\tau + g + o(\Delta\tau), t + \Delta\tau)], \qquad (15.3)$$

with boundary condition

$$S(x, T) = x^2. \qquad (15.4)$$

This yields, taking expectations and passing to the limit, the partial differential equation

$$0 = \min_u [bu S_x + (u^2\sigma^2/2)\,S_{xx} + S_t] \qquad (15.5)$$

which we also would obtain, of course, by the appropriate specialization of Eq. (11.4). Assuming that S_{xx} is positive, and setting the derivative with respect to u equal to zero in order to minimize, we find that u satisfies the equation

$$u = -bS_x/\sigma^2 S_{xx}. \qquad (15.6)$$

Substituting result (15.6) into Eq. (15.5), we obtain the nonlinear partial differential equation

$$0 = -(b^2/2\sigma^2)[(S_x)^2/S_{xx}] + S_t. \qquad (15.7)$$

Letting

$$S(x, t) = h(t)x^2 \qquad (15.8)$$

with

$$h(T) = 1 \qquad (15.9)$$

and substituting into (15.7), we conclude that $h(t)$ must satisfy the ordinary differential equation

$$0 = -(b^2/\sigma^2)h(t) + h'(t). \qquad (15.10)$$

Solving for $h(t)$, and substituting into Eq. (15.8), we obtain the result

$$S(x, t) = x^2 \exp[-(b^2/\sigma^2)(T - t)], \qquad (15.11)$$

where $\exp[c] = e^c$. Now, by Eq. (15.6), the optimal policy function is given by the equation

$$u = -bx/\sigma^2. \tag{15.12}$$

16. Discussion

It can be shown for this problem that the open-loop-optimal feedback control scheme leads to the rule

$$u(t) = \frac{x}{b(T - t + (\sigma^2/b^2))} \tag{16.1}$$

for the control as a function of state (Dreyfus (1964)). Observe that this result differs from that of Eq. (15.12).

Furthermore, were the certainty equivalence principle mentioned in Section 14 valid, one would determine the control by solving the deterministic problem: minimize

$$\xi^2(T) \tag{16.2}$$

subject to the dynamical equations

$$\dot{\xi}(\tau) = bu(\tau), \tag{16.3}$$

where the initial value of τ is t and

$$\xi(t) = x. \tag{16.4}$$

A little reflection shows that any of an infinite set of controls reduces $\xi^2(T)$ to zero. Hence, the concept of an optimal control, using certainty equivalence, is meaningless. Consequently, we have a "certainty difference" principle in this case. The validity of replacing a stochastic problem with a deterministic one by means of replacing random variables with their expected values can be established for only a very restricted class of problems, with the above problem obviously not included. This is particularly interesting because the above problem has exclusively linear and quadratic elements and yet certainty equivalence fails.

17. A Poisson Process

For dynamic programming to be applicable to a continuous stochastic control problem, it must be possible to express the underlying stochastic process in terms of the repeated occurrence of some random event. The probabilities underlying each occurrence of this event must be defined during an interval of time of length $\Delta\tau$ that is allowed to approach zero. Roughly speaking, such a process would be called *infinitely divisible* by a statistician. There are two interesting and fundamentally distinct types of such processes. We have treated an example of one type, the Brownian motion process. The other type is called a *Poisson process*.

The basic assumptions for a Poisson process are, perhaps, even more physically intuitive than those for the Brownian motion process. It is assumed that during each nonoverlapping time interval of length $\Delta\tau$ there is a probability $\lambda \Delta\tau + o(\Delta\tau)$ of an "event" occurring and $(1 - \lambda \Delta\tau + o(\Delta\tau))$ of no "event" occurring. The probability of two or more events occurring is $o(\Delta\tau)$. Various assumptions can be made about what happens if an "event" occurs. We shall treat one of the simplest, and assume that the state vector ξ is incremented by a specified vector z if, with probability $\lambda \Delta\tau$, an "event" occurs during a given time interval of length $\Delta\tau$.

18. The Fundamental Partial Differential Equation for a Poisson Process

We return to the general problem of Section 9, with criterion $J[u]$ given by

$$J[u] = E\left[\int_{t_0}^{T} F(\xi_1, \ldots, \xi_n, \tau, u) \, d\tau + \Phi(\xi_1(T), \ldots, \xi_n(T))\right], \quad (18.1)$$

and with the stochastic dynamical equations given by

$$\xi_i(\tau + \Delta\tau) = \xi_i(\tau) + f_i(\xi_1, \ldots, \xi_n, \tau, u) \, \Delta\tau + g_i, \quad i = 1, \ldots, n,$$
$$(18.2)$$

where g_i is now a stochastic process of the Poisson type described above.

Defining the optimal expected value function in the familiar manner, we see that the recurrence relation

$$S(x, t) = \min_u \{\lambda \Delta\tau \, [F(x + z, t, u) \, \Delta\tau + o(\Delta\tau)$$

$$+ S(x + z + f \Delta\tau + o(\Delta\tau), t + \Delta\tau)]$$

$$+ (1 - \lambda \Delta\tau)[F(x, t, u) \, \Delta\tau + o(\Delta\tau) + S(x + f \Delta\tau + o(\Delta\tau),$$

$$t + \Delta\tau)]\} \quad (18.3)$$

holds, where x, z, and f represent n-dimensional vectors. Expansion in Taylor series, cancellation, division by $\Delta\tau$, and passage to the limit yields

$$0 = \min_{u}[F(x, t, u) + \lambda S(x + z, t) - \lambda S(x, t) + S_x f + S_t]. \quad (18.4)$$

Notice that the term of Eq. (18.3) associated with the occurrence of an "event" contributes only one term, the second, to Eq. (18.4). Equation (18.4) is a partial difference-differential equation and it is extremely difficult to solve analytically, even under the most simple assumptions.

The proper boundary condition for this problem is

$$S(x, T) = \Phi(x). \tag{18.5}$$

19. Adaptive Control Processes

We turn now to a type of process that differs significantly from the stochastic processes we have considered thus far. An *adaptive control process** is one for which a complete description of the process (be it deterministic or stochastic) is not known initially and the state of knowledge about the process changes (hopefully improving) as the process evolves. An optimal control scheme in an adaptive environment hedges initially against the uncertainty concerning the process, perhaps even probing the environment if different controls yield differing amounts of information, but ultimately seeks to optimize some well-defined criterion function that depends on the states and control.

We begin our brief survey of adaptive control processes by presenting and treating a simple numerical example of such a process. We feel that the ideas that are involved will be better illustrated by an example than by an abstract discussion.

20. A Numerical Problem

Consider the network shown in Fig. VII.5, in which at each vertex a decision affecting the subsequent transition is to be chosen. Transitions are always diagonally to the right, either upward or downward. If the problem we are posing were to be deterministic, we would now assume that transitions could be chosen with certainty. Were it to be stochastic,

---

* The basic reference in this area is Bellman (1961).

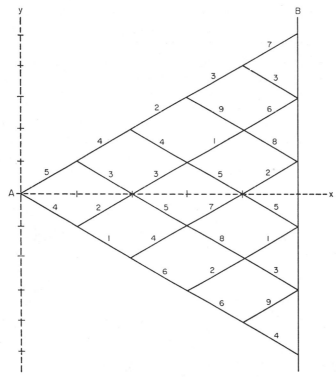

FIG. VII.5

we would associate known probabilities of transitions with the admissible decisions. To construct an adaptive problem, we do neither.

Let p_1 be the probability that decision 1 (independent of the vertex) yields a diagonally-upward transition. We assume that the constant p_1 has been determined, prior to the actual evolution of the decision process, by sampling a random variable with probability density function g_1; i.e., when p_1 was generated, $g_1(\xi_1)\ d\xi$ equalled the probability that p_1 assumed a value between ξ_1 and $\xi_1 + d\xi$. We, the decision-makers, know the function g_1 but do not know the actual value of p_1. The function g_1 is called the *prior* probability density of p_1, since it represents our state of knowledge about p_1 prior to the observation of any events that might alter our assessment.

To recapitulate: At the moment the control process begins at point A, we know the precise statistical mechanism by which p_1 has been determined, but we do not know its actual value. Similarly, p_2, the probability that decision 2 when chosen at a vertex will yield an upward transition, is determined prior to the evolution of the process by sampling a random variable with a known density function g_2 and the result of the sampling is unknown to the decision-maker. We assume that the random variables p_1 and p_2 are independent, although this assumption is not necessary.

At each vertex we are asked to choose either decision 1 or 2. A transition is then determined using the appropriate probability (p_1 or p_2) by the chance mechanism. We are merely told the transition that results. Of course, after rendering several decisions and observing the resulting transitions, we will have acquired more information about the actual numbers p_1 and p_2 than merely their prior distributions g_1 and g_2. Hence learning is possible. Our ultimate goal is to influence the five transitions that occur in the evolution of the process (see Fig. VII.5) in such a way that the expected sum of the five arc-numbers encountered is minimized.*

21. The Appropriate Prior-Probability Density

When the process described above commences, the functions g_1 and g_2 represent the densities, as known to the decision-maker, of p_1 and p_2. Actually, of course, p_1 and p_2 are fixed numbers determined by the use of g_1 and g_2 as indicated above, but the controller has no further information than that p_1 and p_2 were determined by sampling random variables with densities g_1 and g_2.

Suppose that, at an intermediate point in the process, the controller knows that decision 1 has been previously chosen k times and l upward transitions resulted. Given this information, what then is the decision-maker's appropriate density function for p_1? This question is answered by an application of Bayes' formula.† Defining $f_1(\xi \mid k, l)\, d\xi$ as the probability that p_1 lies between ξ and $\xi + d\xi$ given k and l as defined above, Bayes' formula yields the result

$$f_1(\xi \mid k, l) = K_1 \xi^l (1 - \xi)^{k-l} g_1(\xi) , \tag{21.1}$$

where K_1 is a normalizing constant chosen such that

$$\int_0^1 f_1(\xi \mid k, l)\, d\xi = 1 ; \tag{21.2}$$

---

* For some analysis of a related and potentially more practical problem, see Bradt *et al.* (1956).

† In its discrete form, Bayes' formula states the following: Let each one of n events A_i, $i = 1, \ldots, n$, have probability $P(A_i)$ of occurring. One of the events A_i has occurred, but *which* one is unknown. Suppose that a related event B has occurred, and that $P(B \mid A_i)$, the probability of the event B given that A_i has occurred, is known for all i. Then the probability that event A_i occurred, based on the further information that B occurred, is written $P(A_i \mid B)$ and given by the formula

$$P(A_i \mid B) = [P(B \mid A_i)P(A_i)/\sum_{i=1}^n P(B \mid A_i)P(A_i)] = KP(B \mid A_i)P(A_i).$$

i.e., so that f_1 is a density function. A similar result holds, of course, for p_2 and will be developed in the following.

22. The State Variables

As usual, we define the state of the system to be the set of information that is needed to render an optimal decision. Certainly the current vertex is part of the state, as are the current probability density estimates of p_1 and p_2. It turns out for our particular example that if the vertex is known, and if k and l as defined in the previous section are known, then the density for both p_1 and p_2 can be calculated. This is because, given that we are at the vertex $x = i$, $y = j$ (see Fig. VII.5) and given that decision 1 has been chosen k-prior times and resulted in l upward transitions, we can deduce that decision 2 must have been chosen $(i - k)$-prior times and must have led to $\frac{1}{2}(i + j) - l$ upward transitions. Consequently f_2, the density for p_2 at the particular vertex, depends on $i, j, k,$ and l, and by Eq. (21.1), is given by

$$f_2(\xi \mid i, j, k, l) = K_2 \xi^{\frac{1}{2}(i+j)-l}(1 - \xi)^{i-k-\frac{1}{2}(i+j)+l} g_2(\xi) . \qquad (22.1)$$

Hence, $i, j, k,$ and l are the four state variables for our problem, since they characterize the current vertex and current density functions for p_1 and p_2.

23. The Fundamental Recurrence Equation

Let us define

$S(i, j, k, l) = $ the expected value of the process starting at stage $x = i$ in state $y = j$, where k-prior choices of decision 1 led to l upward transitions and where an optimal adaptive policy is followed.

Of course, S also depends upon the prior densities g_1 and g_2, used to generate p_1 and p_2, but we suppress this in our notation. Note that the function S defined above is not the expected value of the remaining process, *given p_1 and p_2* and the optimal adaptive policy, but is the value expected by the decision-maker, who must view p_1 and p_2 as random variables.

Let $a_u(i, j)$ represent the value attached to the arc leading diagonally up from vertex (i, j) and $a_d(i, j)$ designate the value of the downward arc emanating from (i, j). If we choose decision 1 and if p_1 equals some particular number ξ, then with probability ξ we experience an upward transition with value $a_u(i, j)$ and we find ourselves in state $(i + 1, j + 1, k + 1, l + 1)$. With probability $1 - \xi$ we move diagonally downward, accruing a value of $a_d(i, j)$ and entering state $(i + 1, j - 1, k + 1, l)$.

Hence, if $p_1 = \xi$ the future expected value of the process is given by

$$\xi[a_u(i, j) + S(i + 1, j + 1, k + 1, l + 1)]$$

$$+ (1 - \xi)[a_d(i, j) + S(i + 1, j - 1, k + 1, l)]. \quad (23.1)$$

But, according to our current information, p_1 lies between ξ and $\xi + d\xi$ with probability $f_1(\xi \mid k, l) \, d\xi$ given by Eq. (21.1). Consequently the expected future value using decision 1 at present and optimal decisions thereafter is found by weighting the expected value, given $\xi \leq p_1 \leq \xi + d\xi$, by the probability that $\xi \leq p_1 \leq \xi + d\xi$, and integrating over all ξ. This gives the value

$$\int_0^1 \{\xi[a_u(i, j) + S(i + 1, j + 1, k + 1, l + 1)]$$

$$+ (1 - \xi)[a_d(i, j) + S(i + 1, j - 1, k + 1, l)]\}f_1(\xi \mid k, l) \, d\xi . \quad (23.2)$$

Reasoning similarly for decision 2, we have the fundamental recurrence equation for our adaptive process

$$S(i, j, k, l) = \min \begin{cases} 1: & \int_0^1 \{\xi[a_u(i, j) + S(i + 1, j + 1, k + 1, l + 1)] \\ & + (1 - \xi)[a_d(i, j) \\ & + S(i + 1, j - 1, k + 1, l)]\}f_1(\xi \mid k, l) \, d\xi \\ & \qquad\qquad\qquad\qquad\qquad\qquad (23.3) \\ 2: & \int_0^1 \{\xi[a_u(i, j) + S(i + 1, j + 1, k, l)] \\ & + (1 - \xi)[a_d(i, j) \\ & + S(i + 1, j - 1, k, l)]\}f_2(\xi \mid i, j, k, l) \, d\xi \end{cases}$$

with boundary condition

$$S(5, j, k, l) = 0 . \quad (23.4)$$

For our particular example, Eq. (23.3) can be further simplified by denoting the expected value of p_1, given that k choices of decision 1 led to

l upward transitions, by $\bar{p}_1(k, l)$ so that

$$\bar{p}_1(k, l) = \int_0^1 \xi f_1(\xi \mid k, l) \, d\xi, \qquad (23.5)$$

and by defining $\bar{p}_2(i, j, k, l)$ by

$$\bar{p}_2(i, j, k, l) = \int_0^1 \xi f_2(\xi \mid i, j, k, l) \, d\xi. \qquad (23.6)$$

Then Eq. (23.3) becomes

$$S(i, j, k, l) = \min \begin{cases} 1: & \bar{p}_1(k, l)[a_u(i, j) + S(i+1, j+1, k+1, l+1)] \\ & + (1 - \bar{p}_1(k, l))[a_d(i, j) + S(i+1, j-1, k+1, l)] \\ & \qquad\qquad\qquad\qquad\qquad\qquad\qquad\qquad\qquad (23.7) \\ 2: & \bar{p}_2(i, j, k, l)[a_u(i, j) + S(i+1, j+1, k, l)] \\ & + (1 - \bar{p}_2(i, j, k, l))[a_d(i, j) + S(i+1, j-1, k, l)] \end{cases}$$

Not all combinations of stage and state on the left-hand side of (23.7) are possible. The possible ones are generated by the rule

$$i = 4(-1)\, 0, \qquad j = -i(2)i, \qquad k = 0(1)i,$$

and

$$l = \max[0, \tfrac{1}{2}(i + j) - (i - k)]\,(1)\, \min[k, \tfrac{1}{2}(i + j)],$$

where the expression $m = a(n)b$ means that the variable m takes on values $a, a + n, a + 2n, \ldots, b$. In writing these bounds, we have in mind computing $S(i, j, k, l)$ by first evaluating S with each argument equal to the first value given above (i.e., $i = 4, j = -4, k = 0, l = 0$), and then varying l until it reaches its last allowable value. Then k is incremented by 1 and l again varied; next j is incremented by 2 and the variations of k and l are repeated; and finally, i is reduced by 1 and the whole process is repeated.

24. A Further Specialization

Let us now assume that the prior distributions used to generate p_1 and p_2 are uniform distributions; i.e.,

$$g_1(\xi) = 1, \qquad g_2(\xi) = 1, \qquad 0 \leq \xi \leq 1. \qquad (24.1)$$

This specializes Eqs. (21.1) and (22.1). We now have the results

$$\bar{p}_1(k, l) = \int_0^1 \xi f_1(\xi \mid k, l) = \frac{l + 1}{k + 2} \qquad (24.2)$$

and

$$\bar{p}_2(i, j, k, l) = \int_0^1 \xi f_2(\xi \mid i, j, k, l) = \frac{\frac{1}{2}(i + j) - l + 1}{i - k + 2} \qquad (24.3)$$

for use in Eq. (23.7). This reduces Eq. (23.7) to

$$S(i, j, k, l) = \min \begin{cases} 1: \dfrac{l + 1}{k + 2} \left[a_u(i, j) + S(i + 1, j + 1, k + 1, l + 1) \right] \\[2ex] \quad + \left(1 - \dfrac{l + 1}{k + 2} \right) \left[a_d(i, j) + S(i+1, j-1, k+1, l) \right] \\[2ex] 2: \dfrac{\frac{1}{2}(i + j) - l + 1}{i - k + 2} \left[a_u(i, j) + S(i + 1, j + 1, k, l) \right] \\[2ex] \quad + \left(1 - \dfrac{\frac{1}{2}(i+j) - l + 1}{i - k + 2} \right) \left[a_d(i,j) + S(i+1, j-1, k, l) \right] \end{cases} \qquad (24.4)$$

which renders it easily computable. (Note that Eq. (24.2) asserts that the expected value of p_1, given that k choices of decision 1 led to l upward transitions, is $(l + 1)/(k + 2)$, an eminently reasonable result.)

Results almost as simple as the above would occur if g_1 and g_2 are taken to have the form $K\xi^\alpha (1 - \xi)^\beta$. This form is the density function of a beta distribution on the unit interval and reduces to the density of the uniform distribution when $\alpha = \beta = 0$.

25. Numerical Solution

Computation using the above scheme generates the table of minimum expected values $S(i, j, k, l)$ and of optimal decisions $u(i, j, k, l)$, as shown in Table VII-1. The value 4.8333 of S that is associated with the argument $(4, -4, 0, 0)$ was computed as follows: Since $i = 4$, $j = -4$, $k = 0$, and

TABLE VII–1

THE OPTIMAL EXPECTED VALUE FUNCTION AND OPTIMAL POLICY FUNCTION
FOR THE PROBLEM OF SECTION 20

i	j	k	l	$S(i, j, k, l)$	$u(i, j, k, l)$
4	−4	0	0	4.8333	2
4	−4	1	0	5.0000	2
4	−4	2	0	5.2500	1 or 2
4	−4	3	0	5.0000	1
4	−4	4	0	4.8333	1
4	−2	0	0	2.0000	1
4	−2	1	0	2.2000	2
4	−2	1	1	1.6667	1
4	−2	2	0	2.0000	2
4	−2	2	1	2.0000	1
4	−2	3	0	1.6667	2
4	−2	3	1	2.2000	1
4	−2	4	1	2.0000	2
4	0	0	0	3.5000	1 or 2
4	0	1	0	3.2000	2
4	0	1	1	3.0000	1
4	0	2	0	2.7500	2
4	0	2	1	3.5000	1 or 2
4	0	2	2	2.7500	1
4	0	3	1	3.0000	2
4	0	3	2	3.2000	1
4	0	4	2	3.5000	1 or 2
4	2	0	0	6.6667	2
4	2	1	0	6.4000	2
4	2	1	1	6.6667	1
4	2	2	1	6.5000	2
4	2	2	2	6.5000	1
4	2	3	2	6.6667	2
4	2	3	3	6.4000	1
4	2	4	3	6.6667	1
4	4	0	0	5.0000	1
4	4	1	1	5.6667	1
4	4	2	2	6.0000	1 or 2
4	4	3	3	5.6667	2
4	4	4	4	5.0000	2
3	−3	0	0	7.3333	1
3	−3	1	0	8.8333	1
3	−3	2	0	8.8333	2
3	−3	3	0	7.3333	2
3	−1	0	0	10.1000	1
3	−1	1	0	10.1667	1
3	−1	1	1	9.7500	2

TABLE VIII-1—Continued

i	j	k	l	$S(i, j, k, l)$	$u(i, j, k, l)$
3	−1	2	0	9.7500	1
3	−1	2	1	10.1667	2
3	−1	3	1	10.1000	2
3	1	0	0	7.9333	1
3	1	1	0	7.6000	2
3	1	1	1	7.8333	1 or 2
3	1	2	1	7.8333	1 or 2
3	1	2	2	7.6000	1
3	1	3	2	7.9333	2
3	3	0	0	9.5333	2
3	3	1	1	10.4167	2
3	3	2	2	10.4167	1
3	3	3	3	9.5333	1
2	−2	0	0	13.5250	2
2	−2	1	0	14.6111	1 or 2
2	−2	2	0	13.5250	1
2	0	0	0	13.0000	1
2	0	1	0	12.1222	2
2	0	1	1	12.1222	1
2	0	2	1	13.0000	2
2	2	0	0	11.6333	2
2	2	1	1	12.2222	1 or 2
2	2	2	2	11.6333	1
1	−1	0	0	14.6833	2
1	−1	1	0	14.6833	1
1	1	0	0	15.6722	1
1	1	1	1	15.6722	2
0	0	0	0	19.6778	1 or 2

$l = 0$, we conclude that

$$\bar{p}_1(0, 0) = \frac{0 + 1}{0 + 2} = \frac{1}{2},$$

$$\bar{p}_2(4, -4, 0, 0) = \frac{1}{6}.$$

The expected value of the remaining process if decision 1 is chosen at the vertex $(4, -4)$ is then

$$\frac{1}{2} \cdot 9 + \frac{1}{2} \cdot 4 = 6.5000,$$

while the expected value under decision 2 is

$$\frac{1}{6} \cdot 9 + \frac{5}{6} \cdot 4 = \frac{29}{6} = 4.8333.$$

The smaller value is chosen and decision 2 is recorded as optimal under this condition.

These results are interpreted as follows: Initially it does not matter which decision is chosen, since nothing is known about either p_1 or p_2 other than that both were generated by sampling random variables with uniform distributions. If decision 1 were chosen initially and the transition were upward, decision 2 should be chosen next (since $u(1, 1, 1, 1) = 2$). If the resulting transition after this second decision is downward, then decision 1 becomes the preferable next decision (since $u(2, 0, 1, 1) = 1$). If the second transition is upward instead of downward, decision 1 and decision 2 appear at the moment to be equivalent (see $u(2, 2, 1, 1)$), because $\bar{p}_1(1, 1) = \bar{p}_2(2, 2, 1, 1) = \frac{2}{3}$, and each estimate is based on the same amount of information. Similar paths, and justifications, exist for each contingency. Note that if decision 1 has been chosen twice and has resulted in one upward transition and one downward move,* the next decision is *not* immaterial (see $u(2, 0, 2, 1)$), although $\bar{p}_1(2, 1) = \bar{p}_2(2, 0, 2, 1) = \frac{1}{2}$, because p_1 is now known with greater assurance than p_2 and the rules for the modification of the probability distributions based on the next result are not symmetric.

26. Discussion

Observe that the problem is of a familiar type, once the rule is determined by which decisions and transitions influence the densities f_1 and f_2. The state description at a given time is expanded to include all information gained up to that time, but a recurrence relation of the usual form characterizes the optimal value and policy functions.

As the problem formulation becomes more complex and admits adaptation, the number of potential nonoptimal and suboptimal solutions proliferates. For adaptive control processes, many pitfalls surround the true optimal control policy. Let us mention just one. Note that the method used for the solution of the adaptive problem does not merely accept the current densities of p_1 and p_2 at any given vertex as describing the valid underlying probabilities and go on to determine the optimal solution of

---

* According to the optimal policy function, this event can occur if decision 1 is chosen initially and results in a downward transition. Since $u(1, -1, 1, 0) = 1$, decision 1 would then be chosen again. If decision 1 initially yields an upward transition, it would not be chosen as the second decision. The reader should observe that S may be computed for some hypothetical initial states that cannot possibly occur when the optimal policy function is implemented. This is a property common to most dynamic programming solutions, whether the problems are deterministic, stochastic, or adaptive.

the remaining *stochastic* problem in order to render the optimal decision
at that vertex. Rather, the recurrence relation reflects and exploits the
fact that each transition from each state after each decision will result in
an updated density of p_1 or p_2. To use names reminiscent of the presentation of Section 3, one should clearly distinguish *optimal adaptive control*
(such as was computed for the example) from *stochastic-optimal adaptive
control*. The latter scheme would actually use adaptation to update estimates after a transition had occurred, but each decision would be rendered
on the basis of the solution of a stochastic problem of the type discussed
in Section 3. Such a scheme is no more optimal for the information it uses
than is the open-loop-optimal feedback scheme of Section 3, but the
distinction here is perhaps even more subtle than it was in Section 3.

Remember that the formulation of our simple discrete problem assumed
that the prior densities g_1 and g_2, of the unknown parameters p_1 and p_2,
in the dynamical equations were known. Under this assumption, the
control scheme that was computed above is demonstrably optimal. If
the relevant prior distributions are not known, as is often the case in
practical situations, they could be subjectively assessed in order to apply
the foregoing reasoning. Then the resulting control scheme is only as
good as the subjective assessment. But at least one can rest assured that
x is as good as possible, given the subjective assessment and the expected
value criterion. Of course, a different, perhaps more conservative, criterion
might be chosen in this case and then a different control policy would
emerge, but in this case dynamic programming might not prove applicable.

The example treated in the previous sections involves learning about
the dynamical equations. The state (the vertex and previous decisions
and results) is completely observable at all times. A second important
kind of adaptation, considered next, concerns optimal control in the
presence of uncertainty concerning the values of the state variables.

27. A Control Problem with Partially Observable States and with Deterministic Dynamics

We turn now to the problem of optimal control in the presence of unknown, but partially observable, states. Our mathematical model is as
follows: We assume that the state variables evolve deterministically.*
We further assume that the initial values of the state variables, though
fixed, are unknown to the decision-maker and that the values of the state

---

* Our method is also applicable to stochastic or even adaptive state dynamics, but
we strive here for simplicity.

variables can never be observed with certainty. However, a probability density function $p(\xi, t_0)$ exists which specifies the distribution of the state vector ξ at the initial time t_0. Furthermore, as the process evolves, observations of the values of some or all of the states or of functions of the states are made. These observations, which we denote by $h(\tau)$, are corrupted by measurement errors, with the statistics of the noise corrupting the observations assumed to be known. Were the measurements errorless, the precise values of the state variables could in general be determined and the states would be termed observable. Since the observations are error-corrupted, the system is called partially observable. The observations $h(\tau)$ permit the probability density function $p(\xi, t)$, representing the decision-maker's knowledge of the state vector ξ at time t, to be modified as time passes on the basis of incoming information.* We consider first a discrete process where, at time t, a constant control $\bar{u}$ to be used over the interval $t \leq \tau \leq t + \Delta\tau$ must be chosen on the basis of prior observations $\bar{h}(\tau)$, $t_0 \leq \tau < t$. Essentially, control in the environment that we have described is a problem of adaptation of the state variables, rather than the adaptation we discussed earlier upon certain parameters of the dynamical equations.

Letting a criterion functional J, given by

$$J = \int_{t_0}^{T} F(\tau, u)\, d\tau + \Phi(\xi(T)) , \qquad (27.1)$$

associate a value with each evolution of the process, we can define the *optimal expected value functional* by

$S[p(\xi, t), t] =$ the expected value of the process which starts at time $\tau = t$ when the state vector has probability density function $p(\xi, t)$ and in which the optimal control functional $u[p(\xi, t), t]$ is used during the process.

Note that the optimal control is given by a functional which assigns a

---

* This procedure differs from that of determining a state vector ξ that constitutes an estimate of the unknown true state ξ. There is a variety of properties that an estimate can have (e.g., minimum variance, maximum likelihood, minimum bias, etc.), and given a particular set of observations and assumptions, different desired properties lead to different estimates. There is a vast literature on this subject. Concerning dynamical models with sequentially updated estimates, the reader might consult Swerling (1959), Kalman and Bucy (1961), Ho (1962), and Cox (1964). The Kalman-Bucy paper computes the conditional density of the state, given the prior observations, in order to determine an estimate. Consequently, under rather restrictive assumptions, it carries out in practice the program that we have described in general terms here. The Cox paper uses a dynamic programming approach to determine its estimate of the state.

number, the value of the optimal control, to each state density function $p(\xi, t)$ at time t. Note also that S is a functional, and associates a number, the expected value of the criterion, with each state density function $p(\xi, t)$ at time t.

Given $p(\xi, t)$ at time t, we can compute the probability of each reading $\tilde{h}(\tau)$, $t \leq \tau \leq t + \Delta\tau$. Consequently, for a particular choice of control $\tilde{u}$ (assumed constant) to be used over a time interval of length $\Delta\tau$, we can determine the probability of each resulting new state probability density function $\bar{p}(\xi, t + \Delta\tau)$ at time $t + \Delta\tau$. We can also compute the value of the contribution to the criterion integral accruing during the interval $[t, t + \Delta\tau]$. If we knew that value of $S[\bar{p}(\xi, t + \Delta\tau), t + \Delta\tau]$ for all $\bar{p}(\xi, t + \Delta\tau)$, we could, for each value of $\tilde{u}$, calculate the expected value, starting at time t with state density $p(\xi, t)$, of the remaining process. Then, we could choose the control at time t, given $p(\xi, t)$, that yields the minimum expected value of the remaining process. Written mathematically, our discussion takes the form

$$S[p(\xi, t), t] = \min_{u}[F(t, u) \, \Delta\tau + o(\Delta\tau) + \underset{\tilde{h}}{E}[S(\bar{p}(\xi, t + \Delta\tau), t + \Delta\tau)]],$$

(27.2)

where the probability density function of $\tilde{h}$, the error-corrupted observations that help determine $p(\xi, t + \Delta\tau)$, depends upon $p(\xi, t)$, t, and the statistics of the noise in the observation; and the density of ξ at time $t + \Delta\tau$, $\bar{p}(\xi, t + \Delta\tau)$, depends upon the dynamical equations and upon $p(\xi, t)$, $\tilde{h}$, u, and t. Using Eq. (27.2), a minimizing u and an associated value of S are found for each possible density function $p(\xi, t)$. Then, $S[p(\xi, t), t]$ is used to compute $S[p(\xi, t - \Delta\tau), t - \Delta\tau]$ by the usual dynamic programming recursive method.

The boundary condition for the functional recurrence relation (27.2) is

$$S[p(\xi, T), T] = \underset{\xi}{E}[\Phi(\xi)], \qquad (27.3)$$

where the random state vector ξ, over which the averaging is done, has probability density function $p(\xi, T)$.

28. Discussion

We have defined and characterized a functional S that associates numbers with arguments that are functions. In the limit as $\Delta\tau$ approaches zero, we are led to an expression involving the partial derivatives of a functional. These partial derivatives, when evaluated in terms of a given argument function, are functions.*

Straightforward numerical solution of a relation like (27.2) is not practical, since the functional would have to be evaluated, at time $t + \Delta\tau$, for all possible argument functions (or a discrete approximation thereto) in order to be able to compute the value of S corresponding to a particular argument function at time t. However, such an equation, with appropriate boundary conditions, is a mathematically meaningful characterization of the solution. While it is usually impossible to *construct* a functional that satisfies such a relation, it is fairly easy to *test* a *given* functional to see if it satisfies the equation. If the shoe should fit the foot, the adaptive control problem is solved. The contribution of dynamic programming toward the eventual complete solution of adaptive control problems is the discovery of the foot. And just as it is necessary to be able to walk before one can run, one must have feet before one can walk.

In this connection, recall that for several hundred years mathematicians were content to express the solutions of deterministic variational problems in terms of nonlinear ordinary differential equations. They had no means, at that time, of determining the solutions of their equations. Now the digital computer has made routine the solution of even large sets of nonlinear ordinary differential equations, but the numerical solution of partial differential equations with more than about three independent variables requires what is today considered prohibitive quantities of computational time and computer storage space. No special insight is necessary to foresee machines that can easily produce numerical solutions of high-dimensional partial differential equations and probably even the functional differential equations of the type deduced in Section 27. When bigger and better machines are made, dynamic programming will use them.

29. Sufficient Statistics

The state density can always be calculated at a given time, if the previous history of the process is given. In general, as many possible state densities can be foreseen at a future time as possible histories of the process up to that time. This leads to an expanding set of possible states at future times. However, in certain cases, the relevant facts about possible previous results can be summarized in terms of a finite, nongrowing, set of numbers. For example, in determining f_1 in Section 21, the sequence of previous

---

* For more on a problem of this sort, see Bellman and Kalaba (1962).

transitions could be sufficiently summarized by the pair (k, l). Such summarizing data is called a *sufficient statistic* since the posterior distribution depends upon the sample outcome only via the statistic—in Section 21, the order of the upward and downward transition was irrelevant—regardless of the prior distribution.*

For a process admitting a sufficient statistic, it is always possible to parameterize the family of possible posterior distributions by means of the sufficient statistic.†

30. The Decomposition of Estimation and Control

Some authors have considered the possibility of solving an adaptive control problem involving deterministic dynamics and partially observable states by the following procedure. The optimal control policy $u(x, t)$, as a function of the state, is determined for the deterministic problem. Since the state at time t is not known, this control policy is of no immediate value. However, at time t the actual state can be estimated on the basis of previous observations. Usually this is done by defining a criterion for the goodness of an estimate $\hat{x}$ and then choosing the value of $\hat{x}$ that optimizes this criterion. (See the second footnote to Section 27.) Once $\hat{x}$ has been determined, the control $u(\hat{x}, t)$ is used. New observations of the state are used to continually update $\hat{x}$ as time passes and the control $u(\hat{x}, t)$ is exerted.

Under the very special conditions of linear dynamics, of quadratic criteria for both the actual control process and for the optimal estimator, and of Gaussian random disturbances, it can be shown (see Joseph and Tou (1961)) that the separation of estimation and control leads to the same control policy as does the general model of Section 27. Consequently, the control determined on the basis of decomposition is optimal.

31. A Warning

One should be grateful when simplifications such as certainty equivalence or the separability of the estimation and control portions of a problem are valid, and one must expect the worst (i.e., no special properties) until

---

* For more on this subject, see Raiffa and Schlaifer (1961), pp. 28–76.

† For the treatment of control problems for which this reduction can be carried out, see Florentin (1962a, b).

proven otherwise. While most of the literature concerns those cases that exhibit special structures, the majority of actual problems possess no such properties. This leads to various forms of approximation. It is important that the control theorist be aware as to whether he is (1) finding the optimal solution of an approximate problem, (2) approximating the optimal solution of an actual problem, or (3) characterizing (but all too rarely finding) the optimal solution of an actual problem. All three approaches have their values—values that are enhanced by clearly recognizing the above distinctions.

32. Summary

We have devoted this final chapter to the study of stochastic and adaptive control problems, and have seen that a wide variety of optimization problems, apparently outside the domain of the classical variational theory, can be treated systematically by means of the dynamic programming formalism. A fundamental auxiliary function (or functional) associating a value with each state is introduced. The function is seen to satisfy a recurrence relation or a partial differential equation reminiscent of the fundamental equation of the more classical problems of earlier chapters. Unfortunately, the solution of stochastic and adaptive problems can seldom be expressed in terms of associated ordinary differential equations. The contribution of dynamic programming is the reduction of a variety of quite complex problem statements to mathematical relations of rather conventional and familiar forms. While at present the resulting mathematical relations can seldom be solved, analytically or even computationally, the precise and unambiguous characterization of what constitutes the solution of a stochastic or adaptive problem leads to useful concepts and distinctions. In this chapter we have developed some of these concepts and illustrated some of these distinctions.

Bibliography

Akhiezer, N. I. (1962). "The Calculus of Variations" (Aline H. Frink, transl.). Ginn (Blaisdell), New York.

Bellman, R. E. (1957). "Dynamic Programming." Princeton Univ. Press, Princeton, New Jersey.

Bellman, R. E. (1961). "Adaptive Control Processes: A Guided Tour." Princeton Univ. Press, Princeton, New Jersey.

Bellman, R. E., and Dreyfus, S. E. (1962). "Applied Dynamic Programming." Princeton Univ. Press, Princeton, New Jersey.

Bellman, R. E., and Kalaba, R. (1962). Dynamic Programming Applied to Control Processes Governed by General Functional Equations, in Proc. Natl. Acad. Sci. U.S. 48, 1735–1737.

Bellman, R. E., and Kalaba, R. (1964). Dynamic Programming, Invariant Imbedding and Quasi-Linearization: Comparisons and Interconnections, in "Computing Methods in Optimization Problems" (A. V. Balakrishnan and L. W. Neustadt, eds.), pp. 135–145. Academic Press, New York.

Berkovitz, L. D. (1962). On Control Problems with Bounded State Variables, in J. Math. Anal. Appl. 5, 488–498.

Berkovitz, L. D., and Dreyfus, S. E. (1964). A Dynamic Programming Approach to the Nonparametric Problem in the Calculus of Variations. The RAND Corporation, RM-4329-PR.

Berkovitz, L. D., and Dreyfus, S. E. (1965). The Equivalence of Some Necessary Conditions for Optimal Control in Problems with Bounded State Variables, in J. Math. Anal. Appl. 10, 275–283.

Blaquiere, A., and Leitmann, G. (1964). "On the Geometry of Optimal Processes—Part I." Institute of Engineering Research, California Univ., Berkeley, California.

Bliss, G. A. (1959). "Lectures on the Calculus of Variations." Chicago Univ. Press, Chicago.

Bradt, R. N., Johnson, S. M., and Karlin, S. (1956). On Sequential Designs for Maximizing the Sum of n Observations, in Ann. Math. Stat. 27, 1060–1074.

Breakwell, J. V. (1959). The Optimization of Trajectories, in J. SIAM 7, 215–247.

Bryson, A. E., and Denham, W. (1962). A Steepest Ascent Method for Solving Optimum Programming Problems, in J. Appl. Mech. 29, 247–257.

Bryson, A. E., Denham, W. F., and Dreyfus, S. E. (1963). Optimal Programming Problems with Inequality Constraints. I: Necessary Conditions for Extremal Solutions, in AIAA (Am. Inst. Aeron. Astronaut.) J. 1, 2544–2550.

Caratheodory, C. (1935). "Variationsrechnung und partielle Differentialgleichungen erster Ordnung. Teubner, Leipzig and Berlin.

Chang, S. S. L. (1963). Optimal Control in Bounded Phase Space, in Automatica, 1, 55–67.

Cox, H. (1964). On the Estimation of State Variables and Parameters for Noisy Dynamic Systems, in IEEE (Inst. Elec. Electron. Engrs.), Trans. Auto. Control 9, 5–12.

Dreyfus, S. E. (1962). Variational Problems with Inequality Constraints, in J. Math. Anal. Appl. 4, 297–308.

Dreyfus, S. E. (1964). Some Types of Optimal Control of Stochastic Systems, *in J. SIAM Control, Ser. A*, **2**, 120–134.

Fleming, W. H. (1963). Some Markovian Optimization Problems, *in J. Math. Mech.* **12**, 131–140.

Florentin, J. J. (1961). Optimal Control of Continuous Time, Markov, Stochastic Systems, *in J. Electron. Control* **10**, 473–488.

Florentin, J. J. (1962a). Optimal, Probing, Adaptive Control of a Simple Bayesian System, *in J. Electron. Control* **13**, 165–177.

Florentin, J. J. (1962b). Partial Observability and Optimal Control, *in J. Electron. Control* **13**, 263–279.

Gamkrelidze, R. V. (1960). Optimal Processes with Bounded Phase Coordinates, *in Izv. Akad. Nauk (SSSR) Ser. Mat.* **24**, 315–356.

Gelfand, I. M., and Fomin, S. V. (1963). "Calculus of Variations" (Richard A. Silverman, transl. and ed.) Prentice-Hall, Englewood Cliffs, New Jersey.

Halkin, H. (1963). The Principle of Optimal Evolution, *in* "Non-Linear Differential Equations and Nonlinear Mechanics" (Joseph P. LaSalle, ed.). Academic Press, New York.

Hestenes, M. R. (1949). Numerical Methods of Obtaining Solutions of Fixed End Point Problems in the Calculus of Variations. *The RAND Corporation, RM-102.*

Hestenes, M. R. (1964). Variational Theory and Optimal Control Theory, *in* "Computing Methods in Optimization Problems," (A. V. Balakrishnan and L. W. Neustadt, eds.), pp. 1–22. Academic Press, New York.

Ho, Y. C., (1962). The Method of Least Squares and Optimal Filtering Theory. *The RAND Corporation, RM-3329-PR.*

Howard, R. A. (1960). "Dynamic Programming and Markov Processes." Technology Press and Wiley, New York.

Joseph, P. D., and Tou, J. T. (1961). On Linear Control Theory, *in Trans. AIEE* **80**, Part II, 193–196.

Kalman, R. E. (1963). The Theory of Optimal Control and the Calculus of Variations, *in* "Mathematical Optimization Techniques" (R. E. Bellman, ed.), Chapter 16 California Univ. Press, Berkeley, California.

Kalman, R. E., and Bucy, R. (1961). New Results in Linear Filtering and Prediction Theory, *in J. Basic Eng.* **83**, 95–108.

Kelley, H. J. (1962). Method of Gradients, *in* "Optimization Techniques" (G. Leitmann, ed.), Chapter 6. Academic Press, New York.

Kelley, H. J., Kopp, R. E., and Moyer, H. G. (1963). A Trajectory Optimization Technique Based Upon the Theory of the Second Variation, *in AIAA Astrodynamics Conf., New Haven, 1963, AIAA Reprint No.* **63-415.**

Kushner, H. J. (1962). Optimal Stochastic Control, *in IRE (Inst. Radio Engrs.) Trans. Auto. Control* Vol. **7**, 120–122.

Kushner, H. J. (1964). On the Stochastic Maximum Principle: Fixed Time of Control. *in Res. Inst. for Advanced Studies, Techn. Rept.* **63-24** *(rev. ed.).*

Leitmann, G. (1963). Maximum Range for a Rocket in Horizontal Flight, *in J. Appl. Math. Mech.* **27**, 867–872.

Miele, A. (1962). Extremization of Linear Integrals by Green's Theorem, *in*, "Optimization Techniques" (George Leitmann, ed.), Chapter 3. Academic Press, New York.

Pontryagin, L. S., Boltyanskii, V. G., Gamkrelidze, R. V., and Mishchenko, E. F. (1962). "The Mathematical Theory of Optimal Processes" (K. N. Trirogoff, transl., L. W. Neustadt, ed.). Wiley Interscience, New York.

Raiffa, H., and Schlaifer, R. (1961). Applied Statistical Decision Theory." Division of Research, Graduate School of Business Administration, Harvard University, Boston.

Savage, L. J. (1954). "The Foundations of Statistics." Wiley, New York.

Simon, H. A. (1956). Dynamic Programming Under Uncertainty with a Quadratic Criterion Function, *in Econometrica* **24**, 74–81.

Swerling, P. (1959). First Order Error Propagation in a Stagewise Smoothing Procedure for Satellite Observations, *in J. Astronaut. Sci.* **6**, 46–52.

Theil, H. (1957). A Note on Certainty Equivalence in Dynamic Planning, *in Econometrica* **25**, 346–349.

Valentine, F. A. (1937). The Problem of Lagrange with Differential Inequalities as Added Side Conditions, *in* "Contributions to the Calculus of Variations, 1933–1937," pp. 407–448. Chicago Univ. Press, Chicago.

Von Neumann, J., and Morgenstern, O. (1947). "Theory of Games and Economic Behavior." Princeton Univ. Press, Princeton, New Jersey.

Wald, A. (1950). "Statistical Decision Functions." Wiley, New York; Chapman and Hall, London.

Author Index

Numbers in italics refer to pages on which the complete references are listed.

Subject Index